Psychoneurosis
&
Schizophrenia

AUTHORS

Hilde Bruch, MD
Professor of Psychiatry, Baylor University College of Medicine, Houston; Clinical Professor of Psychiatry, Columbia University College of Physicians and Surgeons, New York (on leave)

John Donnelly, MD
Psychiatrist-in-Chief, Institute of Living, Hartford; Associate Clinical Professor of Psychiatry, Yale University School of Medicine

Stuart M. Finch, MD
Professor of Psychiatry, Director, Children's Psychiatric Hospital, University of Michigan Medical School, Ann Arbor

Robert W. Gibson, MD
Medical Director, Sheppard and Enoch Pratt Hospital, Towson, Maryland

Edward H. Knight, MD
Senior Associate, Division of Psychiatry and Neurology, Touro Infirmary; Associate Professor of Clinical Psychiatry, Louisiana State University School of Medicine, New Orleans

Reginald S. Lourie, MD
Professor of Psychiatry and Pediatrics, George Washington University School of Medicine, Director of the Department of Psychiatry, Children's Hospital, Washington, DC; President, American Academy of Child Psychiatry

Judd Marmor, MD
Clinical Professor of Psychiatry, University of California at Los Angeles School of Medicine Medical Center; Chief, Department of Psychiatry, Cedars-Sinai Medical Center, Los Angeles; President, Academy of Psychoanalysis

Jules H. Masserman, MD
Professor and Co-Chairman, Division of Psychiatry, Northwestern University Medical School, Chicago

Howard P. Rome, MD
Professor of Psychiatry, Mayo Graduate School, University of Minnesota, Rochester; President, American Psychiatric Association

Elvin V. Semrad, MD
Clinical Professor of Psychiatry, Harvard Medical School; Director of Psychiatry, Massachusetts Mental Health Center, Boston

Charles Shagass, MD
Professor of Psychiatry, State University of Iowa School of Medicine, Iowa City

James N. Sussex, MD
Professor and Chairman, Department of Psychiatry, University of Alabama Medical Center, Birmingham

Harvey J. Tompkins, MD
Director, Department of Psychiatry, St. Vincent's Hospital and Medical Center; Clinical Professor of Psychiatry, New York University School of Medicine, New York; President-elect, American Psychiatric Association

Gene L. Usdin, MD
Chief, Division of Psychiatry and Neurology, Touro Infirmary, Associate Professor of Clinical Psychiatry, Tulane University School of Medicine, New Orleans

Psychoneurosis & Schizophrenia

Edited and With a Foreword by

GENE L. USDIN, MD

Chief, Division of Psychiatry and Neurology, Touro Infirmary, New Orleans
Associate Professor of Clinical Psychiatry, Tulane University
School of Medicine

A classic of contemporary psychiatric thought in which fourteen of the leaders of American Psychiatry present provocative yet fundamental concepts of Psychoneurosis & Schizophrenia

Philadelphia J. B. LIPPINCOTT COMPANY Montreal

Distributed in Great Britain by
Pitman Medical Publishing Company, Limited, London

Library of Congress Catalog Card No. 65-27617

PRINTED IN THE UNITED STATES OF AMERICA
SP-B

Foreword

DESPITE WIDE DIVERGENCIES, A BASIC SUBSTRUCTURE EXISTS IN PRESENT-day American psychiatry that accommodates various theoretical concepts without compromising autonomy.

As in any fledgling science, the early years of "modern psychiatry" were fraught with insecurity, intransigencies and power struggles. Psychoanalysis was viewed as a challenge by descriptive, organically oriented psychiatrists, and also as a revolution against the rigid cultural standards of the Victorian age. Resistance by organic psychiatry stirred up a counter reaction from those in the psychoanalytic movement, which was also having conflicts within itself. A polarization occurred between somaticists and members of the psychodynamic groups. The psychoanalytic movement tended to look down on the other as inferior and second class, considering itself, to a degree, the avant garde of the still-new science. This was reflected in a social class distinction in selection of patients.

In the past decade, these attitudes have relaxed. Various frames of reference used in analytic theory have begun to demonstrate eclecticism, and analysts are now welcoming many contributions from organic psychiatry. Many psychiatrists, as well as nonpsychiatric physicians, in a spirit of broadening their scientific knowledge, have taken courses in psychodynamic theory and undergone analysis without any intention of ultimately becoming psychoanalysts.

Psychoanalysts have become less hesitant and negative regarding use of psychopharmacologic drugs, and many have recognized the advantages of working with patients in a hospital. This has had the "therapeutic" effect of maintaining psychoanalysis in the main stream of medicine. Not infrequently today it is the psychoanalyst who proclaims the importance of constitutional factors in the etiology and prognosis of emotional and mental illness. Freud was organically minded at the outset of his medical career and, although some may disagree, remained organically minded. The marriage of psychoanalysis and organic psychiatry is a sine qua non for the healthy practice of psychiatry.

Whereas analysts have endorsed constitutional elements as having a bearing on mental illness, until recently they have made no significant contributions to the basic matrix in this regard.

On the other hand, organically oriented psychiatrists have dealt with personal relations, environmental manipulation, occupational therapy and other important areas of interpersonal relationships intuitively, often quite soundly, for many years. Because the somaticists endorsed no specific psychological theories, they were accused of being antipsychological.

In this environment, the Division of Psychiatry of Touro Infirmary held a symposium to bring together some of the leading thinkers in contemporary psychiatry. The subject matter had to be limited: psychoneurosis and schizophrenia touch on all major areas of our discipline. Speakers were selected who could best exemplify a broad spectrum of contemporary thought. They were brought together to express their views, share ideas, confront each other and contrast perspectives.

Psychoneurosis and Schizophrenia is the outgrowth of that symposium held in New Orleans. An educational grant from Roche Laboratories, Division of Hoffmann-La Roche Inc., made possible the securing of the outstanding speakers, who came from the West to the East Coast, from the North, the Midwest, and the South. Academicians and clinicians, private and public hospital physicians, child and adult psychiatrists, analysts and nonanalysts, drug researchers and theoreticians, all were represented among the distinguished speakers.

In the opening chapter, Dr. Howard Rome presents the concept that behavioral anthropometry is now possible and describes the utilization of the Minnesota Multiphasic Personality Inventory by the Mayo Clinic. Over 50,000 medical (nonpsychiatric) patients have been given personality inventories, and the entire staff has been involved in utilization of the results. The inventories have revealed to internists the unsuspected presence of emotional problems and aided them in making borderline decisions; but what is most important is that this is added information for nonpsychiatric physicians so that they can be helped to deal more effectively with emotional and mental illnesses. Rome concludes that clinical judgments can be leavened in a manner well established in other areas of medical study by the use of ancillary laboratory procedures.

Dr. Reginald Lourie, in considering the genesis of neurosis, emphasizes the importance of constitutional factors together with the early days of the infant's life. He points out some of the hazards that organic problems can pose in the infant's adaptation to relationships. With his emphasis on the importance of the prenatal period and the child's first year, Lourie raises the question of where true preventive efforts can be directed. He discusses the points that he considers basic to understanding the genesis of the neurosis: *1.* the nature of the individual's pattern of inborn instincts and defenses, *2.* the types of early life experience that can come into conflict with the qualitative and quantitative differences in an individual's instincts, and *3.* the influence of the organic components of the ego on the form taken by the neurosis. He points out that what we might later perceive as a child's being rejected can begin, in reality, by the parents' being rejected.

Dr. Jules Masserman, in an erudite fashion, reviews earlier theoretical concepts of anxiety, emphasizes its omnipresence and constructiveness and presents studies and conclusions from his Northwestern University laboratory. He considers anxiety to have one final therapeutic connotation: a state of tension ranging from unpleasant to unbearable. Psychotherapy should provide the most effective utilization of every pharmacologic or other medical means to relieve the patient's symptoms, helping him to recognize *1.* that earlier patterns of behavior are no longer either necessary or suitable, and *2.* that other, more "mature" (that is, socially rewarding) modes of conduct are really more pleasurable and profitable. There should be no limited or stereotyped mode of treating anxiety.

Dr. James Sussex warns against using traditional diagnostic groups as a basis for selecting drugs. His section on target-symptom approach is well developed, and he emphasizes that utilization of drugs in the treatment of a patient does something to the therapist as well as to the patient. In the search for more effective predictions of the way in which the individual neurotic patient may respond to drug therapy, he suggests that aspects of basic ego function be assessed, particularly the degree of the patient's dependency on environmental stimuli to maintain the feeling of ego intactness. Sussex cautions that in the presence of stimulus dependency, drugs that reduce or distort incoming stimuli are contraindicated and that alerting drugs would be more effective. Like others, he sees no compelling conflict between drug and psychotherapy.

Drawing on studies at St. Vincent's Hospital and a rich clinical experience, Dr. Harvey Tompkins documents the value of, and necessity for, short-term and limited therapy in the treatment of neuroses. He questions whether different schools of psychotherapy get better or worse results. He urges more varied research in comparing various technics and their theoretical backgrounds. Tompkins believes that ultimately it will be possible to earmark one patient for guidance and counseling, another for reconstructive therapy, another for drug therapy, and still another for a combination of drugs used with some form of psychotherapy. This chapter is a clear call for greater flexibility in therapeutic approach by psychiatrists.

Dr. Judd Marmor reviews the nature of the psychotherapeutic process and strikes at many psychiatric shibboleths, noting that patients respond to the implicit as well as explicit expectations of their therapists and that therapists must become more aware of their interpersonal relationships with their patients. The "reflecting screen" of the psychiatrist is fully taken down by Marmor. He makes many of us feel more comfortable about certain countertransference factors, which tend to make us feel uncomfortable. He feels that operative in effective psychotherapy are initial and continuing catharsis, cognitive awareness, corrective emotional experience, identification and reality testing. Marmor concludes by emphasizing the need for understanding the psychotherapeutic process because "the origin of most psychoneurotic disorders will continue to lie in the life experiences and early interpersonal relationships that have distorted the perceptions and the ego-integrative mechanisms of the people we see as patients."

In the opening chapter of the section on Schizophrenia, Dr. Robert Gibson, drawing on lengthy experiences at Chestnut Lodge and Sheppard and Enoch Pratt Hospitals, presents concepts that he views as paramount in treating schizophrenia. He develops the concept that the schizophrenic patient suffers from a need-fear dilemma; the patient desperately needs personal relationships to compensate for an ego deficit, yet at the same time is terrified by the fear that these relationships will engulf him. Activation of this dilemma is crucial to therapy, permitting new object relations and the opportunity for the patient to identify with the therapist. In a way the therapist commits himself not only to entering the patient's life, but also to permitting the patient to enter his.

Dr. Stuart Finch reviews current knowledge of childhood psychosis and presently accepted therapeutic approaches, outlining valuable studies being carried out at his and other centers. Finch assumes the presence of both psychological and biologic factors in the etiology of schizophrenia. He develops three subtypes of childhood schizophrenia that, while based on severity of illness, are recognized to be in a continuum. He notes that schizophrenic patients tend to retain a basic hypersensitivity and a need to avoid closeness. He concludes with the opinion that few, if any, psychotic children are really cured.

Dr. Hilde Bruch, in a challenging paper relating obesity to schizophrenia, stresses the basic defects in the personality of these patients and decries "giving insight" as useless for correction of the schizophrenic state. She supports the view that schizophrenia is a deficiency disease, with deficits in basic tools of orientation and communication essential for effective personality organization. Bruch maintains that the cardinal problem is not so much one of avoidance of contact with others because contact is painful, but rather a sense of being helpless, an alien, because the ability to experience human contact as gratifying and rewarding has never developed. She believes the therapist's function is to aid these patients in learning to identify their feelings and sensations, and to distinguish between basic bodily needs and emotions and affect. Only then can a patient develop further understanding.

Dr. Charles Shagass presents an encyclopedic review of drug therapy and his own studies. He believes that phenothiazines definitely exert normalizing effects on the schizophrenic processes and that these effects are achieved more readily in patients with acute rather than chronic disease. Shagass questions the influence of drugs on the long-term course of schizophrenia, but emphasizes their value in managing disturbed patients. He points up the important, unanswered questions of proper dosage and duration of drug therapy, the need for clinical guidelines relative to reduction and discontinuance of medication, and the question of whether or not there are special difficulties in reinstituting psychotherapy. He credits drug therapy with having been instrumental in involving a large number of investigators from various basic disciplines in mental health and illness.

Dr. John Donnelly points out the practical value of short-term psychotherapy in schizophrenia. He indicates that the therapist is obliged to take an active role from the outset of therapy in an effort to establish rapidly the positive relationship; his development of technics for doing so provides many useful ideas. Donnelly emphasizes that although there is a risk that great anxiety and considerable hostility may be aroused, the nature of the relationship and the therapist's skill should enable him to control the degree of arousal, while the quality of the relationship enables the patient to tolerate and utilize such experiences. He cautions against the development of an intense transference in the schizophrenic patient and reminds the reader that violent emotions are usually present, although often—but not always—deeply repressed. He suggests that, within the framework of short-term therapy, the therapist has two possible approaches: he must choose whether to reinforce the power of the tyrannical superego or to ally himself with the ego of the patient. There is a clear feeling of Donnelly's willingness, within such an alliance, for therapeutic confrontations of his nuclear problems by the schizophrenic patient, when indicated.

Dr. Elvin Semrad reviews some of the history of American psychiatry and stresses the necessity for continued intense study. Like Bruch, he submits the hypothesis that we are only catalysts in the patient's attempt to get well. Semrad sets forth the premise that in long-term therapy of schizophrenia, the ego-corrective experience should be the major operative concern because of the patient's overwhelming anxiety and dread of the outside world. Semrad cautions against permitting too much pain to develop in the patient. He emphasizes, as do many of the other writers in the section on schizophrenia, the intricacies and importance of understanding the patient-doctor relationship, and cautions against too much emphasis on symptom relief without analysis of the psychosis-vulnerable ego, which then permits ultimate maturation.

As the speakers are considered representative of present-day American psychiatric thinking, an overview of the symposium brings several points to mind. Although neuroses are supposed to be less enigmatic than schizophrenia, we have clearer views of the therapeutic limits in dealing with schizophrenia; at least, we make more clear-cut statements about schizophrenia. Although the psychoneuroses certainly are more amenable to therapy, we have to be careful to avoid thinking that there is a conceptual framework.

If schizophrenia is viewed as a disease with a predominant organic component (or organic defect disease), the therapeutic potential must be recognized as exceedingly limited. If schizophrenia is viewed in terms of social maladaptation, with some constitutional factors, then there is reasonable hope that the illness can be modified to the extent that the patient is relatively indistinguishable from the average person. With schizophrenia, we have been able to observe the natural history of the disorder because we were unable to interrupt its course; with neuroses, we can break up the course.

What keeps coming through as having first and decisive importance in psychotherapy is the establishment of an honest and consistent relationship between two people. This relationship is refreshing to both the patient and the therapist because so much of life is veneer, composed of artifacts. Neurotic persons doubt themselves more in terms of honesty than in terms of ability. They contend with feelings that nothing about themselves is spontaneous and decent. In a way, healthy personality remnants that exist in these persons are hidden or unrecognized by them. For example, tenderness may be viewed as weakness and all expressions of kindness as false. Therapists must speak up without hesitation or fear, emphasizing to the patient that the relationship is trustworthy, even though the therapist may be wrong at times. Then the patient can recognize that therapy is to point out strengths as well as weaknesses; then too, therapy requires an interaction between the patient and the doctor with both maintaining an awareness that certain processes are going on within the patient unknown to either.

This volume emphasizes the need for a further refining of the definition of the therapeutic role and process, and stresses that while therapy must, perforce, be a fairly massive effort, it has also to be tempered by a guiding principle of noninterference: the natural recuperative processes of the patient must be supported and dealt with as a constant factor in the therapeutic relationship. Symptoms, it must be remembered, are disturbances of equilibrium due to excess or deficiency, and regression is an attempt to "hold the line."

Some critics undoubtedly will take issue with almost any of the chapters in this volume, but I believe that most of what these contributors said in this symposium of the mid-60's will be of value in the mid-70's, mid-80's, mid-90's and the twenty-first century.

GENE L. USDIN, MD

Contents

Schizophrenia

Howard P. Rome, MD
Mayo, Minnesota

1

Automated Psychological Tests as Heuristic Devices

AN UNDERSTANDING OF BEHAVIOR ON A MOLECULAR LEVEL IS INDISPENSABLE for an understanding of the vagaries of patients and for efficient psychotherapy. Another parameter of behavior also requires the same kind of careful definition: its molar aspects.

Background: Molar Behavior

The natural history of disease and disability reflects the prevailing attitudes and values of the times. These subtle but pervasive influences shape community responses. These can mean a greater tolerance of difference and its benefits for patients, and they also determine the therapeutic sets and the diagnostic criteria used by various professionals. Molar behavior in this context means the modal attitudes and conduct of large sectors of a community that can be taken to represent society as a whole. The study of demography and other social characteristics has been a contribution of the social sciences. These insights into individual and group behavior replicated on a large scale have changed every segment of the communications network that links us. We have had a recent dramatic example of this. What a few years ago would have been called *pre*science is now a science of a high order of sophistication. The predictive power of opinion polls, one form of a specal brand of demography, has been demonstrated in the recent national election. The wedding of computer technology and scientific social assessment has generated a reliable data base that illumines the variables of individual and group behavior.

A behavioral anthropometry is now possible. It rests on the definition given certain parameters of human behavior. These are capable of statistical refinement and validation in large samples of persons if they are ordered and classified in accordance with a defined set of characteristics. Equipped with such refined measures, it is neither 5th-century Athenian optimism nor 19th-century starry-eyed positivism to say that the time is near when it will be possible to build a lever and construct a suitable fulcrum with which to move the world of idiosyncratic judgments. Hopefully, the sagacious insights of investigators who work on the molecular level of behavior can be extrapolated to the molar level. Every serious student of human behavior these days must agree that the paramount problem of our time is that of second-order organization: the organization of organizations. Rivalry and similar interface problems, the conflict of overlapping jurisdiction, segregated territoriality, sacrosanct domains, status, competition and the rest are social phenomena that psychiatrists must recognize as important, as intrapsychic conflicts.

Justification

The data that follow are presented as an heuristic device, an experimental attempt to gauge the utility of incorporating routinely a clinical inventory as part of a comprehensive medical examination. If the principle can be proved valuable in this setting, its general application in the study of individuals and groups is assured.

It has been accepted that a large segment of the medical population has what is vaguely termed "a psychiatric component" as part of the syndrome for which it seeks help. An evaluation of its significance depends on the patient's information and the physician's time and skill in the interpretation of its clinical relevance. Even in those medical settings where clinical psychological and clinical psychiatric consultation is available, the pressure of demands, as well as the limitations of available specialists, coupled with the mounting cost of comprehensive studies, precludes its inclusion as a routine part of every medical examination.

However, its inclusion would be possible if some more or less automatic means were devised that could sample the patient's store of information about himself and reorder it in accordance with a model based on valid concepts. This labor-saving operation would obviate dependence on human operators for the time-consuming, expensive and perfunctory part of the examination, and thereby a more effective medical-information system could be realized. The logic and many of the components of such a system have been available for some time.

Methodology

For example, the Minnesota Multiphasic Personality Inventory (MMPI) is the most widely used of the structured and empirically validated clinical psychological tests. It consists of a series of 566 statements descriptive of those categories of general and psychiatric health, occupational adjustment, educational capacity, social attitudes, values and relationships that commonly are the data base for psychiatrist's clinical judgment.

FORMAT

The yes-no format (worded "True"—"False") of its statements is similar to the typical question and response history-taking employed by physicians. The familiarity of this method of inquiry reduces the likelihood of the test's being viewed as an unacceptable intrusion in the physician-patient relationship. It has been demonstrated that the style of an inventory is congenial to both patients and the nonpsychiatrist physicians. Also a large body of interpretative studies has been gathered over the more than 20 years of MMPI use. These provide a diagnostic and predictive base for subtle analysis. In the routine use of the MMPI by clinical psychologists it is usually scored on a total of 14 keys or scales; however, more than 200 other sets of item-clusters have been developed and studied by investigators. These augment the useful data base.

As they have been used routinely in the past, the inquiry statements of the inventory are presented in a serial fashion to a subject. He either sorts or notes his response to each statement as being "True" or "False" or "Cannot say". In the totally automated version of the MMPI, it was necessary to modify the form of presentation. Several considerations obtained. It was desirable that the inquiry statements be collated in a form that would require no special handling or physical arrangement for its administration, collection and processing. If these constraints are met, there is no insuperable limitation to a collection system for processing and reporting the test. It can be given and taken in any physical location: its portable form permits collection at a number of stations; batches of tests are easily transported to a central-processing facility where, without much handling, each test can be scored electronically by either an electronic marked-sense reading device or an electronic optical reader.

The format used consists of 24 standard-size computer cards. On both sides of 23 cards are printed the inventory statements. The first card is a header card that contains address information on its face side; the obverse side displays the detailed test-taking instructions. These cards are held together by a plastic-ring binder, and can be removed easily prior to processing.

SCORING

The scoring program, stored in the memory of the computer's central processing unit, is divided into several logical parts. Each of these is complete within itself and, inasmuch as it forms interdependent logical compartments, can be modified, or additional routines may be inserted without having to rewrite the entire program. The header-card routine is essentially an address-format check. It reads the name, date, sex, age, patient-registration information, and these are the punched identification for the next 23 cards. A second routine is concerned with the certification of the proper card sequence, the orderly contents of successive decks in each batch processed, the accumulation of raw scores for all scales and tallies of statements not-answered or both-answered.

There is a routine for scoring, according to the item requirements of the 10 standard and three validating scales. A modification of this template will permit the addition of other test scales by assigning their component items to a scale-set. Inasmuch as certain items are significant members of more than one scale-set, and its significance is either in its "True" or "False" mode, the program has to specify these special requirements. Essentially, these routines are locations assigned in the computer memory. Each item may be tallied according to its significance for one or more scales and ordered to the location assigned to the set of items that comprise this scale. Another series of memory locations is reserved for the basic complement of 13 positions, one for each of the standard scales. These have assigned values 0 or 1, which indicates their significant registration in the scale-set.

Then, too, each of the 23 cards has its unique punching format, determined by the spatial location on the card of the printed inquiry statement, with an appropriate space on the left and right margins in which balloon-like check areas may be marked true or false, by filling them in with a special electrographic marking pencil. The subsequent operations in sequence require the transformation of the tallied numerical scores, gotten from the sorting and accounting procedure, into language print-out statements. The rationale for this phase of the project rests on an extensive background of evidence provided by Meehl, Sarbin, Hunt and others.

The point has been made that the problem of the unit of measurement can be solved only by reference to empirical data. Once these data are assembled and ordered according to a standard notation system, the number of phenotypic and genotypic attributes to which they refer as Meehl has observed, is finite. Consequently, no logical reason exists why the frequency of the associated characteristics, within the limits of predicted probability, cannot be used to establish an automatic associational linkage. If this is logically permissable, then all that is required to complete the steps from the raw data of the patient's input to an English-sentence interpretation of these as output, are those interpretive statements stored in computer-memory and corresponding to the particular scale elevations.

These requirements have been met in the following ways: For years MMPI scales have been scored for various reference populations whose demographic-diagnostic-clinical criteria have been carefully defined. A statistical device is used to convert each set of item-statements to its T-score numerical equivalent. It is contrived so that, with a T-score of 50 as the mean average score for each scale, each standard deviation represents an increase or decrease of the T-score by 10. The distribution of responses to the items of each scale has made it possible to associate a standard set of descriptive words with each of the various T-score elevations. In effect, this becomes a dictionary or a library of interpretive statements. It is as definitive, as comprehensive and as sophisticated as the intent and the empirical data on which it is based. Further, it has the possibility of being extended to a thesaurus by the use of clusters of scales instead of single ones for the interpretive statements.

If ambiguity is avoided, redundancy kept to a minimum, and apparent inconsistencies cleared by a more precise choice of words, it is possible to categorize the T-score range for the standard scale into a 5-step grouping: low, normal, mild, moderate, marked. Furthermore, within each of the 5 groups for each of the scales, acceptable T-score (or raw score) limits can be established as allocating criteria. Then, each of these cells in the T-score library can be assigned an English-language statement as an equivalent. Once this decision is made, it is a simple programming operation to pair the T-score (or the raw score) with its equivalent statement stored in computer memory. A punched card actuates the print-out statements by call-out routine triggered by the T-scores.

Based on data collected on reference populations, this can be modified in accordance with any set of criteria equatable with T-scores. It was found, shortly after the pilot phase of this project was undertaken in 1961, that the commonly used clinical psychological criteria were not sufficiently discriminatory for our medical population. Apparently, the doctor's office-patient normal person in MMPI scale elevation terms, at least, was a more anxious, depressed, somatically preoccupied person than the man-on-the-street nomal. Therefore, if the inventory were to meet the needs of practicing physicians, it would better serve this purpose were it scaled on a base derived from data on medical patients. The reasonableness of this association and decision is evident. Obviously, were it not for the patient's consciously expressed concern about his health, he would not be motivated to seek a doctor's advice. That he is concerned, and perhaps with substantial justification, seems to account for the modal depression that typifies the doctor's office-patient.

REPORT

Indeed, found in an item analysis of 50,000 inventories, obtained from medical (nonpsychiatric) patients, is a significant variation in response. This is true not only if the responses are separated by the sex of the responder but also if they are separated by age-group. Again this is in accord with what one would expect: that the percentage of "true" responses, for example, to item number 145—"At times I feel like picking fist fights with someone"—are not only greater in males than in females but are greater in the younger members of both sexes. In the age decade less than 20 years, approximately 40% of males among 50,000 medical patients answered this statement in the affirmative. In the decade 30 to 39 years, this falls to approximately 15%; in that of 60 to 69 years, to 5%, and in that greater than 70, to about 3%.

The library of interpretative statements may be augmented by the inclusion of modifications gotten from the configuration of the profile of the combined scales. These profiles have been numerically coded by Hathaway (1943) and modified by Welsh (1949). The resulting code typology as well as its profile homologue has been useful in permitting test interpreters to consider interscale effects. For such clinical use as is required in a large-scale screening selection-referral procedure, the statement library is programmed to include such print-out information as: "Consider psychiatric evaluation." This statement is generated when four or more scales have T-score elevations of 70 or more.

Similarly, statistically infrequent profiles can be defined clinically. When they recur in a population sample, a notice in the print-out is taken in the form of a special advisory. Also, with large samples of data, it is possible for a given population to be classified according to coded base rates. Thus, on a simple frequency distribution base, it is possible to include in each print-out a statement indicating the frequency with which a patient of the stated sex and age (and whatever other typifying characteristic may be available) has a profile of the same general (or specific) type.

The print-out, the report made available to the clinician user, is the ultimate product of such an automated scaling and interpretation system. It has to meet several specifications. Generally speaking, it has to resemble the kind of report that is ordinarily the final product of a clinical psychologist's examination. Thus, it contains a series of statements that interpet in relatively simple language the meaning of the scale profile. These have been derived from the published data on MMPI scales and clusters. They represent, therefore, a condensation of the information gleaned from an analysis of accumulated records over a period of many years. In addition to the usual identifying information on subject's name, age, sex, date of test and location of the station, to which the report is to be sent, the test preface includes notations on the number and the scale-locus of unanswered and both-answered statements. A minor addition to the program will permit an indication of the item number of the unanswered and both-answered statements. The raw and T-scores for each scale, as well as the raw score with a K-score factor, are also printed.

The body of the print-out lists in serial fashion those statements which correspond to scale elevations. It begins with branching statements that denote interpretations of scale clusters. The next to be printed in order of highest scale elevation are those statements from the library that correspond to the T-scores of the individual scales.

Inasmuch as these reports are designed for use by clinicians who are relatively unsophisticated in the interpretation of psychological test data, several precautions must be observed. First, the language used had to avoid technical psychiatric terms. It was recognized that while this is a semantic restriction to psychiatrists and psychologists, inasmuch as it tends to eliminate the connotations conveyed by such concepts as ego-strength, paranoidal, psychosexual conflict, acting-out, and so on, what terms are used convey meanings understood by and acceptable to a non-psychiatrist clinician.

Obviously, much more can be said on this question. Practically, the choice of the terms used in the reports is made on the basis of the user-audience for whom they are intended. To be sure, in the transliteration much information is lost that otherwise would be useful to a clinical psychiatrist or psychologist. Experience has demonstrated also that rather than the report's being limited to a description of the normatively deviant aspects of the profile, most physician-users are aided by the inclusion of statements that describe those personality characteristics within the normative range.

Comment: Conclusion

This entire program rests on its ability to facilitate an exchange between the physician and his patient. It strives to highlight those aspects of the patient's problem that lie beyond a descriptive evaluation of his anatomic and physiologic integrity. Therefore, the intended function of the print-out report is primarily catalytic. The physician is asked to incorporate these data as background information of both diagnostic and therapeutic relevance. Obviously, it does not replace the psychologist or the psychiatrist as consultants. Neither is it capable of being used to its optimal extent other than in the context of a complete and comprehensive examination.

Granting that such a device has a role in facilitating the processing of medical information by a clinician dealing vis-a-vis a patient, there are other benefits to be derived. Base-rate information necessarily requires the use of a standardized notation system employed in the tabulation of adequate samples of data on large populations. This epidemiologic approach to the psychiatric problem of sickness and well-being permits the more accurate assessment of patients. Comparisons and contrasts with patient peers, holding one or more variables constant, can be made with actuarially defined certainty. Thus, the accumulated data on various subpopulations of patients, categorized according to clinically established syndromes or sites of pathologic findings or diagnostic entities, or remedial procedures applied or any other criterion, can be gotten from frequency distribution tables or similar codification technics. In this fashion, clinical judgments can be leavened, in a manner well established in other areas of medical study, by the use of ancillary laboratory procedures.

Manifestly, this is an early, obviously primitive, attempt to augment the ordinary resources of clinical psychiatry. It attempts this by the use of a computer technology. It uses experience gained on a molecular level as an heuristic device to determine the relevance of these concepts to molar behavioral phenomena.

Reginald S. Lourie, MD
George Washington, Children's, Hillcrest

2

Constitutional Factors in the Genesis of the Neuroses

IF WE ARE TO ADHERE TO GENESIS, WE SHOULD OBSERVE THAT IN THE beginning neurosis was not. Children are not born neurotic: all that goes into the making of a neurosis had to develop from the basic ingredients with which an individual begins life and from what happens to them in the course of life experience. From what we know, these components of a neurosis have their origins in the first years of life. To understand their beginnings, let us examine these years.

Basic Mental Apparatus

The mind, to illustrate with a theoretical model of mental structure, is like a box (Fig. 1). The infant is born with a set of instincts, also known as urges or drives (1A), present and active at birth, with all the rest of the mental apparatus roughed in but not organized and functioning. As

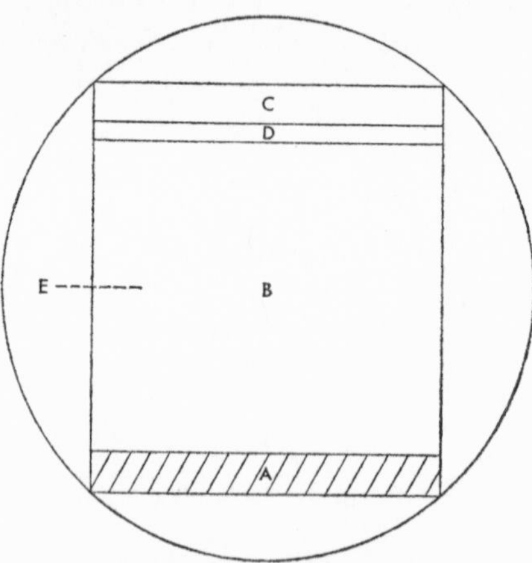

Fig. 1. Model of mental structure. *A:* instincts (*id*). *B:* unconscious and *C:* conscious (*ego*). *D:* censor-conscience (*superego*). *E:* environment.

myelinization proceeds and gray matter is laid down, the mental apparatus becomes a storehouse for every experience the individual encounters, most of which will remain out of his awareness (1B). As perception proceeds, there develops a part of the mind which the individual is aware of (1C), usually known as the conscious mind, in contrast to that out of awareness, the unconscious.

The body of experience in the unconscious mind is used to develop a control system, which determines the best way for the instincts to be expressed; it is made up of thousands of falls, bumps, no's, don'ts, and yeses. This process is part of building a defense system, which will be able to change the forms in which the instincts are expressed in accord with this body of experience and in such a way as to keep the organism in a state of homeostasis. A super control system between the conscious and unconscious part of the mind also develops (1D), which operates as a value system, censor, policeman, and includes what is usually described as the conscience. This system makes the ultimate decisions whether what is coming from the unconscious should be allowed in awareness, and whether what is in awareness, and what comes into consciousness from the outside world, should be allowed to stay in consciousness. The environment (1E) is where the signals and experience come from, and therefore it determines what kind of control system over the expression of drives and what type of censor or conscience is represented in the individual's mental apparatus. It takes three to five years for this process to crystallize sufficiently for the individual to begin to see himself as independent and able to function with the values and patterns of the environment now built in and ready for him to experiment with as a person in his own right.

The Programming of a Neurosis

Given these ingredients and structural components, let us review, a purposely oversimplified way, how a neurosis occurs. Usually, when the instincts plus the life experience to which they have been exposed are in conflict with the control system and the censor, the wish dictated by the instinct is repressed. However, later in life experience a large dose of inner or outer stimulus or a life situation may reactivate the conflict. Then there is the threat that what has been pushed out of sight and walled off (the repressed wish) can become a storm center again. It may threaten even to come out of the unconscious and into the individual's awareness. In order to prevent the breakthrough, since the walling off defense threatens to be ineffective, another defense or set of defenses is necessary to prevent this material from coming into awareness. When this defense pattern takes the form of exaggerated or extreme displacements, compulsiveness, projections, the resulting symptom picture often can be classified as a neurosis. For example, the displacements may take the form of conversion manifestations, the projections of phobias, the compulsiveness of a constricting type of warding off, isolating behavior or thinking. In these ways, compromises are made between the great pressure for conscious awareness and action from the stimulus reinforced instinct and the almost overwhelmed control system. The wish dictated by the instincts actually comes into awareness but in one of these disguises,

Some Significant Early Steps in Personality Development

Parallel to and intertwined with this process of mental development, a pattern of personality development is proceeding. Although often intertwined facets of development are evolving at the same time, for our purposes, especially for seeing the influence of constitutional factors, let us consider the evolution of one of the most important components of personality development, the development of relationships in the first year of life of the newborn.

Although, as is described later, multiple constitutional factors which have developed in prenatal life are already involved, when we look at a newborn in terms of relationships, he is not related to anyone. If we diagram this in the form of circles representing baby and mother (Fig. 2), we see that the newborn infant functions in relation to his mother tan-

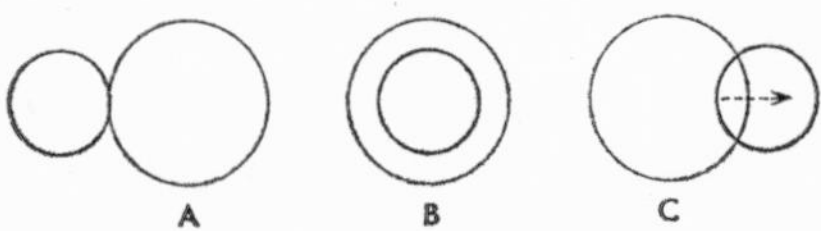

Fig. 2. Model of the newborn's development of relationships. *A:* at birth—with mother, tangential. *B:* by 3 to 5 months—complete dependence. *C:* about 8 months—beginning separation, slightly on his own.

gentially (2A). The equipment with which to be aware of people or of what goes on around him is not activated yet. He functions in terms of demonstrating that he has needs determined by the instincts. When these needs are met, he turns away; he sleeps 20 to 22 hours out of the 24.

As the mental apparatus matures and some perception is available to him, the baby begins to realize that his needs are met by recognizable, predictable objects: at first experienced as a breast or a bottle, then, slowly, as a person attached to breast or bottle. This person begins to mean a great deal more than meeting the needs for supplies, warmth, comfort and the pleasures of being close to and involved with another person. By 3 to 5 months, this process has advanced sufficiently that the baby begins to see himself, if development proceeds in uncomplicated patterns, only as part of and completely dependent on another person (2A).

If there is a single most important stage of development, it is this concept of being part of another person, of being dependent. If an individual does not learn what it is like to be part of another person, knowing that its dependency needs will be met, this concern with dependency has priority over any other drive and type of relationship, even on into adulthood. The first interest in any relationship of such a deprived individual at any age will be to determine first whether dependency needs will be met. We can picture therefore how serious it would be if something were to interfere with the achievement of this step.

In the constitutional makeup of the infant, and in his early life experience, are many possible hazards to making this first move toward relationships. If there is such a hazard, an individual baby can decide not to invest in relationships, and if so, he can remain in the unrelated state (2A). We then call it autistic, and if he continues in this pattern until later in childhood, we call him schizophrenic. However, the drive for normality is so great and the need to establish dependency is so strong that even despite handicaps, constitutional distortions or life experience, the individual often makes efforts to achieve this concept of being able to trust another to meet needs. Sometimes this step can be made with only partial success, so that he may not be able to see himself completely as part of another person. He can reserve the right for himself to retreat from relationships when necessary, thus going back and forth between relatedness and unrelatedness. Some children may be able to make only tentative gestures in the direction of being dependent. In the process of early mother-infant adaptation, when a mother is not able to read the signals given by the baby, or interprets his needs in distorted ways, or provides too little or too much or the wrong kind of stimulation, we also have hazards to the development of this first and most important stage of personality development, particularly when there is some constitutional distortion to start with.

The last stage of personality development to illustrate the point of this chapter also occurs within the first year. It appears when the infant has so matured that he is capable of being on his own for at least short periods of time. He develops enough motor control to be able to crawl, so that he can begin to explore. This phase is usually at its height at about 8 months of age. The infant now, on his own, can begin to emerge from his picture of being completely part of another person and move out at least a little from within his mother's orbit (2C). This stage is made possible also by increased perception, which allows him to be aware of the differences between the people closest to him and strangers.

At the same time that the baby is enjoying his new-found ability to expand his horizons and explore his environment, clouds appear on the new horizons. New people, new situations present dangers. Fear is in evidence. We may think of it as normal fear, because it is almost universal. This fear, usually called separation anxiety, shows up in terms not only of strangers and unfamiliar places, but also of new routines, new foods and such.

This is the prototype of many of the later, more sophisticated fears that we expect in the developing child, and is at its height with each major step toward independence. If it is not dealt with in ways that will allow its resolution in its earliest form, separation anxiety, the later fears are often exaggerated. They may continue for the rest of an individual's life even in their earliest forms, and can provide the groundwork for the development of a neurosis. We all have seen adults still afraid of strangers and new situations, often with phobic defenses.

When we examine these fears, it becomes apparent that not only poor handling but also constitutional factors can help perpetuate them.

Constitutional Factors in the Instincts

The constitutional factors are involved in creating the conflicts or fixations that are the core elements in the neuroses which may develop later in childhood. The instincts underly every stage of personality development. What are they? From the constitutional point of view, they are physiologically determined pressures, such as are involved in metabolism and in as yet incompletely understood organic and tissue pressures, that build up and call for relief in order to maintain homeostasis within the organism. Constitutionally in each individual, these instincts vary qualitatively and quantitatively. Let us put them, for our purposes, into three categories:

1. *The instinct for self-preservation.* These instincts put pressures on the organism to keep the body going, growing and intact, free from damage, metabolic needs met with necessary supplies.

2. *The instinct for race preservation* (the sexual drives). This group of instincts may be more difficult to understand in an infant. Perhaps they may be thought of best, constitutionally, in terms of hormonal pressures on the organism, requiring relief from organic tensions that they create. In the blood streams of all infants and children, male and female sex hormones circulate. We cannot assume that only in adolescence is the individual called on to respond to these pressures. We can assume, however, that only after the child is past at least infancy can it begin to respond to these drives in ways that would be called sexual in the usual, genital terms. The infant is obviously unable to respond physically or mentally in any way that would resemble adult or even later childhood sexual expression. However, since it is under pressure to relieve these hormone-induced tensions, the avenues open for such relief are in the use of the body and its functions in pleasurable ways. This may be accomplished in terms of mouth function, as thumb sucking, of the motor system, as rocking or other rhythmic patterns of motor activity, and so on.

3. *The aggressive drives.* These are the forces that push the individual into action in order to satisfy the pressures exerted by the other two sets of drives. Constitutionally, this drive force illustrates well the qualitative and quantitative variations in the strengths of the instincts. Some infants are born with a very small amount of aggressive drive, while others are born with much more than they would need simply for use in the service of the other two sets of instincts. Thus, in the newborn nursery, we can see the differences between the infant who when hungry will demand, fuss, kick and yell, in contrast to the infant who when hungry lies back and waits.

Constitutional Factors Influencing Personality Development

Ingredients for the Genesis of Neuroses

Let us now see how the process of personality development is influenced by the constitutional factors in both the instincts and the components that make up the control system (Fig. 1B, D). Each new step in personality development is influenced by the interaction of all the instincts with the emerging body components and functions as they become activated. Once a new step in development is achieved or a new function is mastered, the individual then experiments with the ever-present problem: How can this new-found part of me be used for the satisfaction of the drives? Growth and maturity thus involve a continuous process of finding more and more new appropriate ways of satisfying the pressures on the organism to deal with these drives. As this process takes place, very often the drives fuse with each other. Biting, for example, necessary for intake of supplies, may become a pleasurable, aggressive activity.

If there are constitutional variations in the instincts, some of them, conceivably, could be such that they might interfere with the orderly progression of personality development. Suppose something in the makeup of the instincts gets in the way of the first step in relationships, which we indicated as the most important—that is, moving in the first 3 to 5 months from the unrelated to the completely dependent state. Taking the instinct for self-preservation as an example, one of its manifestations would be hunger. The feeding process is one large part of the infant's experience that helps him become attached to the person involved in relieving hunger. One of the components in producing the feeling of hunger is uropepsinogen in the stomach. The studies of Mirsky indicate that it is possible to think of some babies as being born with an extremely large secretion of uropepsinogen. Such a baby would always feel hungry, no matter how much food he was given. Thus, he is asked to make his first step in personality development, toward dependency, on a basis in which he feeling that the people he is dependent on cannot satisfy him, cannot ever completely meet his needs. Thus, the first step may never be accomplished, since some children may feel so mistrustful or so much anxiety that they feel safer in an unrelated or autistic state. Even if they do establish a shaky type of dependency relationship, their expectation, from the beginning, is that in closeness with other people they will never be taken care of properly. We can see then how we have the basis for a conflict situation—a basic ingredient of the neurosis in process.

The organic components of the ego apparatus include the various forms of perception. Suppose something in the makeup of one of the forms of perception—for example, the sense of touch—represents a constitutional distortion. Some babies are born with tactile hypersensitivity, and experience being touched as painful. We tell mothers to hold their babies, cuddle them, fondle them, in order to facilitate the first step in relationship development, to help to see themselves as part of another person. The baby hypersensitive to touch, however, experiences this cuddling and fondling as so painful that he turns away from the mother. Again we see a situation in which the baby may elect to remain unrelated. The pain involved may make it more comfortable for the child to be aloof and distant rather than close. Immediately we have a hazard to the accomplishing of the most important first step in personality development. We may look at this situation a few years later and say that this is a rejecting mother because she has little to do with her child, especially in terms of closeness. However, if we discover how this situation evolved in the presence of this special sensitivity, we can see that it is the mother who was rejected. A mother, some more tolerant than others, can be expected to pour herself out to a child only for so long; she eventually gives up.

However, we do not always end up with autistic, unrelated children under these conditions. The tactile hypersensitivity may be in a child whose need to be dependent on another person may be so strong that he will make the first relationship step in spite of the resulting pain and discomfort. One way he can accomplish this is by "saying": "If pain is necessary for me to achieve this dependence, then pain must be part of the relationship." In fact, some individuals with this makeup can go further and "say": "Pain is my pleasure." You will recognize in this the development, even in the first year of life, of masochism, shown as a need and sometimes pleasure in being hurt. We can also recognize here a component found in many of the later neuroses, which can originate from constitutional influences. In a neurotic symptom such as claustrophobia, there is classically the need to ward off the wish to be dependent, i.e. to be completely taken care of, as symbolized in the closed space. However, if dependency is remembered as painful, then being in the dependency relationship—i.e. symbolically the closed space—must be defended against at all costs. We can see the roots of such a concept in the interaction of constitutional factors, such as we are describing, being "imprinted" in the relationship concepts of the individual.

Because we have better obstetrics and pediatrics, we save more babies who might otherwise have died or not been born. Some of those that we save have brain damage, which, often mild, not only may include perceptual defects, such as hypersensitivities, but also may contribute to organically based conditions, which can be hazards to orderly development. Visual-motor difficulties leading to motor awkwardness, or even delays, can lead to a change in the timetable of the stages of personality development. Thus, a child may need to be dependent longer than usual and therefore to be afraid of separation longer than usual. If he is pushed into independence too early, again we find the nucleus of a later neurosis in a continuing wish for dependency that is forbidden. Also in such situations we find that the developmental delays can lead to exaggerated and perpetuated fears of bodily hurt (which normally appear in the second and third years of life). So again we see coming from the original constitutional determinants a potent factor in later neurotic patterns.

Where there is overstimulation of the organism, the defense systems move in to attempt to maintain homeostasis. A high level of uropepsinogen secretion might create such a situation, but other types of overstimulation can have origins in the constitutional makeup of the infant. One of the most difficult combinations to deal with clinically is the child who has a constitutionally determined high level of motor activity (which may already be evident in the prenatal period) and a poor control apparatus. Another is the child born with a large component of interest in mouth stimulation and activity in the presence of a poor control apparatus. To defend against the organism's being flooded by a high level of excitation, various solutions are sought.

One solution that paves the way for later difficulties is the development of rigidity of affect and constriction of thinking as a device to keep from being overwhelmed by excitation. Thus, the child gives up its potential for flexibility in personality development, a most important asset in learning how to deal with the multiple standards that children are expected to adjust to later. We can also recognize in this type of rigidity the precursors of compulsive thinking, another core element of some neuroses. When brain damage exists as the basis for the poorly controlled hyperactivity, there may be accompanying concreteness of thinking, also of organic origin, which in itself predisposes to lack of flexibility. This combination may make flexibility much more difficult to achieve.

When overstimulation on an internal level is met with encouragement to continue or even enhance its manifestations, this may result in a given stimulus–response becoming a major goal or preoccupation. This can lay the groundwork for a fixation, again a starting point for some neuroses. When constitutionally based overstimulation is uncontrolled, some young children feel helpless. This not only leads to increased dependency but can lead to a quite poor self-image. Feelings of inadequacy can progress, and as concepts of right and wrong develop, move on to having a picture of themselves as being bad. A depressive core of this kind can be laid down by preschool, leaving the way open to depressive forms of neurosis, among other possible solutions.

Another symptom complex that can result from this constellation of overendowment of drive, especially aggressive drive, is the impulse disorder. Its later manifestations, such as impulsive character formation, can have neurotic as well as constitutional roots (Michaels).

Recent work at the Children's Hospital of Washington, DC, has shown that young children born with a great deal of interest in mouth satisfaction and stimulation can develop pica if exposed to care in which mothering is unavailable to keep the impulses under control. This form of craving for objects and substances not fit for food has not only been dangerous when children have turned to eating plaster, paint and woodwork resulting in lead poisoning from their pica; there is also some early evidence that these early cravings represent a neurotic predisposition for the development of similar cravings later in life. Oral cravings thus seem to reappear when a similar type of lack of dependency in the face of helplessness is encountered later in the life of the individual. Thus a constitutionally determined symptom leads to a personality response which might be thought of as indicating "addiction proneness." In an "addiction prone" adult, when such a craving recurs, the individual may turn to alcohol or food with familiar results.

Using Lois Murphy's (1965) concept of a vulnerability check list, it is possible to catalogue the constitutional distortions with which an individual is struggling. In addition to the more obvious physical handicaps, such as gross auditory, visual, motor and vestibular deficits, there may be structural differences in body build leading to sufficient unusualness in appearance or functioning that it may make for difficulties in social acceptability and/or the child's own feelings of acceptability (obesity [Heald], short legs, ectomorphism [Sheldon], asymmetries.) Special sensitivities in perception or poor tolerance for anxiety, displeasure, sudden change or stimulation, marked autonomic lability and excessive somatic responses to stress—these are additional examples of hazards that may complicate the developmental tasks of infancy and childhood. Persistent imbalances, such as drives being more intense than control capacities, may lead to impulsiveness. Deviations in rates of development, though still in normal ranges, are among the more common constitutional factors responsible for adjustment and body-image problems. When such growth differences occur in the school years, they can lead to alienation from the individual's peer group.

One of the most important yet least well understood constitutional determinants of behavior is the individual's degree of flexibility, particularly in being able to cope with anxiety, stress, changes and more than one standard. Murphy suggests that innate passivity, predisposition to restriction (inability to adapt the body to the environment), limited ability for physical and communicative expression, wide diffusion and overflow of affect (leading to poor control), and direct impulse-expression (requiring no delay in response) are organically based components of the capacity to respond with flexibility.

Another important and yet relatively undefined constitutional component is a tendency to a disorganization of thinking and acting under stress. This has been called a perceptual-cognitive vulnerability, experienced as a loss of integration or optimal level of functioning in cognitive areas in the presence of anxiety. It may lead to inhibitions, paralysis of action, loss of impulse control, loss of clarity and appropriateness.

To diagnose even mild degrees of constitutional disturbance, which have not been compensated for or satisfactorily modified in the earlier phases of development, is important. Personality distortions and behavior patterns stemming from or protective of even the mild constitutional difficulties are not prone to change if their determinants are taken into account.

Patterns of Behavior

The constitutional makeup of a given child results in an individual temperament or style. Fries's description of activity types and, more recently, the studies of Chess, Thomas and Birch have made available an understanding of the handling which certain types of children need if neuroses and other defensive patterns are to be avoided. The latter authors have cataloged the individual, constitutionally determined patterns of behavior under nine headings, described as follows:

1. Activity level. Some babies are from early infancy much more active than others. Even toward the end of feeding, when most babies are quiet and sleepy, they move their arms, lift their heads, kick, or—if they are on their backs—move their bodies till the covers are off. This goes on right to the moment their eyes shut. Even when asleep, they often move from spot to spot in the crib. Their mothers can never turn away for a moment if these infants are in the bathinet, for fear they will squirm out; diapering them is a problem because they twist and turn so much.

In contrast, the quiet babies tend to lie where they are placed and move both little and slowly. Sometimes they are almost as still when awake as when asleep; often only their eyes move.

2. *Regularity.* Babies differ in the regularity of their biologic functioning. Some seem born with built-in alarm clocks. By the second or third week they are hungry at regular times. Their mothers can plan the day's activities around the babies' predictable nap and feeding times. Their bowel movements are regular. Others are quite different. There is no telling when they will be hungry, how hungry they will be, or when they will be hungry next. Their naps might be short one day and long the next.

3. *Approach or withdrawal as a characteristic response to a new situation.* Young babies have new experiences every day—the first bath, the first taste of orange juice, the first solid food. New people are constantly coming into their lives. They go out in the carriage for the first time. A bonnet is put on. They get a first injection. They go into a playpen for the first time.

The category of approach-withdrawal characterizes the child's initial reaction to any new stimulus pattern, whether food, people, places, toys, or procedures. Some babies have no trouble with these new experiences: in the first bath they take to the water like ducks. Others, however, do not splash and kick, or coo and play with their mothers: they scream when put into the bath for the first time. They spit out many new foods at first, cry at a stranger and react negatively to strange places.

4. *Adaptability to change in routine.* Babies' routines constantly shift. When they begin solid foods, the number of meals gradually declines. In the first days, they almost constantly sleep or doze, but then their naps become less frequent. In considering a child's adaptability there is the step-by-step development of responses to new situations or altered routines. In contrast to approach-withdrawal, here the concern is not with the initial response, but with the ease or difficulty with which this response can be modified in socially desirable ways.

Some babies shift easily and quickly with a changing schedule. They readily learn to eat a little earlier or later and go to bed at a different hour. In general, they change their behavior to fit in with the pattern the mother wants to set. With others, a change in routine brings fussing and crying or screaming and kicking. Only with difficulty and much repetition are mothers successful in shaping the child's behavior. On occasion these babies do not adapt at all. Instead, it is the mother who often adjusts to the child's pattern rather than continue the unsuccessful struggle to impose her preferences.

5. *Level of sensory threshold.* Some mothers feel fortunate because they can have a houseful of visitors without worrying at all about awakening the baby. Babies with a high "sensory threshold," as it is called, do not startle at loud noises; bright lights don't bother them. Whether clothes are smooth or rough, wool or cotton, hot or cold, makes little difference. They are not particularly discriminating about food. Their mothers can easily disguise something the baby doesn't like by adding it to something 'good.' They do not react to being wet or soiled.

At the other extreme are babies who cry the moment they are soiled. There are sensitive ones who, even in the first weeks, wake when a light is turned on in the room or a door latch clicks. Some literally shudder at even a whiff of a disliked food. A slight sound will attract their attention, and their eyes will move towards it. One mother can always tell when her husband is home, because her six-month old can hear his footsteps in the hall outside the apartment and will start to coo and kick.

Response to pain varies. One baby can bang his head hard against the crib bars without a whimper. For another, a slight bump will bring howls of discomfort.

6. Positive or negative mood. Some children react negatively from the beginning, crying when awakened, when a door closes, when put down. Others smile before getting a bottle, gurgle when being dressed, coo in the bath, babble when they wake. Some are neutral.

7. Intensity of response. One baby lets his mother know he is hungry with a loud piercing cry; another cries softly—two examples of the range of intensity of the children's reactions. Both children are crying, but one is expending considerably more energy than the other. When a behavior is characterized by a high level of energy expenditure, it is judged as intense. When the energy expenditure is low, the response is considered mild. One baby may open his mouth for a second spoonful of food he likes without any other movements: a response of mild intensity. Another may open his mouth, turn toward the dish, and strain actively toward the spoon with his whole body: a response of high intensity. The child of preponderantly low intensity smiles gently, but his more vigorous companion chortles, gurgles, and kicks when he is happy.

The intensity of response does not relate to whether the child is showing positive or negative mood, but to the energy expressed in his behavior.

8. Distractibility. Some babies seem able to concentrate better than others. The nondistractible child will usually drink from his bottle until he is full, no matter what is going on around him. The ringing of the telephone will cause only the most momentary pause in sucking. He will ignore passers-by or even active efforts to win his attention. The distractible infant, crying when hungry or hurt, can be diverted with a rattle or by being picked up or talked to. The nondistractible one continues to bellow until he tastes milk. No amount of juggling, cooing, or stroking will alter his direction of behavior.

9. Persistence and attention span. It may sound strange to talk about persistence in newborn babies, but it can be seen even in very young infants. There is great variation in the ability of different babies to continue an activity in the face of difficulties or to resume it after interruption. Some children suck very persistently at the nipple with small holes, even if little milk is coming through; others give up quickly. The persistent infant keeps trying to reach a toy that is out of reach; the nonpersistent tries for only a few minutes. If he objects to having his face washed, the persistent baby keeps pulling his face away; the nonpersistent gives in after a brief struggle. The child with a long span of attention gazes at his cradle gym intently for half an hour; the same baby, a year later, will stick with one toy for quite a long period. A baby with a short attention span, on the other hand, will focus only briefly on any activity or aspect of the environment; at a year and a half he might flit from toy to toy, spending very little time with any one of them.

Summary

An attempt has been made in this chapter to picture how psychiatry in the mid-60's is turning increasingly to emphasize the constitutional components that influence the mental makeup of the individual. This has been done by taking a traditional (psychoanalytic) concept of mental structure, early personality development and psychodynamics underlying a neurosis, and illustrating how recent developments in defining individual constitutional differences add dimensions to our understanding of this concept. (Any other theory of the genesis of neuroses could have been similarly used). Currently, even more detailed studies of infant responses and basic makeup, such as those by Wolff and by Richmond and Lipton, give promise of more definitive understanding of the role of these factors in later mental health and pathology.

The emphasis on the role of the individual's constitution is not new. However, the recent developments make possible a new subspecialty in psychiatry that might be called infant psychiatry. It is in this earliest period of life that our greatest hopes for primary prevention of mental illness must turn, even in our poverty programs. The next steps require the application in programs of what is being learned about constitutional differences—at least until there are technics developed to deal with these factors even before an individual is born.

Jules H. Masserman, MD
Northwestern

3

Anxiety: Aspects and Answers*

IN THE BEGINNING WAS THE WORD—AND THAT WORD, THEN AS NOW, MIGHT well have been *anxiety*. Since the English language has no more protean term, not excepting the almost equally poetic concepts of *narcissism* or *love*, a survey of its multiple meanings, in their philologic, historical, and clinical perspectives, may be our first task.

Aspects of Anxiety

Dictionary definitions, which reflect the semantic origins and evolutionary wealth of our language, are often more illuminating than technical strictures: thus, the *Oxford English Dictionary* (unabridged) notes that *anxiety* was derived from the Latin *angere*, indicating an intuitive link between hostile impulses and fear of retribution. From this sprang three derivative meanings: *anguish* (anticipated distress), *solicitude* (empathy with a fellow victim of fate), and *vital endeavor* (man's motivations to explore and control). But it is relevant to all three that German *Angst*, as used by Freud, also has the echoes of *limitation* and *constraint*.

Historically, the ancient Hebrews recognized the eternal struggle between *Yetzer Haráh* (Force of Destruction) and *Yetzer Hatóv* (Spirit of Good), just as the Hindus counterposed *Siva* and *Vishnu* and the Taoists *Yin* and *Yang*. Without adequate reasons, classical Western sages were more confident both of man's intellectual powers and his moral self-determination: the Ionic philosophers anticipated modern physical and cosmic theories, Socrates taught that a "rational social order" would solve all of man's anxieties, and Aristotle assured his complacent Academicians that man's knowledge of physical and biologic phenomena would eventually establish his supremacy over nature. When it did not occur during the next eight centuries, St. Augustine, tiring of Manichaean mysteries and Dionysian satisfactions, authoritatively advised everyone else to practice Ambrosian religious austerity.

However, most men, faced with environmental stresses they could not dissipate by currently available physical and technical means, characteristically reverted to what I have called our ultimate (Ur) defenses:

---

* Portions of this chapter, in another version, have been published in Masserman, J. H., ed.: *Science and Psychoanalysis: Communication and Community*, vol. VIII, New York, Grune and Stratton, 1965.

dereistic denials, demographic deployments or deistic demonologies. In effect, men who could not cope with what they regarded as overwhelming threats got drunk and dissipated, or contracted opportunistic human alliances against fellowmen, or sought magical power by cajoling or bribing a pantheon of gods conceived and controlled in man's image. A classical example of the first Ur-escape is furnished by Thucydides, who thus described the Plague of Athens in 480 B.C.

> Men resolved to get out of life the pleasures which could be had speedily and would satisfy their lusts, regarding their bodies and their wealth alike as transitory. No fear of gods or law restrained them; for on the one hand, seeing that all men were perishing alike, they judged that piety and impiety came to the same thing; and on the other hand, no one expected that he would live to be called to account and pay the penalty for his misdeeds. On the contrary, they believed that the penalty already decreed against them and now hanging over their heads was a heavier one and that before it fell it was only reasonable to get some enjoyment out of life.

So also, when the Black Death had ravaged Europe for 300 years, despite man's futile devices of fires, philters and fasts, Michelangelo confessed "no thought is born in me that has not Death engraved on it," and George Wicher observed:

> Some streets Tavernes had, rude revelles keeping.
> Some had churches full of people weeping.
> Within some houses, Psalmes and Hymnes were sung.
> With rayling and loud scoldings others rung.

Again, in a later outbreak when all human life seemed to be as much in danger as it is in our nuclear age, the three anxiety-relieving maneuvers —escape, aggression and mysticism—were once more brought into full play: drunkenness was rampant; Queen Elizabeth, by divine right, hanged anyone who dared approach Windsor Castle; those less privileged killed Jews by the tens of thousands to please the gentle Jesus, and the revels of the Dancing Manias and the Black Sabbath spread throughout Europe.

Only as man's trepidations abated did gentler self-reassurance in the classic manner reappear in the art of the Renaissance and the reawakened confidence of the *nuova scienza.* DaVinci now glorified bodily strength and beauty; Vives founded associationist psychology as the basis of all human knowledge and understanding, and Nicholas Cusa and Nikolaj Kopernik founded modern astronomy—although, in a continuation of man's cosmic arrogance, they regarded the movements of the planets as also designed to predict the fate of the minor princelings who were their patrons. Only when the Religious Wars had almost completely abated did men resume the even more complacent egocentricities epitimized by Descartes' *Cogito ergo sum* or Spinoza's more reflective solipsism:

> I saw that all the things I feared, and which feared me had nothing good or bad in them save insofar as my mind is affected by them. . . . Fear cannot be without hope, nor hope without fear (for) all is Nature and God.

Leibnitz, in accord with the new Baconian spirit, felt called on to materialize this hope that all that exists is in the service of mankind, by postulating that, whereas the ultimate "monads" which constitute the universe were "completely discrete and independent," they must nevertheless conform to the "laws of cosmic harmony" and thus create for humans a "perfect social order." But Pascal, reverting to Jansenite mysticism, was once again less sanguine:

> When I consider the brief span of my life, swallowed up in the eternity before and behind it, the small space that I fill, or even see, engulfed in the intimate immensity of spaces which I know not, and which know not of me—I am afraid.

Regarding such premonitions of what is now called existential anxiety as being intolerable, subsequent emphathizers with man's dilemma again compounded more or less nebulous Ur-negations, Ur-norms or Ur-nepenthics. Berkeley denied reality; Kant restructured the universe according to his own convenient "categories"; Schopenhauer imperiously subjugated the world to his Will and Idea; Nietzsche extolled the amoral Superman; Marx advocated revolution leading to the abolition of all politico-economic controls, and Goethe (emulating Luther) used his Faustian inkwell to defy the Devil himself. With even greater monothetic fervor, Comte tried to reduce all sociology to a mathematical science (and ended by worshipping his dead wife as the Supreme Goddess of a new religion); Kafka pleaded piteously with man's unknown judges to specify their dark accustions; Santayana justified theology because of its "beauty"; Thoreau sought an earthly Walden, and Kierkegaard abandoned all reason in favor of an intensity of vital experience that was at once an acknowledgment and a defiance of a death-dealing God—an heroic stand that, minus even the comforts of a theistic faith, was also assumed variously by Sartre and the late Albert Camus. Yet despite such fervid philosophies, man's manifold anxieties remained.

Psychoanalytic Concepts

Sigmund Freud, idolized by his family as a genius and raised in an Hebraic-Hasidic tradition that included the notion of innate but unrecognized evil (the "Id"), preoccupation with sexuality ("libido"), the ritualized confessions to the rabbi as teacher ("emotional catharsis"), the hidden meanings of dreams ("symbolic interpretation") and other protoanalytic concepts and practices (*cf.* D. Bakan), took readily to the introspective philosophies of his day and, in his own narcissistic-syncretic manner, colored them with his 17th-century faith in "pure reason" ("Where Id was, there shall Ego be"), a melange of Hartmann's arcane fantasies about the "unconscious," a transposition of the neural hierarchies of Hughlings Jackson (psychologized topologically as Id, Ego and Superego) and the quasierotic interpretations of mesmeric phenomena he had observed in Charcot's and Bernheim's clinics. Then, with charismatically effective conviction, Freud also claimed that his new doctrines would modify many of the social and sexual prohibitions of his day, and thus imparted to his teachings (as Comte had done to his mystic version of sociology and as, with different pseudoscientific pretensions, Mary Baker Eddy had done with Christian Science) not only the attractions of avant-garde social protest but also the trappings of a newly revealed and ritualized religion.

In the latter respect, indeed, "classical" psychoanalysis offered a recorded and annotated bible of Freudian gospels setting forth simple concepts of an intrapsychic Trinity, other dogmatic propositions exquisitely religious in form in that they were quite insusceptible of either proof or disproof (*cf.* Popper), a quasimystic ritual of indoctrination that held forth salvation through faith in the teachings of the Master, a roster of early disciples (later to be individually canonized), and special studies of their exegetical writings, with the apocrypha of Jung, Adler, Rank, Sullivan, Horney and others fallen from grace specifically proscribed. Finally, after years of service as an acolyte, the seminary graduate received a public anointment that conferred on him the priestly privileges of hearing the confessional in a soundproof retreat sanctified by the order's ikons and images, receiving liberal tithes and comforting the laity by the absolution of sin and the revelation of Ultimate Truth.

Parenthetically, the current movement among orthodox analysts (e.g., Gitelson, 1964) to extend these special privileges to our nonmedical confreres may be related in part to the likelihood that some (fortunately not all) members of these latter groups, in contrast to physicians with more disciplined scientific training and clinical experience, are more likely to believe that a solemn verbal incantation presented as an "analytic interpretation" can in itself change any cherished pattern of behavior. I have elsewhere defined "insight" in such circumstances as "that mutually happy state in which the patient shares the current illusions of his therapist." Of particular interest here, however, are Freud's own successive (but unfortunately less comprehensive) definitions of anxiety and its neurotic manifestations.

In 1894, Freud first attributed "anxiety neurosis" to a supposed "toxin . . . produced by frustraneous sexual excitement, the free floating anxiety being ready to attach itself to any ideational content, such as phobias and obsessions." In later writings, Freud wisely abandoned such elementary biologizing and instead traced anxiety to the experience of external restraint and prohibition. "Anxiety as a signal of danger . . . mediated by the Ego" now *produced* "repression" rather than vice versa, the "impulses repressed" being those that might entail "loss of love, castration and social [internalized "superego"] condemnation." Freud then assured us that analytic therapy "will bring this unknown *instinctual* danger (again, not an acquired apprehension of external consequences) into consciousness and, in this way, the neurotic or instinctual anxiety becomes a *real* anxiety, anxiety over a *known* danger [italics mine]. . . . Real anxiety—that is, fear of others—is then resolved in the transference which . . . should end in a heartfelt human relationship." However, since Freud also implied that all reality is "psychic" and equated all social punishment, including "loss of love," with symbolic "castration," these subdivisions of anxiety remained somewhat tenuous, as did his distinction between "real" and "neurotic" anxiety. The subsequent analytic literature on anxiety has unfortunately continued to be similarly equivocal.

Post-Freudian. Otto Rank's concept of birth trauma has often been interpreted too literally as physical suffering or injury to the neonate; actually, Rank meant what is now called "separation anxiety," whereas it was Freud who, in accordance with his first formula for anxiety, conceived of the birth trauma as a "flooding" of the newborn's immature nervous system with unaccustomed stimuli. Piaget and Odier, like Rank, thought of birth in terms of "abandonment," a precondition of what Fromm-Reichmann discerned in the adult as "loneliness."

For Alfred Adler and Karen Horney, anxiety represented the apprehension of a threat to the "life style" or the "self-image" of the subject; as Erik Erikson has more recently pointed out, this could lead to an agonizing confusion of "partial identities" in adolescents who have not been helped to develop clear values and goals.

Other current combinations and permutations of these concepts may be summarized.

Roy Grinker, Sr., believes that whereas "animals may become alert and vigilant," only self-reflective humans can know anxiety as conscious dread of the future—though this would in turn raise the question what else the animals could be "vigilant" about. Paul Tillich is predictably more somberly reflective: "Normal anxiety is equatable with the finiteness of man," whereas for Rollo May, "Anxiety is occasioned by a threat to *any* value considered essential"—hence anxiety-relieving drugs may prevent or confuse effective conduct.

Kurt Goldstein differentiates "fear, which leads to adaptation," from "anxiety, which may result in catastrophic paralysis"; hence, psychotherapy should be deliberately designed to convert vitiating anxieties into realistic fears leading to appropriate action. Yet, on the basis of extensive military experience, A. J. Glass has once again come full circle in questioning the validity of sharp distinctions between fear and anxiety, since both cover widely overlapping ranges of helplessness in the face of variably sensed insecurities, both are inextricably mixed with trepidation, dread, anger or other equally protean "affects," both are expressed in identical physiologic reactions, and both are relieved when the anxious or fearful subject believes, with whatever illusions, that his safety and well-being have been restored through the efficacy of his Ur-defensive gadgets, groups or gods.

Ur-anxieties. If, then, the *essential* features of all of these concepts were to be combined, anxiety could be operationally defined as a repressed apprehension of earlier dangers easily reevoked by situational symbols to which the individual has become psychologically hypersensitive and somatically hyperactive. In 1953, I attempted to correlate this definition with the deeper and perhaps ultimate Ur-sources of man's trepidations:

Man's Ur-anxieties are three: first, his abhorrence of physical injury and death; second, his uncertainty as to the reliability of his human alliances; third, his utter rejection of the thought that perhaps he is, after all, a little more than a cosmic triviality. It is equally significant that these triple trepidations of man also motivate his principal modes of presumed mastery: first, his attempt to subjugate his material milieu through various sciences and technologies; next, his efforts to safeguard his social security by familial, economic, political and military alliances; and finally, his endeavors to encompass the entire universe in his philosophic and religious systems.*

Physiologic Substrate of Anxiety

Since, then, anxiety has connoted almost every conceivable combination of motives, experience,† affects and ideas, it is hardly surprising that the more carefully conceived and controlled the search for its anatomic nidus or physiologic accompaniments, the less definitive the results. In this regard, history again furnishes the proper perspective.

Two and a half millennia ago, Aristotle traced the source of "entelechy" of all behavior to the heart, Erasistratos to the cerebellum and Herophilus to the third ventricle; more wisely, Democritus distributed the functions of the human soul among the liver (desire), heart (anger), and brain (reason). Galen taught that "will and feeling" originated in the rhombencephalon, whereas Descartes, always seeking concentric symmetry, designated the pineal. Turning to the periphery, William James (1884) proposed that all "emotions," including anxiety, were perceived as secondary to visceral reactions; almost simultaneously, G. C. Lange (ergo, the James-Lange theory) stressed the vascular component, and a decade later John Dewey, and subsequently H. Kantor and J. Drever, called attention to the necessity of bodily *frustrations* in the genesis of affect.

However, all such visceropoetic speculations were challenged by the clinical observations of Sherrington (1900) and the experimental work of Cannon, Lewis and Britton (1927), which demonstrated that interference with the afferent somesthetic or efferent spinal pathways to the viscera did not markedly influence affective reactions. On this and other evidence, H. Head (1921) returned to the thalamus as the affective center, and W. Cannon (1931) and P. Bard added the concept of emotional-ideational resonance *via* thalamocortical radiations. Leeper (1948) pointed out that since "affects mobilized action" rather than disorganized it, distinct cere-

---

* T. R. Sarbin has very recently pointed out that the term anxiety was not used in psychology before Freud's writings and that, like Descartes' concept of "soul," it is still merely a metaphorical reification unnecessarily postulated between distal events in a "real" world and their physiologic, subjective and behavioral consequences in a designated individual. Sarbin, without reference to my earlier concepts of the three basic Ur-defenses, expands the sources of anxiety to five "cognitive strains" or threats: self-concept (*what* am I?), time-space orientations (*where* am I?), social function (*who* am I?), normative performance (*how well* am I doing?), and transcendental concern (*why* am I?).

† The observations of Divenberg and Whembey throw a sidelight on the "familial" transmission on early experiences: when rat pups are raised by adult mothers who had been mishandled in their own infancy, the pups show various behavioral disturbances not shown by controls raised by normal natural or foster mothers. Cf. Harlow.

bral circuits for the various "emotions" were unlikely; nevertheless, Arnold (1950) assigned separate cortical pathways for fear, anger and sexual excitement.

Diencephalon. Meanwhile, on the basis of observations by Cannon, Bard, Rioch, Ranson, *et al.*, that stimulation of the hypothalamus produced "sham rage" or "pseudoanxiety" in cats, this portion of the diencephalon had been designated by Alvarez, Serota and others as the "center of emotion." However, stimulation of the hypothalamus in human subjects by J. C. White produced only cardiac slowing and drowsiness, and a series of animal studies by Masserman *et al.* indicated that whereas the hypothalamus was undoubtedly a coordinating way station on the visceromotor pathways for emotional expression, it was in all probability not a "center" that either "originated" or "experienced" subjective affect.

Limbic circuits. As long ago as 1878, Broca had noted that the limbic lobes were prominent in all mammals capable of versatile "emotional" responses, and von Economo, a generation before Moruzzi and Magoun, had attributed activating functions to the periaqueductal gray and mesencephalic reticulum. In 1937, J. W. Papez suggested that the rhinencephalon, in which the neural circuits of olfaction had been primarily concerned with escaping from danger, securing food and finding mates, now also mediated "emotions" via connections to the hippocampus, amygdalae, cingulum, cuneus and diencephalon. P. McLean (1955) then proposed that these circuits constituted a "visceral brain," which receives affectively charged stimuli significant to sex and survival through the brain stem and midthalamic nuclei, regulates their intensity in the reticular system, marshals appropriate visceral responses via the fornix and hypothalamus, enlists the endocrine organs through tuberopituitary tracts and hormones, and then relays these neural transactions to the cortex for conscious ideational evaluation.

Striking illustration of the interrelationships of brain function and experience appeared in our own work (1960–60), which showed that lesions of the dorsomedial thalamic nucleus induced aggression to a far greater degree in adult animals that had been exposed to neurotigenic conflicts than in normal controls, whereas bilateral amygdalectomy produced an irreversible Kluver-Bucy syndrome in only young animals. In other investigations, J. Olds, K. Pribram, J. Delgado and others isolated special regions in the septum and lateral amygdalae which, when stimulated, mediate presumably pleasurable seeking and repetition, as contrasted with other points in the tegmentum, fornix and posterior hippocampus, which induce avoidance; however, these neural nodes, too, change or even reverse their functions under overstimulation, external satiation and various other experimental contingencies (N. Miller[36]).

Experiential effects. But perhaps the most clinically significant animal studies were behavioral rather than strictly neurophysiologic. Begun by Pavlov and continued by Shenger-Krestovnikova, Gantt, Liddell, Jacobson, Hoff, Schenker, myself *et al.*, these showed that, irrespective of lesions or stimulation of the hypothalamus, thalamus, cortex or other portions of the central nervous system, most of the manifestations of "anxiety" and its accompanying behavioral deviations (e.g., symbolic inhibitions, phobic and compulsive aversions, somatic dysfunctions and disturbances in social relationships) could be predictably induced by subjecting an animal to disruptive conflicts between incompatible motivations and opposed patterns of adaptations. Our experiments have shown that such conflicts need not involve fear; "positive" but mutually exclusive goal-seeking patterns may be almost as neurotigenic.

As examples of recent work, Curt Richter observed that hungry rats, offered poisoned food, froze into bizarre postures, or ran to exhaustion if a wheel was available; at higher libidinal levels, A. Wikler reported that pups subjected to an electric shock on their first attempt at coitus developed a "sexual neurosis," i.e., lifelong deviations in sexual patterns. It is relevant here that disturbed maternal and social avidities in adulthood could also be shown to result from infantile deprivations. Green and Gordon[18] summarize their observations:

> Visual exploration was studied in maternally reared and maternally deprived monkeys. When an animal pressed a bar an opaque screen was raised providing a brief view of either of a pair of stimuli. Subjects reared by their mothers pressed more to see animate than inanimate objects. With increasing age, the number of bar-pressing responses decreased for an adult female stimulus, increased for an age peer and for food, and remained low for geometric forms and an empty chamber. *Maternally deprived subjects established uniformly low response levels to all stimuli.*

*Additional Animal Experimental Data**

The general purpose of our program has been to test psychiatric theory and practice by scientifically planned and controlled investigations in animals, thereby to clarify our understanding of human behavior and to improve the treatment of mental disorders. Fundamental to all research are clear and testable hypotheses. Those that have emerged from our work and been integrated as *Biodynamic Principles* into psychiatric teaching here and abroad are, briefly:

1. Motivation. The behavior of all organisms is actuated by physiologic needs, and varies, therefore, with their intensity, duration and balance.

2. Percept and response. Organisms conceive of and interact with their milieu in accord with not an absolute "external reality" but the evolution of their unique capacities and experiences.

3. Range of normal adjustments. In higher organisms, this makes possible many technics of adaptation, and this versatility renders the organism able to meet stress and frustration and to maintain an adequate level of satisfaction by *a.* employing new methods of coping with difficulties when the old prove ineffective or *b.* modifying or substituting goals when the old become unattainable.

* *The research here described is based on studies during the past three decades conducted with me by successive associates: Drs. Charles Fisher, Karl Pribram, Curtis Pechtel, Louis Aarons,* et al., *who have since ably continued similar studies at other universities.*

4. Failures of adaptation. However, when physical inadequacies or environmental stresses or conflicts exceed capacities, innate or learned, the internal tension (anxiety) mounts, neurophysiologic (psychosomatic) dysfunctions occur, and the organism develops avoidance (phobic), ritualized (obsessive-compulsive), socially deviant (regressive or aggressive), or "dereistic" (hallucinatory, delusional) patterns of behavior corresponding to those in human neuroses and psychoses.

FINDINGS

Developmental influences. Our findings have confirmed the principle that the young of all organisms, including man, develop through an orderly succession of stages during which sensory modalities are distinguished, integrated concepts of the environment developed, manipulative skills refined, early dependencies relinquished in favor of exploration and mastery, and peer and sexual relationships sought, through which the animal becomes normally "socialized" in its group. Over the past eight years, the growth of individual animals of various species from infancy to adulthood has been carefully recorded and progressively photographed in motion pictures; these observations have revealed the following important influences on development, again with significant clinical parallels.

1. Early deprivation. Young animals subjected to periods of solitary confinement, even though otherwise physically well cared for, do not develop normal initiative, physical stamina or social relationships.

2. Formative experiences. Conversely, young animals given opportunities for continuously protective and nutritive contacts with adults acquire exploratory self-confidence, motor and interpersonal skills, and social "acculturations."

3. Learning. The growing infants show patterns of dependency, exploration, play, fetishism (i.e., attachment to objects representing early securities), rebelliousness, developing sexuality, and other characteristics significantly parallel to those in human children. However, the surrogate parents involved, whether of the animal's own species or not, impart their own traits to the adopted young. For example, a young rhesus raised from birth in the investigator's home learns to respond sensitively and adequately to human language and action, but may never acquire some of the patterns (e.g., a fear of snakes) "normal" to rhesus monkeys raised by their mothers.

4. Character deviance. Unusual experiences for the young animal may engram peculiar characteristics that persist through adulthood. For example, if a young animal is taught to work a switch and thus subject itself to increasingly intense but tolerable electric shocks as a necessary preliminary to securing food for the rest of its life, it may continue to seek such shocks even in the absence of any other immediate reward—and may thus appear to be inexplicably "masochistic" to an observer unacquainted with its early history.

5. Early "psychological" trauma. If, however, the young animal is subjected to exceedingly severe conflicts between mutually exclusive satisfactions or counterposed desires and aversions, it develops deeply ingrained inhibitions, fears, rituals, somatic disorders, social maladjustments and other aberrations of behavior which become highly elaborate and more difficult to treat than those originating in adulthood.

6. Early brain injuries. A remarkable finding was that adequate care and training in early life could compensate in large part for extensive brain damage in the newborn. Monkeys subjected to the removal of both temporal or parietal cortices at birth, but given a protective and stimulating home environment thereafter, suffered minor kinesthetic and affective impairments detectable by special tests or by periods of sensory deprivation, but developed otherwise normal and adequate individual and social adaptations. In the absence of such special care and training, the effects of brain damage, including lesions in the thalami, amygdalae, and cerebral areas 13, 23 and 24, were much more devastating in the young than in adult animals. Also, cerebral lesions in young animals did not ameliorate induced experimental neuroses as effectively as in adults.

Adult social relationships: group organization. Our studies have also confirmed the observations of ethologists by demonstrating that animal societies in the laboratory, as well as in the wild (or civilized?) state, organize themselves in hierarchies of relatively dominant and submissive members, with leadership and privilege generally preempted not by size or strength alone but in accordance with special aptitudes and "personality" skills. Nevertheless, social relationships could be modified in the following significant ways:

1. Cooperation. Under special experimental conditions, a cat or a monkey could be trained to operate a mechanism that produced food for its partner, who then reciprocated in "mutual service."

2. Parasitism. In most pairs, however, this pattern soon deteriorated into either *a.* a situation in which neither animal would work consistently for the other, or *b.* a relationship in which one animal (the worker) operated the mechanism sufficiently often to feed both himself and a "dependent" or parasite.

3. Technological solutions. Two such workers were sufficiently "intelligent" (i.e., possessed of unusually high perceptive-manipulative capacities) to jam the feeding mechanism so that it operated automatically, rendering unnecessary further effort by either.

In effect, then, the experiments described helped clarify interrelationships basic to partnerships, sitdown strikes, contracts and automation in human society.

4. "Altruism." Gregarious animals were capable of spontaneous "self-sacrificing" conduct without apparent reward other than that of preventing discomfort or pain to another member of their species. For example, recent experiments have demonstrated that hungry macaques will continue to starve for days, yet refuse to pull a lever to secure readily available food if they have learned that this act also subjected another macaque to an electric shock. This "succoring" behavior was apparently less dependent on the relative age, size or sex of the two animals, than on their individual "character" and whether they had been mutually well-adjusted cagemates for a period of 3 to 6 months.

5. Aggression. Conversely aggression, in the sense of actual fighting between members of the same species to establish various relationships, was minimal; primacy and dexterity manifested by only occasional gestures of preemption were nearly always sufficient to establish dominance and privileges. Indeed, physical combat appeared only under the following special circumstances:

a. when an animal accustomed to a high position in its own group was transferred to a group in which it came into direct conflict with new rivals previously accustomed to dominance,

b. when a dominant animal, by being made experimentally neurotic as described below, fell to a low position in its own group, and thereafter expressed its frustrations by physical attacks both on inanimate and living objects in its environment.

Neurotigenesis. Germane to our present interests are our observations on the experimental production of "neuroses" or "psychoses." In accordance with the fourth *Biodynamic Principle,* dealing with the effects of conflict, marked and persistent deviations of behavior could be induced by stressing the animal between mutually incompatible patterns of survival: as, for instance, requiring a monkey to secure food after a conditional signal from a box that might unexpectedly contain a toy snake—an object, harmless or not, as symbolically dangerous to the monkey as a live one would be. We have further amended Freudian doctrine by demonstrating that "fear" in the sense of dread of injury need not be involved at all; i.e., equally serious and lasting neurotigenic effects can be induced by facing the animal with difficult choices among mutually exclusive satisfactions—food vs. mothering or exploration vs. escape or sex; i.e., situations that parallel the disruptive effects of prolonged indecisions in human affairs.

Neurotic symptoms. Either form of conflict induced physiologic and mimetic manifestations of anxiety, spreading inhibitions, generalizing phobias, stereotyped rituals, "psychosomatic" dysfunctions, impaired social interactions and other persistent regressions and deviations of conduct.

Constitutional influences. Animals closest to man showed symptoms most nearly resembling those in human neuroses and psychoses, but in each case the "neurotic syndrome" induced depended less on the nature of the conflict (which could be held constant) than on the constitutional predisposition of the animal. For example, under similar stresses, spider monkeys reverted to infantile dependencies or catatonic immobility and cebus developed various "psychosomatic" disturbances including functional paralyses, whereas vervets became diffusely aggressive, persisted in bizarre sexual patterns, or preferred hallucinatory satisfactions such as chewing and swallowing purely imaginary meals while avoiding real food to the point of self-starvation.

Principles of therapy. Since we induced experimental neuroses in animals not only to study their causes and variations but primarily to search for the principles of therapy, this portion of our work was assigned most time and effort. After the trial of scores of procedures, only a few, significantly parallel to those used with human patients, proved to be most effective in ameliorating symptoms in animals:

1. *Satisfying* one of the conflictful biologic needs.

2. *Removing* to a less stressful milieu.

3. *Forcing the solution* of a motivational impasse by directed stress kept within the animal's tolerance.

4. *Furnishing opportunities* for the utilization of acquired skills for reasserting mastery over the environment.

5. *Providing the companionship* and example of well-adapted ("normal") animals.

6. *Retraining the animal* by individualized and graduated guidance, the experimenter acting as a "personal therapist" acquainted with the origin and nature of the animal's conflicts and their neurotigenic effects.

7. *Utilizing electroshock* or inducing other forms of cerebral anoxia to disorganize deeply ingrained patterns of deviant behavior.

8. *Performing various brain operations* to induce similar disorganization; in monkeys, lesions in regions corresponding to cortical areas 12, 23 and 24 were most effective in this respect. Another highly significant finding was that the aftereffects of any brain operation depended not only on its site and extent but also on preceding experiences and characteristics of the animal. For example, bilateral lesions of the dorsomedial thalamic nucleus impaired the learning capacities of a normal animal but left it gentle and tractable; in contrast, the same operation rendered a previously neurotic animal irritable and vicious.

9. *Using various drugs* for the temporary amelioration of disturbing perceptions and conflictful reactions, thus facilitating other methods of therapy for alleviating experimentally induced neuroses.

a. *Effectiveness.* Our data indicate that most of the recently promoted "tranquilizers" (meprobamates and phenothiazines) were less generally effective than drugs long tested in clinical therapy: e.g., alcohol, paraldehyde, the barbiturates and bromides.

b. *Preventive action.* These more effective drugs, if administered before subjecting an animal to stress or conflict, would also partially prevent the aftereffects of an otherwise traumatic experience.

c. *Drug addiction.* However, a neurotic animal permitted to experience the relief from fear and inhibition produced by alcohol would then prefer alcohol to nonalcoholic food and drink and thus develop a true addiction that would persist until its underlying neurosis was relieved by other means.

Clinical Aspects of Anxiety

Electroencephalography. Anxiety may abolish alpha rhythms or induce high-voltage beta waves[7]; in animals, these affects may be mediated through the ascending reticular formation.[30] The abolition of alpha waves by an auditory signal previously conditioned to a light stimulus may be diminished in patients with both brain damage and prolonged and severe anxiety, which may thus also produce organic cerebral defects.

Biochemical substrates. The most reliable and obvious physiologic indices are the rapid heart rate, raised pulse and systolic blood pressure, vasomotor instability, horripilation and skeletal tensions that accompany the "anxiety syndrome" described in the clinical sections below. As to their biochemical substrate, increased excretions of hippuric acid and of 17 keto-steroids were the *only* predictable variables in severe emotional states,[20], whereas hyperglycemia during "emergency reactions" occurred only in diabetics. The contention that adrenin secretion is increased when "anger is turned inward as anxiety," whereas noradrenin increases when "anger is expressed outwardly in aggression," has been called into question on both psychological and physiologic grounds. However, an excess of acetylcholine as indicated by an increased galvanic skin response (GSR) may occur in "mild anxiety" (as it does also in deep concentration, sexual excitement, etc.), in contrast with peripheral vascoconstriction in "white panic."

Disturbed feedbacks. Using special sound recording and video apparatus, many have demonstrated that a delay of only a fraction of a second in the auditory or visual feedback of a human subject's own voice or motion may produce sensorial confusion, affective apprehension and marked and persistent disturbances in performance.[28, 32–39, 49, 50] On the basis of such data, Bowers *et al.* concluded that any serious disturbances in accustomed configurations of sensation, arrangements, relationships or systems of self-and-reality produce insecurity and hence anxiety—an inference generalized to interpersonal communication.[47]

Nosology. The current *Standard Nomenclature* of the American Psychiatric Association attempts to telescope all of Freud's successive notions of anxiety into this somewhat tortured definition:

Anxiety in psychoneurotic disorders is a danger signal felt and perceived by the conscious portion of the personality. It is produced by a threat from within the personality (e.g., by supercharged repressed emotions, including such aggressive impulses as hostility and resentment) with or without stimulation from such external situations as [*sic*] loss of life, loss of prestige or threat of injury.

The latest revision of the American Psychiatric Association *Diagnostic Manual* retains only one nosologic entity: *Anxiety reaction*, characterized as "diffuse and not related to situations or objects as in the case of phobic reactions [and] to be differentiated from normal apprehensiveness or fear." In clinical practice, however, the following variants, listed in previous editions, are still frequently used:

Anxiety syndrome: Characterized by severe, unformulated apprehension and its physiologic concomitants: generally cardiac palpitation, irregular or rapid respiration (which may lead to hyperventilation and secondary hypotension with syncope), "globus hystericus" (pharyngeal constriction), trembling, flushing, sweating and splanchnic spasms ("flutterings in the stomach") that may require repeated pharmacologic control with ataractic or sedative drugs.

Anxiety hysteria: When accompanied by marked sensorimotor ("conversion"), functional amnestic, or persistent organic (psychosomatic) dysfunctions which may necessitate ancillary medical or surgical intervention: e.g., as in gastric ulcer.

Anxiety neurosis: Recurrent episodes as above, with phobias, obsessions, compulsions and other more deeply ingrained "neurotic" traits and deviations of character amenable, if at all, only to individualized long-term treatment.

Therapy

Anxiety has one final therapeutic connotation: a state of tension, ranging from unpleasant to unbearable, which induces a patient to seek professional aid. Indeed, Freud insisted that analysis "cannot take place in the *absence* of anxiety." But since the myriad somatic and behavioral concomitants of anxiety add a multitude of biologic, personal, metapsychologic and social dimensions to an already almost incredibly complex field of human discourse, it becomes evident that no limited or stereotyped mode of "treating anxiety," although simple prescriptions are always tempting to the bewildered, can cover even a portion of the intricacies and contingencies involved. In broader statement, the alleviation of "anxiety" (or its elicitation in the sense of inducing optimal modes of alertness, concern and effectiveness of response) is integral with all psychiatric therapy, and may most briefly be stated as follows:

In psychiatry, therapy comprises the most efficient utilization of *every* pharmacologic or other medical means to relieve the patient's symptoms, and *every* ethical mode of communication and influence—including subjective analysis, reorientative dyadic transactions and guided resocializing experiences—to help him realize that his previously "neurotic" patterns of behavior, although perhaps once suitable, are no longer either necessary or advantageous, whereas more effective, creative and culturally adaptive modes of conduct will be found on the whole more pleasurable and profitable, and in no sense a stultified abandonment of individuality. Our technics of therapy (Gk. *therapeien*-service) will thus attempt insofar as possible to meet the patient's fundamental seekings (Ur-faiths): through, first, the restoration of his bodily strengths and skills; second, the recultivation of his human companionships, and third, the reinvocation of his transcendent philosophic-theologic securities. Can any mortal do more?

REFERENCES

1. Adler, A.: *The Practice and Theory of Individual Psychology*, New York, Harcourt, 1924.
2. Bakan, David: *Freud and the Hassidic Tradition*, Chicago, Univ Chicago Press, 1962.
3. Bard, L.: Neural Mechanisms in emotional and sexual behavior, Psychosom Med *4*:171, 1942.
4. Basowitz, L., *et al.*: *Anxiety and Stress*, New York, McGraw-Hill, 1955.
5. Brill, N. W.: Controlled study of psychiatric out-patient treatment, Arch Gen Psychiat (Chicago) *10*:581, 1964.
6. Cannon, W.: Against the James-Lange theory of emotion, Psychol Rev *38*:281, 1931.
7. Cohn, R.: The influence of emotion on the human EEG, J Nerv Ment Dis *104*: 351, 1946.
8. Devenberg, V. H., and Whimbey, A. E.: Behavior of adult rats as modified by the experience their mothers had as infants, Science *142*:1192, 1963.
9. Erikson, E. H.: The problem of ego identity, J Amer Psychoanal Ass *4*:56, 1956.
10. Fairbanks, G., and Guttman, N.: Auditory feedbacks, J Speech Hearing Res *1*: 12, 1958.
11. Festinger, L.: *A Theory of Cognitive Dissonance*, Palo Alto (Cal), Stanford Univ Press, 1959.
12. Freud, S.: *The Problem of Anxiety*, New York, Norton, 1936.
13. ———: *Collected Papers*, vol. 1, New York, Basic, 1959.
14. Fromm-Reichmann, F.: Loneliness, Psychiatry *22*:1–15, 1959.
15. Gibbons, J. L.: Cortisol secretion in depressive illness, Arch Gen Psychiat (Chicago) *133*:572, 1964.
16. Glass, A. J.: Psychotherapy in the combat zone, Amer J Psychiat *110*:725, 1959.
17. Gleser, G. C., *et al.*: Anxiety scale applicable to verbal samples, Arch Gen Psychiat (Chicago) *5*:593, 1961.

18. Green, P. C., and Gordon, M.: Maternal deprivation: its influence on visual exploration in infant monkeys, Science *145*:292, 1964.

19. Greenacre, Phyllis: The predisposition to anxiety, Psychoanal Quart *10*:667, 1941.

20. Grinker, R. R., Sr.: Anxiety as a significant variable, Arch Gen Psychiat (Chicago) *1*:537, 1959.

21. Grotjahn, M.: Freud's letters to Oskar Pfister, personal communication, 1927.

22. Haley, J.: *Strategies of Psychotherapy*, New York, Grune, 1963.

23. Head, H.: Release of function of the nervous system, Proc of Royal Soc *92*:184, 1921.

24. Horney, Karen: *The Neurotic Personality of our Time*, New York, Norton, 1937.

25. Kierkegaard, S.: *The Concept of God*, Princeton, Princeton Univ Press, 1944.

26. Kurland, H. D.: Steroid excretion in depressive disorders, Arch Gen Psychiat (Chicago) *10*:554, 1964.

27. Langer, W. L.: The black death, Sci Amer *210*:115, 1962.

28. Lee, B. S.: Delayed auditory feedbacks, J Acoust Soc Amer *22*:824, 1950.

29. Lilly, J. C.: Distress call of the bottlenose dolphin, Science *139*:116, 1936.

30. Lindsley, D. B., Bowden, J., Magoun, H. W.: Effect upon the EEG of acute injury to the brain stem activating system, Electroenceph Clin Neurophysiol *1*:975, 1944.

31. Magoun, H. W.: An ascending reticular activating system in the brain stem, Arch Neurol (Chicago) *67*:145, 1952.

32. Masserman, J. H.: Faith and delusion in psychotherapy, Amer J Psychiat *110*: 324–333, 1953.

33. ———: *Practice and Dynamic Psychiatry*, Philadelphia, Saunders, 1955.

34. ———: Ethology, comparative biodynamics and psychoanalytic research, *in* Masserman, J. H., ed.: *Science and Psychoanalysis*, vol. 3, New York, Grune, 1960, pp. 20–80.

35. ———: The office therapy of psychosomatic disorders, Arch Gen Psychiat (Chicago) *3*:320, 1960.

36. ———: *Principles of Dynamic Psychiatry*, ed. 2, Philadelphia, Saunders, 1962.

37. ———: A tachistoscope glance at recent advances in the neurophysiology of behavior, Isr Ann Psychiat *1*:244, 1963.

38. ———: Contribution of experimental psychiatry to the art of healing, Psychoanal Rev *50*:103, 1963–64.

39. ———: *Behavior and Neuroses*, ed. 2, New York, Hafner, 1964.

40. McLean, P.: A proposed neural mechanism of emotion, Arch Neurol (Chicago) *38*:725, 1937.

41. Mordlsoff, A. M.: The relationship between psychological and physiological response to stress, Psychosom Med *26*:135, 1964.

42. Odier, C.: *Anxiety and Magic Thinking*, New York, Internat Univ Press, 1955.

43. Pascal, B.: *Thoughts*, New York, Peter Pauper Press, 1946.

44. Persky, I., *et al.*: Adrenal cortical functions in anxious human subjects, Arch Neurol (Chicago) *76*:549, 1956.

45. Popper, K.: *The Logic of Scientific Discovery*, New York, Philos Libr, 1958.

46. Powers, W. T., Clark, R. K., McFarland, R. L.: A general feedback theory of human behavior, Percept Motor Skills *11*:309, 1960.

47. Ruesch, Jurgen: *Disturbed Communication*, New York, Norton, 1957.

48. Sarbin, T. R.: Anxiety: reification of a metaphor, Arch Gen Psychiat (Chicago) *10*:630, 1964.

49. Smith, K. U., Bloom, R. J.: Electronic handwriting analysis and motion study in writing, J Appl Psychol *40*:302, 1956.

50. Smith, W. M., *et al.*: Delayed visual feedbacks and behavior, Science *1330*:1013, Sci Amer *204*:86, 1960.

51. Spinoza, B.: *Ethics*, London, Everyman, 1910.

52. White, J. C.: Automatic discharge from stimulation of the hypothalamus in man, Res Publ Ass Res Nerv Ment Dis *20*:854, 1940.

James N. Sussex, MD
Alabama

4

Drugs in the Therapy of the Neuroses

DRUGS IN THE TREATMENT OF NEUROSES MAY BE APPROACHED IN AT LEAST two ways: 1. by naming the various psychoneurotic symptoms and syndromes and then listing those drugs that have, in certain dosages, empirically yielded improvement; or 2. by trying to find some common denominators underlying the use of drugs in the psychoneuroses that can help us, as clinicians, decide whether to use drugs at all, and if so what *kind* of drug, in treating a particular neurotic patient.

Most psychiatrists decide from their clinical experience which drugs may be helpful, and descriptions and clinical reports of the drugs currently in clinical use are easily available. This chapter, therefore, is not a formulary but a speculation on some issues involved in the use of drugs in treating neurotic patients, in order to evolve a framework within which we, as clinicians, may be able, now and in the future, to make decisions that are more rational and less empirical than those we have been making. To accomplish this even superficially, three things are required. First, we must consider what we mean when, in the mid-sixties, we use the term "neurosis." Second, we must examine the bases on which we attempt to predict the results of the use of drugs in general, or of one drug in particular, in such syndromes. Third, we must examine whether the results obtained are consistent with our treatment goals as viewed in the context of the syndromes we presume to be treating.

PSYCHONEUROTIC DISORDERS

We may start with Dunbar's descriptive[1] approach to psychoneurotic disorders as "characterized by the use of one or all of the known mechanisms for handling anxiety except, perhaps, the somatic short circuit and psychotic withdrawal." She goes on to say:

> "The psychoneurotic is fundamentally self-conscious, worried and unhappy. He has not withdrawn from reality, nor has he repressed all anxiety and conflict since his early childhood. He has put up a good fight to grow and adjust to his environment. He has established communication and contact readily with a considerable number of people." The symptoms he presents, she says, "are indicative of some failure in his capacity to compensate under stress."

In the experience of many of us, it is difficult to put a particular label on psychoneurotic patients. More and more of them seem to fall in the borderlands between neurosis and character disorder or between neurosis and psychosis. While these patients are usually ambulant and seldom require hospitalization, they demonstrate a considerable degree of anxiety and sometimes depression, as well as poor production on the job, impaired relationships in the family and unrewarding experiences in the wider social scene. Maybe they should be considered *semineurotic* or *pseudoneurotic.* At any rate, they cannot be planned for or prognosticated in the traditional diagnostic framework, either psychotherapeutically or psychopharmacologically.

Whatever other criteria we establish, it would seem valid to consider neurotics as characteristically more vulnerable than "normal" people to stress, not just the stress stemming from intrapsychic conflict but also that arising in the environment. And being more vulnerable and reacting in symptomatic patterns that reduce significantly the spontaneity, creativeness, and effectiveness of their day-to-day activity, they suffer more crippling than generally realized. Other syndromes may be more spectacular, in terms of more dramatic symptomatology, higher mortality rate or higher incidence of obviously recognized disability, but the neuroses are the syndromes which show, par excellence, what Dunbar[1] termed "high social incapacity."

GOAL OF TREATMENT

Our goal, presumably, regardless of what form of therapy we tend to espouse, is to help the neurotic patient cope more adequately with the stresses he meets in his life so that he will not need to suffer the symptoms of decompensation. When we consider the use of drugs in the treatment of such patients we should, therefore, be interested primarily in whether the drug helps to reach that goal. Ideally, we want to cure the disorder. More practically, we settle for improvement in the patient's ability to live his life without crippling anxiety and its derivative symptoms.

Baselines for Assessing Patient Response to Drugs

What we would like available are drugs that produce absolutely predictable results in emotional and behavioral effects. In clinical practice, however, our prediction of either beneficial or adverse effects is largely an educated guess. What we seem to need are better baselines from which to estimate what a given patient's *response* will be when he is given a drug. What baselines are available to us now in making such an assessment, and what baselines may be increasingly available to us in the future? Possible baselines have been placed under four headings: 1. the standard diagnostic categories, 2. target symptoms, 3. basic patterns of relating to people, 4. basic responses to the "drug experience."

The standard diagnostic labels have long implied that psychiatric disorders were "conditions" or "states" comparable to clinical entities with specific organic cause. When the current nomenclature came into use about 1950, these conditions were renamed "reactions," but largely within the same conceptual framework. Actually, whether we say a patient is suffering from a "conversion neurosis" or a "conversion reaction" makes little difference in how we view him psychodynamically. In either case, he is regarded as using particular defense mechanisms to deal with a conflict, and if this works well enough, he will have little or no anxiety. While such may be appropriate for planning psychotherapeutic strategy, there being an apparently demonstrable psychodynamic common denominator in all patients with conversion symptoms, it does not afford an adequate basis for predicting how a particular patient with a conversion syndrome will respond to a particular drug. The same comments could be made about the other classical neurotic syndromes. A drug, for example, that yields a particular response in one obsessional neurotic patient, as defined in the diagnostic nomenclature, may not yield the same effect in another patient equally validly termed an obsessional neurotic.

Furthermore, though we view obsessional neurotics and conversion neurotics as different enough in their psychodynamic implications to warrant different psychotherapeutic strategy, we frequently find these and the other neuroses, with the possible exception of neurotic depression, grouped together when drug treatment is considered, as though their mechanisms of reaction to whatever effect the drug produces were the same. Our clinical experience with drugs leads us, I think, to question this assumption and to challenge the usefulness of the traditional diagnostic groupings as a basis for planning drug treatment even in the classical psychoneuroses. The difficulties in prediction are even greater when we are considering a treatment plan for a patient of the apparently ever-expanding group of people whose neurotic syndrome fails to fit into any category of the standard nomenclature.

The idea of a "target symptom" treatment approach has been increasingly appealing over the last few years and, to a considerable degree, seems possible. But it may also beg the issue or cloud it dangerously. The fact that aspirin usually reduces the pain of a headache, and thereby the disability incurred, makes it perfectly valid for a physician to prescribe it for a patient with a headache. It does not change the fact, however, that headaches may arise from a variety of sources, with various implications for the future of the patient ranging from the possibility of an hour or so of relative incapacity to death. Some headaches require an elaborate diagnosis and treatment. It is clear that we can't just say that a headache should be *treated* with aspirin or that aspirin is a *treatment* for headache.

In the neuroses, the key symptom is anxiety. Certain drugs apparently reduce anxiety, regardless of the cause of that anxiety. Should we say, then, that the anxiety of the neurotic patient should be *treated* by this or that drug, or that such and such a drug is a *treatment* for anxiety?

If we choose to shoot at a target symptom, we might consider which of the following specific goals we are trying to accomplish: 1. to get the patient back into his normal activity with a minimum of additional psychiatric attention; 2. to make him more comfortable and cooperative while we carry out further diagnostic and exploratory studies; 3. to make him more comfortable and, therefore, more amenable to any changes we may be able to bring about in his environment; or 4. to help him communicate more easily and thereby become more accessible to psychotherapy.

Is it valid to try to get a neurotically disabled patient back to a coping level by symptomatic treatment alone? Even if it is valid, can it be done? Most psychiatrists speaking on the subject of drug therapy, regardless of how "organically oriented" they may be, hasten to mention, sometimes seemingly more as lip service than anything else, the necessity for other forms of help. Usually a specific nod is given toward psychotherapy. This is rarely spelled out, possibly because no one knows much about it. Anyway, the advocate of drug therapy covers what he thinks may be a vulnerable flank by acknowledging that the patient's anxiety reflects problems in meeting the stresses of his life and that working out better ways of handling these stresses may be a good idea. So we are frequently told that drug therapy should always be used in combination with psychotherapy, as an adjunct to it or to facilitate it.

Anxiety is a universal phenomenon. Occasional incapacity from anxiety is probably also universal. One survey, for example, conducted in 1959, reported that about 20% of the industrial population at both managerial and labor levels could be expected *at any given time* to be working at less than maximum efficiency because of emotional difficulties.[10] In many of our complex industries of today, it would be difficult to demonstrate a drop in individual productivity, but Proctor[10] has shown very vividly, in a study involving 50 hosiery mill workers whose earnings depended on piece work production, that anxiety and its related symptoms seriously curtail the individual's effectiveness. In this time of heavy patient loads and the implausibility of providing any other form of therapy for many patients, it would seem untenable to say, after the patient has been adequately studied for possible other-than-neurotic sources of anxiety, that drugs should never be used as an "only" treatment method. Surely many people who are temporarily incapacitated by anxiety at times of special stress could validly be given a drug to reduce their anxiety and enable them to carry out their usual activities, without automatically assuming that they should have psychotherapy.

If we assume that a treatment situation in which there is no *formal* arrangement for any other kind of therapeutic intervention constitutes a "drug only" arrangement, there seems to be some evidence, both clinical and experimental, that a drug alone *can* be helpful in overcoming neurotic symptoms. Proctor[10] found, with his 50 hosiery mill workers, that drug treatment planned essentially on a target symptom basis yielded beneficial effects almost immediately, not only by decreasing the severity of the target symptom itself but also in increased productivity on the job. Furthermore, he found that the improvement in many patients continued indefinitely, without deeper or more extensive psychiatric treatment of any sort.

Masserman[7] cited neurotically constricted animals who, when force-fed alcohol, became uninhibited and explored freely. They sought food and drink that contained alcohol and took it preferentially to the point of intoxication. There was a consequent mitigation of their neuroses, apparently due to their reexploration of the situation that had precipitated their neuroses. That this was not some sort of pseudo-improvement achieved only in an intoxicated state seemed borne out by the fact that after the animals became more comfortable in the neurotigenic situation, and could cope more successfully with it, their avidity for alcohol spontaneously decreased.

BASIC PATTERNS OF RELATING TO PEOPLE

The question could be raised, of course, whether in any ordinary treatment situation we could ever prescribe or administer a drug, even if we wanted to, without *some* additional element operating. The patient-doctor relationship is a subtle thing, and we know that even a five-minute interchange can have a definite positive or negative impact on anything else which is done. Our clinical experience seems to lead us to the inevitable conclusion that factors other than drug action alone contribute to improvement, or lack of it, in a given patient. In prescribing a drug, the psychiatrist is actively entering that patient's life, and the interpersonal aspects of the situation cannot be ignored. The patient's reaction to his psychiatrist cannot be passed off entirely as transference, nor can all negative reactions be called resistance. The characteristic modes that the patient has developed to deal with the people with whom he is involved emerge in the clinical situation as complicating or facilitating factors and must be taken into account if the results of drug therapy are to be predicted with any success.

Does the patient, for example, use the drug to increase his dependency on the physician? Does he use it to defy the physician? Does he take it avidly, spit it back, vomit it, openly refuse to take it, forget to take it, claim to have taken it when he didn't? These are important questions to ask and answers to ascertain, for without having a fair idea of what use the patient is likely to make of the drug in his relationship with his psychiatrist, we can only fail in our prediction of the results.

To answer these questions correctly, we must be willing to look at neurotic symptoms and syndromes not only as having significance for what the patient has done in relationships in his past life, or is doing in his present relationships outside the office, but also as reflecting what he is doing or attempting to do in his relationship with his psychiatrist. Sullivan and Horney have been among the more articulate formulators of the implications of these factors, but regardless of the theoretical framework we use, we should be able to decide *the general ways in which a patient tends to handle situations that involve other people.* Does he, for example, to use Horney's conceptualization of the basic conflict, tend to move toward, against or away from people? And what are the implications for drug therapy once we think we have determined what basic mode of relating he uses? If he moves *toward* people, with an underlying need for establishing a strong dependency relationship, we might assume that drug therapy, although perhaps warranted, may be accepted too readily as a way of life and demanded as a proof of the psychiatrist's willingness to take care of him and prevent him from having to undergo the discomforts of standing on his own feet. The danger of accentuating his neurotic pattern by giving him a drug may outweigh the advantage of relieving his anxiety. At least it would call for special consideration in the psychotherapeutic aspects of the treatment program.

If the patient tends to move *away from* other people as a defense against the danger of dependency and closeness, he may suspect prescription of a drug to be an attempt to invade his privacy or take advantage of him. His distrust of the psychiatrist's motives might be expressed quite openly and directly or might be shown by his sabotaging the treatment plan with passive-aggressive technics. It could be dealt with at an unconscious level within the framework of his neurotic symptomatology as, for example, in the case of a phobic who must avoid the medication because he fears what will happen if he takes it. Or it could be dealt with somatically in the appearance of various side-effects, which results either in his discontinuing the medication himself or in the psychiatrist's having to do so.

If the patient characteristically moves *against* people, he may regard prescription of a drug as an attempt to influence him against his will, and may sabotage the drug treatment plan by openly challenging the physician's judgment and refusing to take the medication, by forgetting to take it, by controlling his own drug regimen (sometimes backed by another physician or even, as did a patient I recall, by a copy of the *Physician's Desk Reference*), or by adhering so rigidly to the drug program, once established, that it becomes part and parcel of an obsessive-compulsive control system and, consequently, ceases to be useful for the purpose for which it was prescribed.

Obviously, bracketed together here are patients who show overt aggressive, passive-aggressive and passive-dependent patterns that may underlie phobic or hysterical syndromes, as well as compulsive personalities and perhaps certain obsessional neurotics. Characteristic patterns of relating to people, then, may be considered to cut across traditional diagnostic categories. In none of these patients is drug therapy necessarily contraindicated. The anxiety each patient shows, however, has somewhat different meaning in each type of personality, in terms of his relationship with the drug-prescribing psychiatrist, and is handled in somewhat different ways. A knowledge of this makes it easier to predict what response to the drug may be expected, how the patient is likely to handle the relationship aspects of it, and what management pitfalls may need to be watched for.

Of necessity we must also take into consideration the person on the other side of the transaction. The psychiatrist, too, has basic modes of relating to people and of defending himself against anxiety-producing threatening aspects of those relationships. If his patient's symptoms are threatening to him, he may choose to prescribe a drug which, he hopes, will result in a "good" patient who is undemanding, unchallenging, unaccusatory, unhostile and unthreatening. We need not belabor this point, but the motives of the psychiatrist do bear looking into when drug treatment is being considered, not only in terms of the validity of giving the drug at all but also in attempting to predict the result. The manner in which the drug is prescribed and the conscious or unconscious motives of the psychiatrist have a bearing on how the patient will respond.

BASIC RESPONSE TO "DRUG EXPERIENCE"

What about the *response of the patient to the drug effect itself?* Here we are handicapped by the relative scarcity of information about response of the human species to drugs generally. For a particular patient, we may have information that he has only to "sniff the cork" to appear intoxicated, or that he remains awake and tense instead of going to sleep when he is given a sedative, or that he reports strange phenomena with a minimal dose of a tranquilizing drug. This leads us to be cautious about using drugs similar to those to which he may have responded adversely in the past or to avoid the use of all drugs if his atypical reactions appear to transcend the boundaries of particular psychopharmacologic groups.

The nonspecificity of the behavioral effects of drugs, even in the laboratory, has been noted by many investigators.[2, 4, 6–9] If the behavioral effects of a given drug in a given dosage cannot be accurately predicted in an essentially controlled laboratory setting, then how can we predict what will happen when we give it to our patients? Obviously we have to take into consideration something other than the drug's chemical structure and specific pharmacologic action, or even the interpersonal factors operating between patient and psychiatrist. We have to consider *the patient's particular and individualized response to what I have called the "drug experience."* Can a particular person be said to have his own unique way of responding to drugs in general or to special drug effects in particular? If so, how can we determine what his unique response may be, and how can we utilize that knowledge in deciding whether he may be a good candidate for drug therapy and, if so, which kind of drug might be most likely to help him?

What we need are ways of establishing baselines of behavioral response to drugs just as we have tried to establish basic types of reaction patterns in interpersonal relationships. Although we cannot yet say for sure, it appears that we should consider drugs as predisposing and facilitating agents rather than as forces that elicit or evoke new behavior. What, then, do the drugs facilitate? What are the factors which are important in predicting what response the drug effect will elicit from a particular patient?

Many investigators have commented on the possible relationship between basic personality factors in an individual and the way in which that individual responds to drugs.

Miller,[8] for example, stated that there is an increasing body of evidence that "differences in personality explain many variations in reactions to drugs, particularly those which are psychoactive." Uhr[12] comments, "A surprisingly large percentage of the studies that have tried to correlate the personality of the patient with his response to drug therapy has yielded positive results. Differences between subjects might well turn out to be crucial in the future untangling of apparently opposing results from different laboratories where, inevitably, different populations are treated and examined."

Kubie[4] noted the relationships between what he calls "the central emotional position of the personality" and reactions to a psychoactive drug such as alcohol. He cites the fact that "the same drug affects different men in quite different ways, or may alter any one man in different directions on different occasions," and states that "in a similar way other drugs can release or make manifest latent central affective positions."

Voth[13] suggested that choice of symptom and choice of syndrome, as well as character style, could be understood in terms of his thesis that "a given individual occupies a 'homebase' position on the ego–close—ego–distant continuum despite temporary fluctuations." One implication of this view is that the action of a drug might cause such fluctuation and that the response of the individual patient to the drug would depend on or be related to his unique "homebase position."

Rapaport[11] postulated "innate and acquired apparatuses" that serve to maintain the "autonomy of the ego" by adapting to the environment and protecting the ego against the onslaughts of the id on the one hand, and by preventing the ego from being a slave of environmental stimuli on the other. This view implies possible impairment of ego function as a result of drug action and leads to speculation whether an individual patient's response to a drug could be correlated with the relative balance of his innate and acquired apparatuses of ego autonomy.

As a derivative, in part, of this concept, Linton[5] and others believe that all people may be placed on a continuum, one end of which represents those who are "stimulus-bound" and the other end "non-stimulus-bound." Stimulus-bound individuals have been observed to react to hallucinogenic compounds with markedly increased anxiety and active efforts to avoid perceiving, acknowledging or being influenced by the effects of the drug. The sense of security of this group of subjects seems to depend on their maintaining a definite and firm anchor in reality and any change, especially one that they have no adequate means of controlling, threatens their security. Faced with disturbing phenomena over which they have no control, they tend to become tense, rigid, withdrawn and "paralyzed."

On the other hand, the non-stimulus-bound individuals take readily and even eagerly to the new, even bizarre experiences of the hallucinogenic drugs, apparently reveling in strange phenomena. Perhaps they are similar in some ways to Masserman's intoxicated neurotic animals in that they welcome new situations even though they may not be actually effective in the ordinary way while under the drug's influence.

We have seen patients whose symptoms—restlessness, pacing the floor, insomnia, various somatic complaints—suggested that they were attempting to increase contact with their environment. These patients presented with a high degree of anxiety and expressed fear of loss of control. Subjected by Linton[5] to administration of an hallucinogenic drug (LSD-25), these subjects made active efforts to constrict their environment, and to avoid responding to the changes produced by the drug itself, by holding themselves rigidly in one position and even by denying that any perceptual changes had occurred. Although apparently not reacting to the hallucinogenic drug by developing hallucinations and other psychosis-like phenomena, and therefore superficially appearing less anxious and more in control of themselves, it would seem that actually they were less expressive, less creative, more threatened and more crippled than the non-stimulus-bound individuals whose responses *seemed* to be more bizarre and pathologic.

IMPLICATIONS

The implications are not entirely clear, but if we consider that perceptual changes are reacted to by some neurotic individuals as though they are changes in their environment by which they are threatened because of their fear that they cannot cope with them, then this would lead to a very tentative conclusion that drugs which cause some degree of perceptual modification, and a great many psychoactive drugs do this, create thereby certain additional stresses for these particular neurotic individuals to handle. Rather than *decrease* the stress such a patient has to cope with, such a drug may *increase* it. Rather than making him *more* accessible to the psychotherapeutic relationship, it may make him less accessible to *any* relationship, as he needs to guard himself against total loss of control.

Most of us must discover which reaction a given patient will have to a psychoactive drug by simply trying it and waiting to see what will happen. If, however, people tend to react to the drug experience itself on the basis of their basic personality patterns, then we may have a means of predicting beforehand what a given patient's response to a drug might be. Most of the data thus far available are just as empirical as the standard diagnostic nomenclature, but some of them may point the direction for future clinical investigation.

Klerman[3] and co-workers, for example, observed that "sedative drug action was ego-threatening to athletic, extrapunitive subjects but anxiety reducing to passive, intrapunitive, anxious subjects."

Linton and Stalker[5] feel that they can predict the general response of a subject to a perception-modifying drug, in terms of the stimulus-bound versus non-stimulus-bound continuum, on the basis of profiles obtained on the Minnesota Multiphasic Personality Inventory. Those subjects who resisted change and fought against feelings of loss of control (the stimulus-bound group), showed elevation of the depression and psychasthenia scales of the MMPI, whereas the non-stimulus-bound subjects peaked on the hypomania and psychopathic deviate scales. The question might be asked whether these results can be correlated with the corresponding clinical diagnoses, especially for subjects in the neurotic group, as I am using this term. It seems likely that they cannot be so correlated—that the clinical syndrome itself, by usual diagnostic criteria, is not an adequate appraiser of deeper and more compelling modes of defense. One may speculate that this is because the clinical syndromes, as they are usually defined psychodynamically, center around and emerge out of conflicts in the Oedipal and late anal stages of childhood, whereas the basic reactions to environmental and internal change, as potential threats to the integrity of the ego and as signals of impending loss of ego control, are laid down in the earlier half of the anal period, the last half of the oral period and possibly even in the earliest six months of life—those phases of development in which establishment of a separate ego and the earliest battles for control of it are lived through.

As we so frequently must in the prediction of sequences of events in clinical medicine, perhaps here too, in the prediction of response to drugs, we must, at least for the present, depend on our skill at perceiving and interpreting the meaning of the symptoms the patient presents. Certain symptoms may indicate that the patient is trying to bolster his basic defense patterns by maintaining or reestablishing contact with those aspects of the external environment that he uses as his anchors to reality. Giving such a stimulus-bound patient a phenothiazine, barbiturate or other drug that makes it more difficult for him to maintain this contact will make him worse, not better. His anxiety will increase, and he may begin utilizing those mechanisms of projection or massive withdrawal that signal the emergence of a psychotic break.

On the other hand, if we give him a drug, like an amphetamine or methylphenidate, which makes him more alert and increases his ability to maintain contact with the environment, the threat to his ego may be lessened and his anxiety decreased. This kind of sequence of events may explain the apparently paradoxical effect when such a stimulant drug occasionally calms patients who are anxious instead of making them more tense and jittery. It is intriguing to speculate that this might also explain why these drugs almost predictably reduce restlessness, distractability and hyperactivity in brain-damaged children.

If the patient's symptoms indicate that he is overwhelmed with stimuli and needs to escape from them, then an alerting drug may be productive of increased tension and anxiety. A phenothiazine or even a major sedative may be preferable.

One group of drugs, those of the diazepine series, seem empirically to be of some benefit to both types of patients. These drugs apparently produce a minimum of sensory reduction and distortion and little change of self-image, and are, therefore, unlikely to threaten the stimulus-bound patient with depersonalization phenomena. On the other hand, they are not stimulant drugs but rather tend to be mild sedatives and so do not artificially compel alertness and increased contact with the environment. They seem to lessen the threat sensed by both types of patients and, therefore, contribute to increased coping capacity in patients of either group.

Summary

In summary, as clinicians using drugs to help our neurotic patients be less anxious and to cope more effectively, we have at least four parameters to help us select a drug and to predict what the result is likely to be. We can use the traditional diagnostic groupings. We can shoot from the hip at a target symptom, most likely anxiety, trusting to the odds that all anxiety stems from the same source and all anxious patients respond alike. We can try to assess what in the patient's way of relating to people contributes to his anxiety and adapt our use of drugs to reduce this. We can assess the likely effect of the drug generally, in terms of its tendency to produce perceptual changes, and try to predict how the patient would react to it by making a clinical judgment whether, to be free of anxiety, he needs external stimuli that he can depend on and control or should have respite from them. And we must keep our own motives in mind too—whether we are giving a drug for a particular effect which, if it occurs, will enable him to cope independently or will break down his inhibitions so that he will feel freer to communicate in psychotherapy, or whether we are simply trying to make him into a "good" patient who does not threaten our own security.

Ultimately, it would seem, there is no compelling conflict between drug therapy and psychotherapy. With each approach, we are trying to contribute to the patient's adaptive capacity by helping him react to various stimuli more selectively, appropriately and effectively and, to this degree, to be less crippled by anxiety and its derivative symptoms.

REFERENCES

1. Dunbar, F.: *Psychiatry in the Medical Specialties*, New York, McGraw-Hill, 1959, pp. 334–335.
2. Kety, S. S.: Chemical boundaries of psychopharmacology, *in* Farber, S. M., and Wilson, R. H. L., eds.: *Man and Civilization: Control of the Mind*, New York, McGraw-Hill, 1961.
3. Klerman, G. L., *et al.*: The influence of personality factors on the effects of phrenotropic agents: an experimental procedure to integrate physiologic and psychologic action. Paper read at Mtg Soc Biol Psychiat, San Francisco, 1958, cited *in* Farber, S. M., and Wilson, R. H. L., eds.: *op. cit.* (ref 2), p. 98.
4. Kubie, L. S.: A psychoanalytic approach to the pharmacology of psychological processes, *in* Uhr, L., and Miller, J. G., eds.: *Drugs and Behavior*, New York, Wiley, 1960, p. 214.
5. Linton, P. H., and Stalker, V. G.: Sensory alteration by drugs as related to personality type (part 1), as yet unpublished.
6. Litchfield, J. T., Jr.: Excerpts from an address before Med Res Ass of Los Angeles (Cal), Mar 9, 1964, in Lederle Res Report, Pearl River (NY), 1964, pp. 20–22.
7. Masserman, J. H.: Norms, neurotics and nepenthics, *in* Masserman, J. H., ed.: *Biological Psychiatry*, New York, Grune, 1959, pp. 90–112.
8. Miller, J. G.: The individual response to drugs, *in* Farber, S. M., and Wilson, R. H. L., eds.: op. cit. (ref 2), pp. 92–109.
9. Nowlis, V.: The concept of mood, address given at symposium, "Man and Civilization: Control of the Mind—II", San Francisco, Jan 26, 1962.
10. Proctor, R. C.: Clinical use of chlordiazepoxide, *in* Nodine, J. H., and Moyer, J. H., eds.: *Psychosomatic Medicine*, Philadelphia, Lea, 1962, pp. 480–488.
11. Rapaport, D.: The theory of ego autonomy: a generalization, Bull Menninger Clin *22*:13–35, 1958.
12. Uhr, L.: Objectively measured behavioral effects of psychoactive drugs, *in* Uhr, L., and Miller, J. G., eds.: op. cit (ref 4), pp. 624–625.
13. Voth, H.: Choice of illness, Arch Gen Psychiat (Chicago) *6*:57–64 (Feb), 1962.

HARVEY J. TOMPKINS, MD
St. Vincent's, NYU

5

Short-Term Therapy of the Neuroses

THIS CHAPTER PRESENTS NOT NEW OR NOVEL TREATMENT MODALITIES WITH more immediate results as applied to the neuroses, but rather possible ways of better utilization of the therapeutic interventions now available to us, with concomitant conservation of manpower, in more realistically meeting the needs and demands of the individual and his community.

Medical Progress and Psychiatric Treatment

While medicine as a whole has constantly attempted, through refinement of technics and procedures, to lessen the time required for therapeutic effectiveness, only in recent years has serious consideration been given to similar possibilities in the various modes of psychiatric therapy, particularly as employed on an outpatient basis. While statistically some evidence indicates that the need for hospital residence is being curtailed, a parallel decrease is not so evident in extramural care and treatment. A popular and tenacious belief continues in the chronicity of mental disease, whether neurosis or psychosis, with the extremes of treatment visualized: that is, the patient hospitalized or, if not, requiring daily sessions with the psychiatrist for prolonged periods of time and at great cost. This popular concept is accentuated, if not initiated, by the residual persistence within the profession of a value structure that continues to give the highest acceptance to technics and therapeutic objectives that are inherently time-consuming and long-term. This is particularly true in relation to the neuroses, where, too often, anything short of the traditional psychotherapeutic approach may be suspect as an improvisation due to lack of knowledge or technical skill.

Social and economic factors have focused general attention on shortening the treatment and still retaining an expectancy of satisfactory effectiveness. After World War II, the Veterans Administration established a national chain of psychiatric outpatient clinics, which in a short time accumulated the usual waiting lists. In an attempt to shorten the period of treatment of the individual veteran, it was suggested that therapeutic objectives should be limited to the preenlistment degree of personal integration and adjustment, based on the rationale that this was the extent of the government's responsibility. While the policy was not accepted, some clinics did institute programs sympathetic to it, increasing the patients seen and not decreasing the effect on their improvement ratios. Whatever the validity of these efforts, pressure for psychiatric attention has now increased demand for readily accessible and definitive treatment opportunities not financially prohibitive. The increase in prepaid insurance plans and the demands for ambulatory coverage have given added impetus to the need for treatment programs economically supportive. Additionally, greater prominence is being given to the need for clarification of the definition of psychiatric illness and, especially, what constitutes improvement or recovery. One is reminded of the remarks, in *Mental Hospitals* under the caption "Who doesn't need therapy?" which conclude: "What this country needs is a psychiatrist quixotic enough to say occasionally—'Diagnosis: no significant psychiatric disorder' or 'Treatment recommended: none'."[3] To this might be added: "Further treatment: not necessary."

1,000 Participating Psychiatrists

The significance of these reflections of current psychiatric practice is brought out in the report of Group Health Insurance, Inc., of New York in its research project to determine the feasibility of financing through prepaid insurance short-term ambulatory treatment.[4] In it were 1,000 participating psychiatrists. Of the patients served, self-referred as well as referrals from other physicians and agencies, only one out of 100 was considered *not* in need of definitive psychiatric treatment. There were 923 patients, with 42% diagnosed as psychoneurotic: 50% had symptoms of over two years' duration; 27% initiated treatment within six months of the onset of disabling manifestations of their illness; and the rest fell in between. The protocol of the project allowed 15 office visits. Of those patients availing themselves of the maximum number of sessions or fewer, 75% were considered recovered or improved. Subsequently, the treating psychiatrists were asked the question: "Do you think further psychiatric treatment would help?" The response was in the affirmative for 94% of the patients completing all the office therapy allowed, and 69% of those terminating before that point—an overall average of 81%. "Since three-quarters of the terminated cases were reported as recovered or improved in response to treatment, it would appear evident that the two questions are not related in . . . psychiatry, as they are commonly in other medical areas." The additional treatment most frequently recommended (in 9 out of 10 cases) was individual psychotherapy. The answer to the question, "Do you think that treatment other than by a psychiatrist would help?" provoked an affirmative response of less than 10%.

One could postulate that what was meant was that the patient had responded favorably but with little or no fundamental personality change; the criteria being used were the manifest comfort and generally added effectiveness of the patient as exemplified in sample quotations from participating psychiatrists.

"The patient was able to continue with active employment and to increase his earnings. For the first time in many years, his wife was affectionate and he could return the feeling. These rewards show the project has yielded human benefits."

"This patient has made excellent progress with brief therapy because of highest motivation. This program was most influential in affecting his seeking therapy.

This is an unusual and gratifying experience in an intelligent compulsive person past 60 years of age."

"This patient has been helped over her present acute reactive depression. The underlying neurosis was of course not touched—to do so would require long-term therapy for which the patient is not prepared psychologically or financially. This has, however, been worthwhile and the patient is welcome to return."

"I have not been too enthusiastic as to the helpfulness of merely 15 sessions but this case has shown remarkable improvement including a lowering of blood pressure as he gains insight and actually changes his 'mode of existence.' In fact, during therapy he was promoted to a higher rank in his work."

Most of the psychiatrists refused to admit that there had been any drastic adjustment in treatment approach or goals for patients in this project, suggesting the presence of an interesting flexibility in therapeutic technic.[6] Those who said that they had adjusted indicated one or more of the following ways:

1. *A more active role on the part of the therapist*
2. *A more directive role with greater use of pharmaceuticals*
3. *Limitations of therapeutic goals*
4. *Early definition of goals*
5. *Emphasis on symptoms (target symptoms)*
6. *Spaced visits rather than intensive treatment—shortening the usual 45 to 50 minute session was suggested to conserve the impact of the therapist which, with the infrequency of the visits, was believed to ease the possibility of excessive dependency by the patient*

Some direct quotations may be illuminating:

"The 15-session limit certainly requires drastic modification of our approach as psychotherapists and this to me is a fascinating challenge as indeed is the whole program."

"I tried to reach goals in 15 visits that ordinarily would take much longer. I became much more active, suggestive, authoritative and much less concerned with insight dynamics and transference."

"It was necessary to appraise the situation more quickly and select certain limited goals quickly; included much more specific advice and recommendations; depended less on interpretation."

Of the psychoneurotic patients, 38% received pharmacotherapy. Drugs were used almost twice as frequently by those believed to be more directive-organic in their practice as compared to others who considered themselves primarily analytically-psychologically oriented. This latter group used the maximum number of visits allowed, 15, for 55% of their patients as against 38% for the directive-organic psychiatrists. On this basis of primary practice orientation, the analytical-psychological segment recommended that 84% of their patients receive further psychiatric treatment as against 70% of the other group.

A Community Clinic

The experiences of our outpatient psychiatric clinic may be pertinent.[1] This clinic draws from a catchment area surrounding the hospital with specific geographic limits. In 1961, we indicated that since electroconvulsive therapy was utilized with only two patients, it could be fairly stated that our clinic employed psychotherapy alone, or psychotherapy combined with drugs, as treatment methods, with a bias heavily in favor of the former. Drugs had not been used extensively except in aftercare patients, who are followed in the clinic after their discharge from the inpatient service. Even when drugs were prescribed, therapy sessions were generally maintained at their usual frequency (1 to 3 per week) and duration (45 to 60 minutes). While results with psychotherapy alone were somewhat better than in the psychotherapy-plus-drug group (60% vs 50%), these results were achieved at the cost of a 50% increase in number of treatment sessions (average number of sessions, 19.4 vs 13.9). Our findings suggested this as a possible area for improvement in efficiency, particularly when one considered that drugs apparently were used as afterthoughts in management of patients who did not respond as well as expected to psychotherapy alone, rather than as a primary modality of treatment. We wondered if more extensive use of drugs and less of individual sessions might not liberate more personnel to deal with more patients.

A report on the activities of our clinic in 1962 indicates that these suggestions were ignored by the clinic staff, for in 1962 drugs were used even less than in 1961. Psychotherapy alone did not maintain its superior efficacy in comparison with psychotherapy and drugs, and the number of sessions for all treated cases rose to an average of 25.4. The greatest number of sessions in patients treated by psychotherapy alone in our clinic occurred in psychoneurotics.

Reporting for the year 1963, we state:

> "Psychotherapy remains the treatment modality favored by our clinic staff and in 1963 was the only treatment for 64% of therapy cases, while drugs were used in addition to psychotherapy in 36% (comparable figures for cases terminated in 1962 are 75% and 26%). It seems highly significant that the number of sessions required for psychotherapy cases remained at an average of 25 per patient, while the number required for drug cases dropped from an average of 27 in 1962 to 17 in cases terminated in 1963. This resulted in an overall drop in number of sessions for treatment cases (from 25 to 22), and the findings suggest that drugs are being used more vigorously and more appropriately than they have ever been before in our clinic."

Our findings continue to suggest that psychotherapy alone is better than psychotherapy plus drugs for psychoneuroses, and also for the schizophrenias and the personality disorders. If one accepted this at face value, he might well ask why all the patients in these categories were not therefore taken off drugs and returned to psychotherapy-alone treatment plans. Such a question, of course, would expose the core of the problem in any reports such as these, for we have no effective way of controlling or reporting on how unsuccessful attempts at psychotherapy alone might have been with patients who also did not respond to drugs. Yet such patients will be reported as drug-treated cases so long as any psychedelic agents were prescribed. It seems clear that within any diagnostic entity, there are variations in prognosis and outcome, no matter what therapeutic approach is employed. It is our hope further to refine our evaluation procedures and our assessment of progress so that ultimately we may be able to earmark one patient for guidance and counseling, another for reconstructive psychotherapy, another for a tranquilizer, and still another for a combination of various psychopharmacologic agents. At present we are far from that goal.

Our clinic is located in a general hospital and is sensitive to the emphasis given the community mental health concept. There is pressure for shorter-term treatment leading to control of the illness and rehabilitation through relief of symptoms as well as for limitation or elimination of residual disability. Thus we emphasize improvement in interpersonal and group relationships and, in general, the betterment of environmental adjustments. Our clinic is increasingly crisis-oriented with dependence on short-term, immediate, definitive and intensive interventions. There is recognition and use of the assistance available from other mental health resources, the schools, industry, the clergy and various social agencies. There is growing involvement in community-wide efforts to support and enlarge the impact of such health-generating forces through socioeconomic and political action. It has been our experience, as well as others, that staffing of such clinics is difficult; that the general orientation of attendings and residents together, with their technics and expectancies, are often alien to such commitments, as it is in their private practice. The greatest difficulty appears to lie in the ordinary practitioner's inability to relate his knowledge and technics to these community demands, particularly in psychotherapy. There is lack of clarity in his concept of what these needs are, how they are to be met by what approach, and the results that can be anticipated. The charge can be made that there is a "lag" in our training and/or orientation in terms of the requirements of today's society.

Hierarchy of Therapeutic Procedures

Psychotherapy has become the shibboleth of psychiatrists, yet what does each of the initiates mean by the term? Is it universally applicable, and what does it accomplish? It is conceded, although reluctantly by some, that the term encompasses much more than what might be called "reconstructive," "deep," or "interpretative" therapy. Yet, all too often, the inference or even conviction is given that one form of psychotherapy is really "better" than another and, unwittingly or not, students are taught a hierarchy of systems: at the lowest level fall exhortatory and persuasive methods, counseling, or other technics that may be considered nothing more than "therapy by suggestion." The highest method may be the one that the speaker identifies himself with, no matter what method this might be, with the explicit claim of better results.

Do all "schools" of psychotherapy report approximately the same results? If such be true (and more research is needed on this question: that patients improve despite rather than because of us) how do we refute the conclusion? No matter how ill-considered this opinion may be, our refutation must be better substantiated than it has been. It is said that each school gets its good results because of factors in selection of patients; if so, we need more study of what those selective factors are. Each approach that has survived must have something to recommend it; but how do we define that something? Could it be that each operates best in a very specific area, and that a more detailed mapping of specific areas would enable us to give each patient the best treatment for his highly individual set of problems?

There is the strong possibility that we often promote "method" without due consideration of results: overall, our concern should be that results *are* obtained, and not so much how. We are enmeshed in the magic of the 50-minute hour X times per week, and we give only perfunctory attention to the recent studies that indicate that patients will often improve as much with ten 30-minute sessions as with 100 (or more) "hours." We have had too few studies on when, during psychotherapy, the sought-after improvement does occur, and none on the effects of factors outside therapy sessions.

Despite our repetitive references to treatment of the "whole" patient by a psychiatrist whose training has been broadly based, how many students are imbued with the tradition of keeping in touch with other disciplines and specialties, with other groups within psychiatry itself? How often is a trainee advised to give up a patient in psychotherapy to a marriage counselor, to a clergyman, to a lawyer? We may find that our own methods uncover maximal pathology in the patient (and we label this part of our training efforts "psychodynamics"). But does this help the patient *most*?

"How well acquainted are we, and what degree of familiarity do we expect in our students, with such areas as sociology, experimental and comparative psychology, the psychology of learning—as well as with other medical specialties and offshoots of our own, such as existentialism and pavlovian reflexology? How adequate is the preparation in the basic sciences, especially in their specialized application to psychiatry, viz., neurophysiology, biochemistry, pharmacology? If we let ourselves be lost in the dogma of a specific group, we jeopardize a workable integration between the 'organic' and 'dynamic' camps."[2]

In a similar vein, we have the comment of a participant at the conference on Training the Psychiatrist to Meet Changing Needs:[7]

"What we know best is dyadic psychodynamic therapy which is the product of our Freudian heritage. This falls far short of the present scope of psychiatry in meeting the demands placed upon us by the public and the community. It therefore follows that we must be prepared to educate ourselves or our younger colleagues to carry on in newer directions. It is manifestly impossible to formalize a curriculum for teaching that which we do not yet know. It is more practical to design a curriculum which permits flexibility and research training and which does not impede, by emphasis on traditional learning, the self-learning process of those whom it is our obligation to train and develop. We must participate in and encourage empirical research in order to create competing theoretical models which are relevant to clinical psychiatry. We must encourage methodological advances, take advantage of newer technology and newer concepts derived from biological and social sciences."

The Learning Theory

An approach to the treatment of the psychoneuroses that has stimulated a great deal of interest is psychotherapy by reciprocal inhibition based on the learning theory. The theory postulates that neurotic symptoms are learned patterns of behavior that are unadaptive. If neurotic symptoms are learned, then they should be amenable to "unlearning," and behavior therapy is directed to the inhibition and/or extinction of the learned neurotic responses. Wolpe in his reciprocal inhibition psychotherapy postulates that if a response antagonistic to anxiety can be developed in the presence of anxiety-evoking stimuli so that it is accompanied by a complete or partial suppression of the anxiety responses, then the bond between these stimuli and the anxiety responses will be weakened. He states that once a neurotic habit of responses to specified stimulus conditions has been eliminated, such elimination is permanent unless the habit is reinstated by new specific conditioning, i.e., learning. He believes that the favorable results obtained by varied types of therapies, other than those based on conditioning, are due to interviews generating emotional responses that inhibit anxiety evoked by verbal stimuli.[8]

Preparation for, and specific utilization of, relationships outside the therapeutic session has been suggested most prominently by Ian Stevenson.[5] Acting on the premise that psychoneurotic behavior is learned maladaptive behavior and that recovery requires unlearning and new learning of behavior, he considered the possibility that the unlearning could be done as readily with other significant persons in the patient's environment as with the therapist. Considering the relatively small amount of time the patient spends with the therapist, he proposed that the emphasis be not studying and improving the patient-therapist relationship, but preparing the patient for improved behavioral responses with others. Interviews were pointed toward the past rather than the present and, for the most part, preoccupied with relationships with persons other than the therapist. Stevenson cited the work of others, including Rado and his colleagues, Cameron and Wolpe. He recognized that modifications of these technics must be made for the overly anxious patient and those so inhibited as to require corrective experiences with the therapist.

Conclusions

A review of the literature, as well as experimental material available to us, would indicate the appropriateness of shorter-term therapies. That the results are impermanent, provisional, unreliable, symptomatic, temporary and given to recrudescence to a greater extent than longer-term technics is at least open to question. However, too much of our evidence pro or con remains anecdotal. We desperately need more valid research, a greater legitimacy in comparison of various technics and their theoretical backgrounds, together with each procedure's specificity for different clinical entities. With this should come a greater flexibility in the therapeutic approach of psychiatrists and avoidance of an either/or approach, which, on the basis of our present dearth of knowledge, has little validity. This is a necessity as we face the community-wide demands now before us.

REFERENCES

1. Annual Reports: Psychiatric Out-Patient Service, Dept of Psychiatry, St. Vincent's Hospital and Medical Center of NY, 1961–63.
2. Campbell, Robert J.: Personal communication.
3. Ment Hosp *15*:560 (Oct), 1964.
4. Psychiatric Insurance: New York, Group Health Insurance, 1962.
5. Stevenson, I.: Arch Gen Psychiat (Chicago) *1*:99, 1959.
6. Tompkins, Harvey J.: Amer J Psychiat *120*:345 (Oct), 1963.
7. Training the Psychiatrist to Meet Changing Needs, 63, Amer Psychiat Ass, Washington (DC), 1964.
8. Wolpe, J.: *Psychotherapy by Reciprocal Inhibitions*, Stanford (Calif), Stanford Univ Press, 1958.

Judd Marmor, MD
UCLA, Cedars Sinai

6

The Nature of the Psychotherapeutic Process

THE HELPING PROCESS IN PSYCHIATRY HAS TWO FUNDAMENTAL GOALS. IT may concern itself with efforts either to modify the environmental stresses that have disrupted the individual's psychic equilibrium, or else to improve the individual's adaptive capacity to these stresses, or both. I shall concern myself primarily with the process involved in endeavoring to improve an individual's ego-adaptive capacity.

Psychotherapy, in its broadest sense, may be defined simply as a method of modifying an individual's symptoms, feelings, thought processes, or behavior by means of communication in an interpersonal relationship. Drugs may or may not be utilized as secondary adjuvants to facilitate this process, but not for the primary purpose of altering the patient's inner reactions or outer behavior. If drugs are used for this latter purpose, we are then dealing with pharmacotherapy rather than psychotherapy. A physician may choose, however, to combine both therapeutic approaches for certain conditions.

I shall begin with two major premises. The first is that all of the major psychotherapeutic approaches have essentially similar objectives, although they may attach different names to these objectives and their approaches may rest on differing theoretical frameworks. Thus, Freudians may talk of genitality, Adlerians of social interest, Rankians of active, creative will, Jungians of the full development of the self, Sullivanians of an integrated self, Horneyites of self-realization, Frommians of the productive personality, and eclectics of improved adaptation or emotional maturity. All, however, are talking of helping an individual to have meaningful and satisfying interpersonal and sexual relationships, to work effectively, and to be a socially responsible and productive human being within the limits of his capacity. These objectives, it should be noted, represent normative standards in our culture and are not unique to psychotherapy. What is unique in modern dynamic psychotherapy is not its *objective*, but rather its *method* of attempting to make an individual aware of his previously unconscious thoughts, feelings, and motivations, and its deliberate and controlled utilization of the patient-therapist relationship for therapeutic purposes.

My second major premise is that, by and large, mature and experienced therapists of different theoretical orientations achieve comparable results. Admittedly, reliable statistics concerning this point are difficult to come by, but I know of no convincing evidence to the contrary—if we omit the personal conviction of each individual therapist that his results are better[10] than anyone else's! Over the past 28 years, I have had the opportunity of working closely with and of observing the work of therapists of most of the leading psychodynamic schools of thought, and my experience has been fully in agreement with the findings of Fiedler[4] and Heine[5] that favorable psychotherapeutic results are less dependent on the theoretical inclinication of the therapist than they are on his personal characteristics, empathic capacity, and clinical maturity.

But how is this possible? How can approaches based on different theoretical orientations be equally efficacious for the patient? The inference is justified that if this is so, there must be some common denominator which underlies these diverse approaches. This brings us to a consideration of the fundamental nature of the psychotherapeutic process. Up until relatively recently, the most prominent assumptions concerning what happens in psychotherapy were outgrowths of psychoanalytic theory. The first of these dealt with the effect of emotional release (abreaction), and the second was based on the role of insight.

Abreaction

The assumption that abreaction—the liberation of repressed emotions or memories—is the core of the psychotherapeutic process was an outgrowth of Breuer and Freud's famous studies in hysteria.[2] This assumption, however, has not been borne out by clinical experience, except in some cases of acute traumatic hysteria where recovery of the repressed memory of the traumatic incident will often cause dramatic disappearance of the hysterical *symptom.* In most instances, however, although the release of repressed emotion may result in transitory feelings of improvement, it does not in itself bring about lasting personality changes.

Moreover, as Franz Alexander pointed out as long ago as 1930,[1] the recovery of repressed memories is often a *result* rather than a *cause* of therapeutic change in the patient. Because the theory of abreaction is such a dramatic one, however, it has taken a powerful hold on the imagination of the public, and has become the basis of innumerable movies, plays, and television dramas, where the doctor, at the appointed minute (just prior to the final commercial or the closing curtain), elicits the crucial concealed memory or emotion, and presto, the patient is magically cured! The lay public may be forgiven for this wishful thinking, but what is harder to understand is the fact that this theory is still clung to by many psychiatrists, who ought to know better. Freud himself discarded this theory more than fifty years ago, yet numerous modern psychiatrists working with such tools as hypnosis, or with drugs such as pentothal, CO_2, or LSD, continue to assume that whatever therapeutic results they are achieving, are on the basis of the release of repressed memories or feelings!

Insight

The second major assumption concerning the psychotherapeutic process has been that it is based primarily on the insight acquired by the patient. What is insight, however? When we begin to examine it carefully, we find that it is a highly complex phenomenon. To begin with, it is necessary to distinguish between insight as it is given by the therapist, and insight as it is perceived by the patient. Insight as given by the therapist is defined differently by practitioners of differing schools of thought, and each school gives its own brand of understanding. The remarkable fact, however, is that patients treated by members of each school seem to respond with more or less equal effectiveness to the insights they are given. But even more remarkably, patients of each school seem to bring up precisely the kind of phenomenological data that confirm the theories and interpretations of their therapists! The patients of classical Freudians bring in dreams and material about Oedipus complexes and castration anxiety; the patients of Jungians, about archetypes; the patients of Adlerians, about masculine strivings and feelings of inferiority; the patients of Rankians, about separation anxiety; the patients of Horneyites, about idealized images; and so forth.

What this indicates is that the material in which the therapist shows interest, the kinds of questions he asks, the kinds of data to which he reacts or that he chooses to ignore, and the nature of the interpretations that he makes, all exert a subtle but significant impact on the patient to bring forth certain kinds of data in preference to others. I shall return to this point a little later in this discussion. What I wish to suggest at this point is that *what we call insight as given by the therapist is essentially the conceptual framework by means of which a therapist establishes, or attempts to establish, a logical relationship between events, feelings, or experiences that seem unrelated in the mind of his patient.* It thus constitutes the rationale on the basis of which the therapist hopes that the patient will accept the model of more "mature" or "healthy" behavior that therapists of all schools, *implicitly* or *explicitly*, hold out to him. Since interpretation in different frames of reference seems to be equally effective for the patient, it seems obvious that the *specific* insight given cannot be the fundamental or exclusive basis for the therapeutic reaction.

I do not wish to imply that insights given by therapists of different schools are capriciously variable, or that they bear little relationship to the actual realities of the patient's life and behavior. On the contrary. Interpretations given by ethical practitioners of different schools all bear a definite relationship to clinical reality and all fit the observable facts to a reasonable degree, although each school, of course, believes that its approach constitutes the most valid frame of reference.

A simple clinical example will illustrate this. Consider a young man whose basic behavioral patterns are those of passive dependency. The classical Freudian will make interpretations revolving around concepts of fixation at an oral receptive level, and of an unresolved Oedipus complex;

the Adlerian will talk of expectations of being taken care of, and of a "life style" of passivity and helplessness; a Horneyite might confront the patient with his neurotic need for affection and with his patterns of "moving toward" people; a Rankian might talk primarily about separation anxiety and the patient's defenses against it; a Jungian might speak of striving for reunion with an archetypal mother; a Sullivanian might make reference to oral dynamisms and disturbances in interpersonal relationships. All of these interpretations, however, deal with essentially the same behavioral problem, and the implicit or explicit message in all the interpretations is also the same—namely, that the patient ought to become more self-assertive, autonomous, and mature. Similar parallel interpretations can be demonstrated with other personality patterns, such as aggressivity, withdrawal, compulsiveness, and so on.

If now we turn to a consideration of the problem of insight as it is perceived by the patient, we run into difficulties also. The literature of psychoanalysis is quite confusing with regard to this point. Sometimes the insight referred to is purely cognitive. It is then described as "intellectual insight." If, however, the insight is associated with a simultaneous release of emotion, it is then "emotional insight." Generally, it is assumed that "emotional" insight will be therapeutically more effective than "intellectual" insight. Experienced clinicians know, however, that even so-called emotional insight does not necessarily lead to more mature patterns of behavior. There are occasions, it is true, in which a patient will have a sudden acquisition of insight with what Karl Buhler[3] has referred to as an "a-ha" feeling, and thereafter is able to modify a particular pattern of neurotic behavior in all of its ramifications, very much the way Yerkes and Kohler's apes were able to do once they grasped the gestalt of the test situation. Such persistent changes of behavior following insight, however, are the exception rather than the rule. The important point here is that whatever therapeutic effect any given insight may have on a patient depends fundamentally on how it is perceived by the *patient*, not as it is given by the *therapist*.

As an example of this point, in 1947 Rosen[13] reported some striking remissions in schizophrenic patients by a technic that he called "direct analysis," in which he made direct interpretations of the patients' supposed incestuous fantasies, castration anxieties, and similar "deep" material. Although Rosen attributed the remissions that he obtained to the "insights" he was giving his patients, most modern students of schizophrenia would agree that what was really producing the remissions was not these "deep" interpretations given by the therapist but, rather, what was being perceived by the patients; namely, that here was a doctor who cared deeply and passionately about them, who spent an inordinate amount of time with them, and who absolutely refused to permit them to retreat into their autistic worlds.

What, then, is the nature of the therapeutic process? I submit that fundamentally it is a kind of learning experience[11, 12] that takes place in a number of different ways. One basic difference between psychotherapeutic learning and any de novo learning situation, however, is that in psychotherapy the previously learned behavior (the neurotic pattern) is particularly resistant to change. It was this stubborn fact that forced Freud to abandon his initial hopes that insight alone could dramatically cure his patients, and to emphasize instead the much more arduous, time-consuming, and difficult process of "working through." This process of working through is the core of the long-term psychotherapeutic process.

The Psychotherapeutic "Field"

Let us consider the factors involved in a typical psychotherapeutic relationship.

1. *There is a patient,* whose discomfort, maladjustment, or unfulfilled needs *motivate* him to seek therapy.

2. *The patient brings with him* something else, however, which is very important —not only a motivation for therapy, but also *faith, hope,* and *expectancy* that therapy will help him.

3. *There is a therapist,* who by virtue of his *social and professional role* is endowed by the help-seeking patient with qualities of knowledge, prestige, authority, and help-giving potential.

4. *There are the real attributes* of the therapist—his actual knowledge, self-confidence, intelligence, objectivity, integrity, and empathy. Here we must also include the therapist's own needs and ambitions as they enter into the therapeutic transaction. The real attributes of the therapist have often been minimized in the psychiatric literature, as though the therapist's personality was of no real significance and as though he were as "neutral" and standardized a factor as a surgical instrument. This has often led to the tendency to interpret all positive and negative reactions of the patient toward the therapist as though they were aspects of positive and negative "transference" and to ignore the reality factors that may be involved in a patient's reaction to a therapist. When a patient dislikes a therapist, it is not always negative transference—it can be a reaction to certain real deficiencies in the therapist's personality. Similarly, a patient's liking for a therapist is not necessarily always positive transference, but may be a realistic response to positive attributes in the therapist's personality. It would be useful to make a distinction between "rapport" as a response to the therapist's real attributes, and "transference" as a response based not on the therapist's real attributes but on experiences and reactions with significant figures in the past.

5. *Finally,* although this does not necessarily exhaust the list of variables in the therapeutic transaction, *there are the value systems of the therapist.* All therapists are purveyors of certain mores of their culture, and these values are inevitably transmitted to the patient in terms of what the therapist considers healthy or unhealthy, properly masculine or properly feminine, "normally" aggressive, emotionally mature, and the like.

Given these five factors, a number of things begin to happen, more or less simultaneously, but in varying degrees. First, the patient experiences, as a rule, some initial relief, not only by virtue of his faith, hope, and expectancy, but also by being able to confide in a trusted and respected authority figure. This latter element involves the principle of catharsis and serves as a tension-reducing phenomenon. Second, the therapist begins to convey to the patient his therapeutic objectives and values in a series of interpretations, confrontations, and questions, by virtue of what the therapist chooses to focus on, by what he chooses to ignore, and *by his nonverbal as well as verbal reactions.*

Nonverbal Reactions

The importance of the therapist's nonverbal reactions is something that has been generally overlooked in the literature. This is understandable when one realizes that all reports of the therapeutic process hitherto have always been made by the therapist himself. As one of the participants in the transaction, the therapist could hardly be expected to be aware of everything that he was doing, particularly his nonverbal reactions. In the five-year study of the nature of the psychotherapeutic process, in which I participated with Dr. Franz Alexander and other colleagues (financed by the Ford Foundation, and carried out at Mount Sinai Hospital in Los Angeles; the voluminous data still being processed), I had a unique opportunity to observe many psychotherapeutic and psychoanalytic hours through a one-way screen, and to witness the impact of the therapist's nonverbal reactions on the patient.

When therapist and patient are in a face-to-face position, these nonverbal reactions, of course, are quite apparent to the patient. The therapist's facial expressions, a questioning glance, a lift of the eyebrows, a barely perceptible nod of the head, or a shrug of the shoulders, are all eloquent bits of communication to the patient. But even with the therapist sitting behind a couch, when and how often he says his "mm-hmms," the length and patterns of his silences, the degree of interest or noninterest in his voice, his shifting movements—these all act as cues to the patient whose highly sensitive antennae are alerted to even the tiniest signal of approval or disapproval, interest or noninterest, on the part of the therapist.

That these cues influence the actual content of a patient's communication has been clearly demonstrated in a number of experimental studies by Mandler and Kaplan,[9] Krasner,[7] and others. These investigators have shown that the "mm-hmms" of a therapist can be used actually to manipulate the content of a patient's "spontaneous" communications. Thus, if a therapist says "mm-hmm" every time the patient talks about his past but is silent when he talks about his present, the patient will begin in a short while to talk considerably more about his past than about his present. If now the therapist shifts the emphasis of his "mm-hmms" to the present, the content of the patient's communications will be reversed! The cues thus act as a kind of reward-punishment operant conditioning system in which the communication and behavior that the therapist approves is reinforced and that which he disapproves is discouraged.

Psychotherapy as Learning

In addition, however, the therapist's interpretations actually *do* teach and clarify things for the patient. One might make a crude analogy between what goes on in the psychotherapeutic process and learning to play golf. (Parenthetically, anyone who has taken golfing lessons knows that golfing teachers belong to different "schools" of theory no less than psychoanalysts!) The golf pro begins by confronting the patient with what he is unconsciously doing wrong. The interpretation, in effect, says "Look what you are doing," and implicitly or explicitly offers a more suitable model of functioning. Over a period of time, however, his "patient" tends to fall back again and again on the old patterns of behavior ("resistance") and the golf pro makes repeated "confrontations" which, in effect, say "There you go again." Eventually, the student begins to become aware of his own errors as he makes them and is able to say, in effect, "There *I* go again." Finally, the student is able to anticipate his errors and not make them, and thus he begins to develop new and more effective patterns of functioning. This, in greatly oversimplified form, of course, is the essence of the working-through process.

Therapeutic change does not always follow this slow and tortuous pattern. Occasionally a bit of insight may, as indicated, result in rapid modifications of patterns of behavior through a kind of gestalt learning. Obviously, also, the "faith" of the student in the teacher, as well as the empathic support of the therapist-teacher and his belief in the patient-student's ability to change are important elements in helping the "student" to persist in the often painful and difficult process of learning new patterns of adaptation.

Still another factor in the psychotherapeutic process is that the therapist's reactions, by being different from what the patient has previously experienced from authority figures, become an important additional basis for the reconditioning of the patient. What has been called the corrective emotional experience is essentially a kind of reconditioning process in which the patient encounters understanding, approval, support, or consistent firmness and dependability in place of the criticism, disapproval, non-interest, or inconsistencies that he has experienced with the significant authority figures of his past life.

Finally, the therapist, largely by virtue of the patient's positive transference reaction, unwittingly becomes a model to the patient, after whom the latter consciously or unconsciously patterns himself. This is a process of unconscious imitation, which psychoanalysts call "identification" and is an important element in every psychotherapeutic process. It tends to take place in a climate of rapport and positive transference, whether the therapist consciously intends it or not.

Factors in the Psychotherapeutic Process

We can now summarize the main factors in the psychotherapeutic process.

1. *Release of tension* through catharsis and by virtue of the patient's hope, faith, and expectancy.
2. *Cognitive learning*, both of the trial-and-error variety and of the gestalt variety.

3. *Reconditioning* by virtue of *operant conditioning*, by virtue of subtle reward-punishment cues from the therapist, and by corrective emotional experiences.
4. *Identification* with the therapist.
5. *Repeated reality testing*, which is the equivalent of *practice* in the learning process.

These five elements encompass the most significant factors on the basis of which change takes place in a psychotherapeutic relationship.

Some Relevant Questions

A number of questions present themselves, however.

1. *Does defining psychotherapy as a learning experience minimize the importance of the patient-therapist relationship?* My reply to this would be an emphatic No. The patient-therapist relationship is not a matter of mystique, although existential psychoanalysts write of it as though it were. It is simply *the matrix* in which the learning process takes place and, as such, a tremendously important element. If the therapist's relationship to his patient is one of gentleness, understanding, and empathy, and if the patient has hope and faith in the therapist, the learning process is thereby facilitated. If there is a less favorable emotional climate between them, the learning process will be retarded or even totally inhibited.

2. More fundamentally: *Does structuring the psychotherapeutic process in these terms not imply that the patient is being pressed into a mold of the therapist's making, with no free choice of his own?* My answer to this would again be strongly No. We must remember, first, that as a rule the therapist's goal is also the patient's. Second, even though the therapist is indeed trying to move the patient toward emotional maturity, his method, if it is nonauthoritarian, permits the patient to follow his own paths. The psychoanalytic concept of the dissolution of the transference, one of the prerequisites to a successful termination of therapy, implies helping the patient to achieve autonomy in his relationship to *all* authority figures *including the therapist.* This is an important difference between directive and nondirective technics of therapy. Although these are obviously relative terms, the more authoritarian the therapist is in relationship to the patient, the more difficult it is for the patient to achieve genuine autonomy, even though he may relinquish his symptoms in deference to the therapist. As Klein[6] has aptly put it, the nondirective therapist, like the progressive teacher, "permits the student to set his own goals, encourages independent and spontaneous expression, shows respect for the pupil's worth and promise, prefers a democratic to an authoritarian learning atmosphere, and abhors techniques of domination and coercion."

3. *Where does suggestion enter in the psychotherapeutic process?* The therapist's value-system is implicit, if not explicit, in every interpretation he makes, in the things he shows interest in, in the things he treats as normal, and the things he treats as neurotic. These reactions of the therapist are inevitably communicated to the patient, implicitly or explicitly. Therefore, suggestion is part of every psychotherapeutic process,

even the most nondirective. Obviously, those patients with the greatest need to please the therapist are going to be most "suggestible."

Behavioral Therapy

Finally, a word seems in order concerning the so-called "behavioral therapies" coming increasingly into vogue and utilizing as their basic therapeutic maneuvers constructs of learning theory such as counter-conditioning, extinction, operant-conditioning, and reciprocal inhibition. This school of therapists, exemplified by Eysenck in England and Bandura and Wolpe in the United States, tends to focus only on the patient's external behavior and symptomatology and considers irrelevant the subjective, cognitive, or emotional processes that go on within the patient. They argue that all that is necessary in psychotherapy is to recondition the patient's external behavior, and his internal processes will then remedy themselves automatically. It is significant that most of the cases reported by the members of this school deal with phobias and circumscribed symptom complexes rather than personality disorders.

The chief defect of this approach, it seems to me, is that it ignores the whole complex area of symbolic abstraction that plays so important a part in human behavior and that distinguishes man from all other animals. To base a psychotherapeutic approach on animal conditioning experiments is to ignore the tremendously important and unique role that symbols play in human behavior, and to return to a kind of renascent Watsonian behaviorism. Can anyone doubt that there is a vast difference between a socially adjusted but delusional schizophrenic who behaves normally to all outward appearances, and a nonschizophrenic whose external behavior is essentially the same? Moreover, we have had decades of experience with counter-conditioning therapy of alcoholism, and even where such technics are successful in temporarily eliminating the desire for alcohol, their failure to eliminate the underlying tension and anxiety of the alcoholic is well known. It is highly significant that Wolpe himself in extolling the value of his reciprocal inhibition therapy, states that it is "applicable . . . to almost any source of neurotic anxiety not involving inadequacies in the handling of interpersonal relationships."[14] One can only be astonished that Wolpe does not realize how stringently his statement limits the applicability of these technics. Very few neurotic conflicts indeed do not involve "inadequacies in the handling of interpersonal relationships."

I do not wish to imply, however, that these behavioral therapies are of no value at all. I believe that they are particularly useful for symptom disorders in which the therapeutic goal is limited: that is, restricted to the amelioration of symptoms rather than to the modification of the patient's adaptive capacity. It should not surprise us that some technics work better than others with certain types of patients and problems. Just as there is no single best way of teaching all people and all subjects, there is no single best way of treating all patients. To assume, however, that basic personality abnormalities and maladaptive technics that have been subtly inculcated by many years of daily disturbances in interpersonal relationships, with resultant complex perceptual and symbolic distortions, can be totally eradicated by a dozen or two counter-conditioning sessions aimed at some specific behavioral symptom, is simply to misjudge the complexity of the problems that are being dealt with.

The Magic Pill

In conclusion, a brief word about the relationship of drugs to psychiatric practice in the mid-sixties. There is no doubt whatever that drugs have made an enormous contribution in recent years to modern psychiatric practice. They have transformed our mental hospitals and given us invaluable assistance in controlling and modifying many of our patients' symptoms. Psychiatric practice would be vastly more difficult without them. However, the fantasy of the magic pill or drug that will some day cure all mental illness is, I believe, based on wishful thinking. It will never materialize. The origin of most psychoneurotic disorders will continue to lie in the life experiences and early interpersonal relationships that have distorted the perceptions and the ego-integrative mechanisms of the people whom we see as patients. In a very fundamental sense, therefore, the heart of psychiatric practice will always be the psychotherapeutic process. The better we understand the nature of that process, the better our chances of helping those who turn to us for critical assistance.

REFERENCES

1. Alexander, F.: The development of psychoanalytic therapy, *in* Alexander, F., and French, T. M., eds.: *Psychoanalytic Therapy*, New York, Ronald, 1946, p. 20.
2. Breuer, J., and Freud, S.: *Studies on Hysteria* (1893–1895), New York, Basic, 1957.
3. Buhler, K.: *Die Krise der Psychologie*, ed. 2, Jena, Fischer, 1929, p. 136.
4. Fiedler, F. E.: A comparison of therapeutic relationships in psychoanalytic, nondirective, and Adlerian therapy, J Consult Psychol *14*:436–445, 1950.
5. Heine, R. W.: A comparison of patients' reports on psychotherapeutic experience with psychoanalytic, nondirective and Adlerian therapists, Amer J Psychother *7*:16–23, 1953.
6. Klein, D. B.: *Abnormal Psychology*, New York, Holt, 1951, p. 521.
7. Krasner, L.: Studies of the conditioning of verbal behavior, Psychol Bull *55*: 148–170, 1958.
8. ———: The therapist as a social reinforcement machine. Presented at 2nd Conf on Res in Psychother, Univ North Carolina, Chapel Hill, May 17–20, 1961.
9. Mandler, G., and Kaplan, W. K.: Subjective evaluation and reinforcing effect of a verbal stimulus, Science *124*:582–583, 1956.
10. Marmor, J.: The feeling of superiority: an occupational hazard in the practice of psychotherapy, Amer J Psychother *110*:370–376, 1953.
11. ———: Psychoanalytic therapy as an education process, *in* Masserman, J., ed.: *Science and Psychoanalysis*, vol. 5, New York, Grune, 1962, pp. 286–299.
12. ———: Psychoanalytic therapy and theories of learning, *in* Masserman, J., ed.: *op. cit.* (ref 11), vol. 7, 1964, pp. 265–279.
13. Rosen, J. N.: The treatment of schizophrenic psychosis by direct analytic therapy, Psychiat Quart *21*:3–37, 117–119, 1947.
14. Wolpe, J.: Quantitative relationships in the systematic desensitization of phobias, Amer. J. Psychiat *119*:1063 (May), 1963.

Gene L. Usdin, md, moderator
Touro, Tulane

7

Panel: Psychoneuroses

PANELISTS: DOCTORS LOURIE, MARMOR, MASSERMAN, ROME, SUSSEX, TOMPKINS

DR. USDIN

TODAY, WE HAVE BEEN TREATED TO AN ECLECTIC APPROACH TO THE PROCESSES *and treatment of neuroses. I was interested in Dr. Rome's description how a microcosm can function in a macrocosm. His unit at Mayo's is a striking example how one can work with other specialties in medicine. A major achievement at Mayo's has been the recognition by nonpsychiatrists how much they could gain from the studies his Department has been doing. He affirmed that men have more worries and more feelings of tension than women; perhaps subsequently he will tell us why. We were shown how to use statistics wisely, and new avenues of sociopsychological inquiry were exposed. I thought of the abundance of research projects that could develop from Dr. Rome's studies, and I know most of the audience were thinking of the same thing.*

Dr. Lourie gave us basic tenets regarding the importance of the early development of the personality. I like the way that he interchangeably utilized relationship development and personality development. This eclectic approach was refreshing. An analyst, he emphasized the constitutional factors. One impression about which I hope Dr. Lourie will elaborate is the degree of hopelessness that one must consider insofar as the diathesis for mental illness is concerned. He challenged our thinking with the concept that quite significant influences on mental development may take place in the prenatal period and strongly emphasized the formative importance of the first year of a child's life. Dr. Lourie reminded us, too, that parents can be rejected.

Dr. Masserman initially treated us to a philosophical, historical and anthropological treatise how man deals with his fellow man. It was pertinent, perhaps, that he concluded with a film dealing with animals, especially cats. The effect of alcohol he adduced in dramatic fashion. His film epitomized the effects of motivational conflict and demonstrated how alcohol can modify ambivalence. He raised the question discussed throughout the day, and I hope that some of the panelists will direct themselves to this question: What are the varieties of anxiety, and how are they related to psychotherapy? This has been discussed, but I think the audience is interested in more definitive ideas. He warned us against oversimplified and stereotyped rational technics of therapy, and to beware of "simple" cures for "simple" cases. It was unfortunate that he could not show the entire film. Many of us were left hanging: we wish to know how you cure these alcoholic cats.

Dr. Sussex's offering would be a credit to any top-notch scientific investigator. He reminded us that in prescribing drugs, the psychiatrist is not only actively entering the patient's life, but should keep in mind that countertransference changes enter in. The psychiatrist's image of himself in relationship to the patient is altered. We heard a scholarly presentation of how, when and when not to use drugs, and many of us should carry away a basic, overall concept. He concluded that there is no compelling conflict between drugs and psychotherapy—a concept that many of us believe but some disbelieve.

Dr. Tompkins emphasized the importance of readily available, immediate and effective psychotherapy. His 15-session study brought up interesting attitudes and opinions of the therapists, especially of the efficacy of their therapy. This recalled the early 30's, when Alexander was reminding us of the value of brief, dynamically oriented therapy. Dr. Tompkins has been among the leading psychiatric figures who have been restressing the importance of this factor. He emphasized the goal of getting the best possible guidelines for patient care and questioned the dogmatic approaches, especially those of the young psychiatrists. Therapy should be tailored to the individual, more elasticity is required, and therapists should be tailored to the individual patient. He argued for a broad-based training curriculum and correctly scolded us for forgetting that the 1 to 5 hours that a patient spends in therapy are but a fraction of the 168 hours of the week. Facetiously, one might note that the other 163 to 167 hours of the week are of some consequence in the patient's life. Again, we heard the mandate for more valid research and could tie this to Dr. Rome's position this morning and recognize that we need more of the large-scale research that Dr. Rome and his group are doing. We need more of the type of research that Dr. Masserman and Dr. Sussex have done, more of the challenges and sometimes painful reminders of Dr. Lourie's thought, and the refreshing perspective regarding psychotherapeutic technics that Dr. Marmor reviewed. With these, psychiatry can be a better science.

Dr. Marmor reviewed the different frameworks, but pointed out the common goals of therapy. He questioned the validity of studies of the results of therapy. As he reviewed the various mechanisms that are operative in the therapeutic process, I wondered whether, if he had to pick one concept that he felt was basic, would it not be that of relationship therapy? He emphasized that working through is the sine qua non of the long-term psychotherapeutic process. Again, trying to have the panel react to something I think was operative through all their remarks, I wonder if they were complaining about the overutilization of nosology and that we must emphasize more ego psychology—that we must look at a patient with his own ego strength and ego weaknesses, that we must recognize that these are based on certain constitutional factors and on life experiences, and that we must consider that patient in his individualized present environment.

We shall begin with the opening speaker, Dr. Howard Rome.

DR. ROME: Dr. Usdin, ladies and gentlemen. The seeming paradox of the uniqueness of the individual and his commonalty as a member of groups is the leit motif of our discussions of communication. Communication is a process concerned with data reduction. The prime function of communication is to establish a language that can act as a common carrier of affect, and this attribute certainly was explicit in the presentations this afternoon. How it is that people arrive at one or a combination of levels of discourse—cognitive, affective, or insightful (the combination of all levels)—really is the process by which clues are detected, cues picked up, subtle meanings sensed: in short, ways in which information is reduced to a state of common meaning. Such a communication process breaks down what otherwise would be insuperable barriers. It allows us to deal with people on both individual and small and large group levels. Thus it defines the parameters of social relations: degrees or grades of affection, measures of empathic distance, the solidity of the feeling of being *en rapport*.

We seem to have conceptualized polarities with the individual as an idiosyncratic instance at one extreme, and as a member of a class at the other; yet both share common features. I wonder whether the panel would agree that while each of us has used his own code as a preferential language, basically what we search for is what the computer experts would expect to find in a universal Fortran, the linguists in Esperanto, and Interlingua—a compiler language that will allow us to communicate intellectually, affectively and insightfully with each other.

This effort inevitably will create subordinate issues. For example, there are the grey boundaries of definition; the difference between being sick and sick-sick-sick. Where draw a line to separate what properly is the province of medicine and psychiatry and what properly that of other disciplines? This is not just an academic or a linguistic or a topological exercise. One of the clear implications of Dr. Marmor's discussion this afternoon was that affective communion is the primary prerequisite of the relationship that leads to change. Accepting this dynamic force, what does it mean to us as physicians and as psychiatrists? Certainly we are not unique in the possession of this therapeutic attribute. If indeed it is shared by other persons, groups and professions, what does this sharing mean to our relationship vis-a-vis the rest of medicine and to our relationships with the nonmedical professionals with whom we work? The problem of resolving the territoriality that fragments what we must do if the comprehensive community programs are to be successful is a problem of communication.

DR. USDIN: *Dr. Lourie, you talked about the communication of your two-year-old child. Could you now respond to Dr. Rome's emphasis on communication, especially as it concerns the early years of life?*

DR. LOURIE: There is a communication problem between young children and adults reminescent of that between psychiatrists and the rest of medicine about which Dr. Rome raised a question. Dr. Wood, the founder of the Hospital for Sick Children in London, would tell his students in the 1840's that to communicate effectively with children, you must learn their language. If you do not, they will not let you know their thoughts. This concept has been brought up to date today by Dr. Rome. We must now learn the language of the computer.

I have been troubled as I listened here these last two days, and I have finally realized what was troubling me. In this symposium on psychiatry, in the mid-60's, nobody has mentioned once the word *prevention*. As I have heard these various papers unfold, I kept feeling that increasing responsibility was being placed on us who work with the earliest years of life to think in terms of prevention. As we were hearing about the various problems around therapy, drugs and so on, it seems evident that these treatment modalities are a patchwork corrective approach to emotional problems many of which have their origins early in life. We already have some access to them if we would only turn our attention to the point at which they are beginning. We learn more and more about the bits and pieces that are fitted together in the jigsaw puzzle of what goes on in early development. Therefore, we begin to have a few entrees to identifying and then modifying early distortions such as we talked about earlier today. A hazard to such an approach is that, both inside and outside our professions, we find it hard to look at an infant under a year of age as having a psychiatric problem or even being a potential psychiatric problem. It becomes apparent that this attitude must change.

Many of the problems don't begin at birth. They begin long before birth in the organ systems and their responses to stresses encountered in the first nine months of life. When we see an infant as a newborn, we are seeing him in the "fourth trimester" of his life. Ultimately where we are going to have to work to find the ultimate answers is with the fetus. We're not facing a hopeless problem, because new technics begin to be available to make such work possible.

The human organism "wants" to be normal. When it starts out life with constitutional hazards, handicaps or distortions, it has multiple opportunities to rework them. The relationship distortions, the separation anxieties, the patterns of dependency, which we reviewed today, come into focus over and again during the unfolding of childhood developmental phases. In each new phase, the organism has an opportunity to rework the poor answers it learned in the earlier stages. If we know where and how to give the organism an assist, we can have a hopeful picture about eventual normality.

Some developmental areas have less hopeful features. For example, when it comes to ego functions such as cognitive development, if there isn't the appropriate stimulation or experience in the first years of life, there may be stunting or failure of such functions. This can be corrected, but only up to a point. Research is showing that up to three, or even five years of age, the developmental distortion can still be corrected Thus, we can still help some preschool children who have developed what is called mental retardation from cultural deprivation growing out of lack of appropriate stimulation and opportunity. However, there is a point beyond which this process cannot be reversed, where it has become fixated, locked in place. Therefore, timing of intervention is important. When an individual hasn't learned what it is like to be part of somebody in the first developmental go-around, he can still learn this at two years of age. He can learn it at three. Some investigators think that's the end point; some of us think that you can still teach such an individual what it is like to be part of another person up to five or six. But wherever we think the end point is, we all agree that there is a point beyond which you can't teach that individual true trust, dependency and closeness to another person.

Judd Marmor indicated that identification is important in the corrective emotional relationship. If you have an individual who can't get close enough to another to identify, you have one who does not, in the process of development, achieve the type of relationship from which one builds into himself a conscience and a set of values. In other words, being part of another person has many additional developmental concomitants that go into the ability to learn, through identification with another person, how to modify undesirable behavior. If this ability to learn and to change from identification isn't present, our therapeutic tools can't reach the person in emotional difficulty. In fact, the adult who has never learned how to be part of another person is probably the only true, irreversible type of psychopathic personality.

If you will permit me, I would like to project this discussion ten years ahead and look at what may be expected to be some of the topics in the symposium that Dr. Usdin will have on *Psychiatry in the Mid-70's.* A child development story illustrates the position in which this places me. Once a mother whale was teaching her baby whale what the rules are for swimming. She said: "Now remember, it's when you go up to the surface and begin to spout off—that's when they throw the harpoons."

In early developmental stages, the stage of separation anxiety seems to be increasingly implicated as having significance in establishing patterns that are the prototypes of later depressions. Further, this stage and its concomitants appear to be among the determinants of intricate psychosomatic involvements. In Rochester, Dr. William Greene is finding that in significant numbers of patients with lymphomas and leukemias, the individuals involved have unresolved separation anxiety. They are reported to have encountered a severe loss or a severe disappointment which, in turn, has reactivated an unresolved early separation anxiety, with resulting distorted tissue responses. It sounds "way out." However, this might not be so far out that it could not be what psychiatry will be dealing with in the mid-70's. Where we may have to look for answers with this kind of problem is much further back than the newborn, further back in development than we have available now. In other words, when we are able to look into the prenatal life, we need to find out when a developing organ establishes how it will respond to stress. We know now that it encounters stress situations long before the newborn period. Stresses, such as a period of oxygen deprivation to an organ during its formative stages, are suspected of establishing patterns of response with which that organ will also respond to later stresses. From the doubting smiles on some of your faces, maybe I should have taken the mother whale's advice.

Eventually, some of the answers to these questions about constitutional factors will come from the neurophysiologists and, particularly, the molecular biologists. Cells have defenses just as individuals do, probably the prototypes of the defenses of the whole organism. If a cell is placed under stress, it has three major defensive responses. It can die, it can multiply, or it can change form. If we look closely at these defenses, we can see the prototypes of the defenses of the whole organism, including the mental mechanisms of defense.

I am afraid that in the 1970's, no matter how many of these developmental facets become clearer and hopefully make prevention more possible, we as psychiatrists will still need to apply what we know in treatment of a large group of people.

DR. USDIN: *Thank you, Dr. Lourie. Now, Dr. Masserman.*

DR. MASSERMAN: I'm really a card-carrying analyst: I make my living, such as it is, treating people; I try to teach medical students and residents how to treat people, and most of my books and articles are about treating people. Yet whenever I am fitted into a program such as this, it's usually as a cat psychiatrist. I'd like to warn Howard Rome of a similar fate: if he keeps giving these marvelous talks on computer technics, people will come up to him, put a punched program card between his teeth, depress the third button from the top and expect an answer to drop out of his pocket.

I try to counter my own handicap by emphasizing that I was concerned with human anxiety, an ubiquitous and universally recognizable human affect outside the laboratory, so I talked about history and philosophy and anthropology and ethnology and sociology, thus leading to one of the minor sciences—comparative and experimental psychology. In this I tried to anticipate Dr. Tompkins' very proper lament about how parochial, narrow-minded and uncultured we let our students remain, and how little basis we give them for understanding human behavior in all its implications and utilizing the vast storehouse of intuitive knowledge that we've acquired in three million years of human development.

I am happy indeed that no one in this audience raised the pre-Darwinian, indeed, pre-Kantian, shibboleth of "anthropomorphism" in reference to our animal studies. Since every datum, concept, inference, conclusion of which we are capable is necessarily "anthropomorphic," that word is the most heuristically and semantically redundant word in any language. Undoubtedly, human behavior, individual and social, is much more *complex* than that of cats and monkeys. But consider this analogy: admittedly, no one can understand the human brain by studying the brains of lower animals—yet no one can understand human anatomy, physiology or conduct *without* such comparative studies.

DR. USDIN: *Thank you, Dr. Masserman. Dr. Sussex?*

DR. SUSSEX: It just occurred to me that it has been a popular thing down through the ages for people to try to come up with something that defines man's uniqueness in the animal kingdom, and if it is true, as Dr. Masserman said this morning, that normal animals dislike alcohol, then either there are an awful lot of neurotic human beings or we've found a new criterion for our uniqueness in the animal kingdom.

Dr. Usdin dignified what I presented as the product of research, and I will have to undignify it. It is not, except that kind of research represented, if you will, by a sort of self-conscious clinical approach. It makes me feel very humble, indeed, when I hear Dr. Rome finding common denominators in 175,000 or so patients a year and, with a multitude of different values and criteria, establishing some 550 different scales—and calling this a "pilot study." At any rate, it was good that he emphasized going from the molecular to the molar. Perhaps in the subject I discussed today, I tried to convey some of the implications for physicians in going back from the molar to the molecular. Unfortunately, we have not had much in the molar areas to help us in our clinical work with patients. I think we have all been guilty, from time to time, of trying to draw sweeping conclusions from a series of one, and yet we do need series of patients, the more the better maybe, to go from an individualization to a generalization. I think the importance of this, as far as most of us are concerned in treating an individual patient, is to get back to an individualized use of these generalizations, this molar information, these baselines.

One implication of the subject material that I discussed occurred to me as I went along. I approached it from the standpoint of trying to determine whether individuals depended on stimuli from their environment, or did not need to do so, for their sense of ego security, so to speak, and of using this as a clinical measuring rod to predict whether they would respond favorably or adversely to certain types of drugs. It occurs to me that we could turn this around and speculate, at least, on whether the response to drugs, which produce certain changes in sensory input, distortion or reduction, could be used as a diagnostic tool in itself, perhaps to find whether a given patient tends to be in one or the other of these idiosyncratic reaction classes, if indeed these classes do exist.

Of particular interest to me, over and above the implications for treating individual patients with drugs, is where this comes from, whether the need for contact with the environment and its stimuli is a genetically determined thing or a learned thing. I recollect a couple of infants about six months of age that Sybil Escalona reported a few years ago. One of them she described as being very materially oriented, dealing with things rather than people, going from one thing to another, perfectly comfortable and satisfied as long as he had *things* to relate to. The other, of the same age (both of them were from somewhat comparable socioeconomic backgrounds), was not bound to things at all but, at six months, demonstrated evidence that he had what might be called a six-month-old equivalent of an active fantasy life.

One wonders how much, at six months old, these infants could have learned from their mothers. It was noted that the mothers were significantly different. One mother gave her child, the first I mentioned, *things* to relate to. At any time he felt any degree of tension or seemed to be frustrated, she relieved this, she comforted him, by giving him some *thing* to relieve him. The other mother did not provide *things* but gave her infant a great deal of physical closeness, and this child seemed to develop a capacity for entertaining himself despite this physical closeness. She was there: she communicated with him and apparently fostered the development of his ability to furnish his own stimuli, as it were. I think that the remarks I made earlier today have far broader implications than the specific subject that I was discussing.

DR. USDIN: *Thank you, Dr. Sussex. Dr. Tompkins.*

DR. TOMPKINS: I had a number of purposes in using the locale of the general hospital as a basis for my discussion—because I not only work in that environment, but also feel that if Dr. Usdin would follow the thought of Dr. Lourie and have a symposium on *Psychiatry in the Mid-*

70's, the image of psychiatry at that time would revolve around the general hospital to the extent that the image of psychiatry has revolved around the state hospital for many years past. When I speak of the general hospital, I mean the modern hospital, which is gradually deemphasizing what previously was a too great preoccupation with inpatient beds for the already ill, and stressing extramural care, prevention and rehabilitation. I tried to indicate the organization of the community hospital and its clinics as it faces these multi-faceted tasks imposed upon it by community forces, exemplified by the treatment mission of the ordinary community hospital's psychiatric services, whatever they may be, almost exclusively predicated on short-term therapy; hence, my emphasis. If you accept this as a proper function of psychiatry in this setting, and most people do, there is a question what we have to offer presently to meet this responsibility. The manner in which we approach this problem will, to an appreciable extent, help fashion the future of psychiatry. I do not believe I exaggerate.

Currently, as we consider the lack of specificity in regard to evaluation of the effects of treatment, whether psychotherapy or drugs or other modalities, we can question the validity of any attempt to develop a hierarchy of therapeutic approaches, which, to an extent, is implicit in many training programs and too often found in actual practice. Also, we can speculate whether such orientation provides the best utilization of what is known, as well as the most efficient use of admittedly too few trained people.

Here I might expand on a subject which I mentioned only briefly and which I don't believe was commented on by others on the panel, although it is of general concern to all of us. I speak of the need for better communication not only amongst ourselves but also with our other colleagues in medicine. The American Medical Association has had two national conferences for the expressed purpose of improving our working relationships with the physician who is not a psychiatrist in order to extend the available medical manpower in the mental health fields. I refer again to the insurance project I discussed in my initial presentation. While about 38% of patients referred to the participating psychiatrists were from nonpsychiatric physicians, in only about 23% of the final reports of all patients was there indication of further communication with the referring physician. Another aspect of psychiatric practice that I believe has not been sufficiently emphasized during these two days is our dependence on and, therefore, need to utilize other health professions and varied community resources if the people we serve are to have an adequate opportunity for prevention, treatment and rehabilitation. Again referring to the insurance project, for only 10% of the patients requiring further support on termination of treatment under the program was there a suggestion that such sources of help be utilized. There is a lag in our training programs. Old habits and approaches not consonant with new demands arising through new understandings, continue to be used; we are tradition-bound. Community psychiatry, however defined, requires new and novel technics; the use of the computer, as we have heard from Howard Rome, offers great possibilities and is an example of what is needed. The public health aspects of psychiatry are receiving only belated attention, both in teaching and practice. Jules Masserman has talked about the advantages of broad training and that too many residents tend to become insular after they leave us. I know one antidote, and that is conditioning the resident through precept and example of the teaching staff to look beyond the individual patient to the community and temper his activities to the requirements of this dual responsibility.

DR. USDIN: *Thank you, Dr. Tompkins. Dr. Marmor.*

DR. MARMOR: I want to look into my crystal ball, as Drs. Lourie and Tompkins have looked into theirs, and project a picture of psychiatry in the mid-70's. Although I would agree with Dr. Lourie that one aspect of our concern in the mid-70's is certainly going to be a greater emphasis on molecular medicine and prenatal influences, I suspect, in line with some of the points that Dr. Tompkins has been making, that we will be concerned with the other end of the spectrum, too. That is, we'll be increasingly concerned with the "*field*" in which our patients are getting ill, the broad sociocultural field. I believe also that ultimately, if we're ever going to tackle this problem of mental illness on a broad scale, we will have to think in terms of prevention rather than of treatment alone. Also the technics of treatment that we employ are going to have to go beyond the worthy but expensive individual efforts that we make and move towards certain kinds of group therapy, family therapy, brief therapy, and so on. As you know, we are already moving in that direction, but I suspect that we'll have to move further. We are also going to have to be concerned with broad problems of community psychiatry and with prevention of the origin of mental disorders by concerning ourselves with the psychiatric implications of such significant social issues as discrimination, prejudice, poverty, over-population and birth control, and war and social violence.

We cannot, in short, ignore a field-theoretical approach to the problems of our patients' illnesses. These people are not growing ill in a vacuum. The families in which they develop their faulty communicative and adaptive responses are not isolated, abstract families. They are families in a particular social context, the members of which are responding to particular kinds of social pressures and taboos and mores. I'd like to close with a little story which I think illustrates the point that how you perceive reality depends on where you sit in the "field." The story is told about a spirochete who found himself traveling along the streets of London one day when he bumped into a female spirochete whose curves appealed to him. So he said to her, "Hi there, Babe, how's about taking a little spin in a taxi?" She replied, "I'd love to." So they got into a taxicab and immediately began to twine their curves around one another, when the cab driver turned around and said to the male spirochete, "Hi sye there, Guv'nor. Hi wouldn't do that if Hi wuz you." Whereupon the male spirochete retorted indignantly, "What's it to you, Cabby; I'll thank you to mind yer own business!" At this, the cabby replied, "As yer wish, Guv'nor, but Hi 'appens to know that that lydie friend of yours is just loaded with penicillin."

DR. USDIN: *Dr. Rome?*

DR. ROME: I would agree that the issue of prevention is a major one, and also suggest that social issues such as those that Dr. Marmor mentioned require definition. Historically, we have been witnesses to the potency of style expressed in fashionable metaphor. Many of these are the symbols with which man has struggled and suffered for a long time. Recall the influence of the notion of witches, and the ways in which that sociopolitical concept affected the treatment of mental illness as well as other forms of deviation of the time. Then latterly it was a miasma as the cause of small pox, and yellow fever which certainly attracted attention and generated a unique therapeusis.

All of this is to say that one can relate anything to anything else. If it is a congenial relationship, as Dr. Marmor suggests, it comes out as insight, as if both are different aspects of the same wavelength. One has need to know what is necessary, what is sufficient, and what are attendant phenomena and/or epiphenomena. My point is that 3 or 5 or 10 or 26 cases extrapolated to a world of 3½ billion people and a world that is likely to be 7 billion people by the turn of the century is somewhat presumptuous. Arrogant intellectually, we depend heavily on unspoken articles of faith. These are important constructs with which we order and structure the world. I suggest that as we look at these closely and scientifically, they change from dogmatic truth into no more than testable hypotheses—hypotheses that have to be tested and empirically demonstrated as being applicable to the persons and to the situation in which they are to be used.

We need to continue to do what we do based on the faith of our convictions, using their unique symbols and metaphors. At the same time there is also need to assemble a common language, based on shared data and demonstrated to be adequate by the empirical test of its utility on a wide scale. It is with this expectation that I would like to come back again in 1970 to examine what hopefully will be a large accumulation of evidence in an effort to substantiate these very convincing, very alluring, but still nonetheless untested hypotheses.

DR. USDIN: *Thank you, Dr. Rome. Dr. Sussex?*

DR. SUSSEX: Maybe I should waive your recognition of me here in favor of someone who might want to respond to Dr. Rome's comments, because the question I wanted to ask Dr. Marmor might be sort of going from the sublime to the ridiculous. . . . If you don't mind the ridiculous. Dr. Marmor was making a point this afternoon that the psychotherapeutic process involves teaching and that there is a teacher-pupil relationship in a sense, but warned against "parentifying" this relationship. He pointed out that nondirectiveness, if I understood him correctly, is the best way to do this. It strikes me that to achieve a nondirective relationship in psychotherapy, truly nondirective, there would be no administrative function whatsoever involved between the psychotherapist and the patient. This, it seems to me, is not the case. For example, the fee. I'm sure nondirective therapists want to be paid a fee just as the directive therapists do, and that if the patient fails to pay the fee, this is something the therapist must pick up with him. I'm wondering if the fact that the fee is set by the therapist, this being a directive matter, isn't a clue that perhaps the psychotherapist can be directive at times when his knowledge, his position, his traditional role as the wise man of the tribe, so to speak, qualifies him to be so, whether or not the patient takes the direction. And whether he does or not becomes grist for the psychotherapeutic mill, in the sense that why he does or why he doesn't is important. Teaching a patient to be autonomous, I agree, is most important. To live autonomously, I guess, means to be able to take responsibility for his own life. On the other hand, he must be autonomous within the framework of a system, the standards of which he has to meet, so I wonder if one job of psychotherapy isn't to teach patients how they can live in a situation in which they cannot be truly autonomous and must accept authority and direction.

DR. MARMOR: I think that much of the confusion around this issue lies in what is meant by directiveness. I'm not sure that I consider the setting of limits, which is implicit in any living in a real world, as being necessarily directive, or that I would consider the contract implicit in the setting of the fee as a form of directive therapy per se. I do feel that there has been a great deal of nonsense about fees in psychoanalytic and psychiatric literature, nonsense that I think has been dictated, to a much greater extent than psychiatrists and analysts would like to admit, by their own self-interest. The assumption that a patient must make a financial sacrifice in order to benefit by therapy has, I think by now, been pretty thoroughly negated by our widespread experience with low-cost and free psychiatric clinics. Certainly the degree to which a patient is willing to pay for therapy may be a *measure* of his motivation, but it is not the *cause* of his motivation. A patient's motivation stems primarily from his inner distress and his wish to be relieved of the difficulties that his maladaptive reactions have got him into. Admitting, however, that we do have to set limits and that we do have to charge fees because that is how we earn our living, once we set the contract, I think there is a difference between a directive and a nondirective approach, or better, between an authoritarian and a non-authoritarian approach. The difference is essentially that between a teacher who tries to have his pupil learn to think for himself and the teacher who tells his pupil everything he should do. Although both pupils may learn the facts of life, the former is much more likely to develop feelings of self-confidence and autonomy, and that, after all, is one of the major goals of psychotherapy whenever possible.

May I make one additional remark in response to Howard Rome's last comment? I think that the work that Rome and his colleagues are doing is a terribly important one to the psychiatry of the future, in that it will free us from the tendency of making snap judgments on the basis of relatively few patients and enable us to explore the effect of some of the sociocultural contexts that I mentioned a while ago, and the relationship of these to different kinds of mental disorder. I look forward with great interest and expectation to the findings that may be forthcoming from that kind of computer analysis.

DR. USDIN: *Dr. Masserman, would you like to comment on these remarks?*

DR. MASSERMAN: I'm inclined to be sympathetic with Dr. Sussex's question. *Every* contract, including that between patient and physician, must be a *mutually* attractive organon: and so lays down pretty definitive rules for *both* parties. I was at the University of Chicago when Carl Rogers was teaching us "nondirective therapy," and I noticed that the nondirective arrangement had some pretty definite rules and regulations. For example, the client had to sit where he was supposed to sit, not in the nondirective therapist's lap; he had to pay his bills, had to contract for ten 45-minute sessions. . . . Then, if he hadn't improved, there was an implicit understanding that this would be reported to the authorities and that he might be considered as not qualified to continue at the University. Perhaps for that reason, when I once gave a talk to the Rogerians, I made a slip of the tongue: I called their rituals "noncorrective" therapy!

If we are going ahead now to fantasy another seminar like this in 1975, I rather think that many of the things we talked about today will still apply. That's why I used *biodynamics:* we will start with biology and go on with dynamics, which means an interplay of all the conceivable forces in a matrix of many influences, which will transcend up to the most humanitarian of our concerns.

DR. USDIN: *Dr. Lourie.*

DR. LOURIE: I'm afraid that magic will always be with us, and we might as well learn how to use it in therapy. It may be a reflection of our picture of what ideas of magic the mind will continue to carry into adult life from childhood that brings this symposium to a close by bringing up magic. In terms of the future, in the mid-1970's, people will still be able to cure some cases of eneuresis with a red wool string around the abdomen at the level of the umbilicus and with the knot over the spine, as has been done for hundreds of years.

DR. USDIN: *It may be appropriate to close our provocative panel this afternoon on a note coupling magic and wisdom. Magic, witchcraft, myth and wisdom are close cousins that show their relationship. We have examined where we stand on many present points and glanced into the future. Whether or not we like it, the public and too many of our medical colleagues will continue to look upon us as mystics whose technics may be likened to those of the magicians of the past—who, in many ways, were our forerunners.*

Robert W. Gibson, MD
Sheppard and Enoch Pratt

8

The Ego Defect in Schizophrenia *

A SCHIZOPHRENIC PATIENT LEFT MY OFFICE SAYING SHE COULD NOT STAND to continue treatment any longer. She had said this several years earlier when we first undertook intensive psychotherapy, and had often repeated it, especially when I saw signs of the greatest ego growth. On this occasion, she complained of the torment of indescribable sensations that were somehow mobilized by seeing me: she was afraid of becoming enslaved to me, afraid that I might find her unbearable and, even, die as her previous doctor had. She left saying I would never see her again. I assured her that I would be available for our regular appointment next day.

On the way home, things seemed different to her. Familiar sights and sounds seemed strange, distant. She was not sure if she could find her way. She heard taunting voices urging her to kill herself. She wanted to talk to someone but had no friends and had resolved not to speak to me again. She dialed the weather report on her telephone and felt some slight relief even from this impersonal contact. This soon failed, however, and she felt a kind of dull desperation. Death seemed the only solution. She went to her medicine cabinet, where she found a bottle of a sedative that bore the simple label "Dr. Gibson." She decided to kill herself by taking all the pills. Then she thought if she did this it would destroy me, ruin my professional reputation. With relief, she recalled my assurance that I would be available: she took just one pill—and kept her next appointment.

The Need-Fear Dilemma

This patient was struggling with a basic dilemma—the *need* for an object from which to borrow ego strength, and the *fear* of the same object because of its threat to ego organization. To some extent, this need-fear dilemma is part of the experience of all human beings capable of relating to an object. Those persons we call schizophrenic are especially bedeviled by it. It pervades their entire existence; again and again it can be discovered running through their life histories. It is especially apparent in psychotherapy, because the very nature of the interaction intensifies the dilemma. The need-fear dilemma arises out of a deficit in ego functioning. I do not think of this defect as limited to a specific area of ego function;

* *This chapter is an outgrowth of research supported by a grant from the Ford Foundation to the Chestnut Lodge Research Institute. This research was done in collaboration with Donald L. Burnham, MD, and Arthur I. Gladstone, PhD, to whom I am deeply indebted for the theoretical concepts presented in this chapter.*

so perhaps it would be more accurate to speak of ego weakness rather than defect.

The ego functioning of the schizophrenic has at least three cardinal features: 1. a vulnerability to disorganization of executive functions of the ego; 2. a relative lack of autonomy from internal drives and external stimuli; 3. an inability to maintain a reliable and enduring concept of reality. These overlap and interrelate. For example, the vulnerability to disorganization makes control of drives exceedingly difficult; poor reality testing presents an obstacle to organized ego functioning, and so forth. Taken together, they all work to make the schizophrenic peculiarly dependent on objects but, simultaneously, seriously threatened by them. His vulnerability to disorganization of ego functions makes him desperately need objects to provide the support and structure that he lacks. His lack of ego autonomy leaves him unable to resist the influence of objects and thus makes them frightening to him. The poor reality testing of the schizophrenic makes all object relations extremely tenuous.

Because schizophrenia is not a discrete entity, no unitary explanation will be found for the impairment of ego functioning. Nevertheless, among those patients considered schizophrenic is a group in whom a disturbance of early object relations interfered with normal ego development, which disturbances disrupt the processes of psychological *differentiation* and *integration.*

Differentiation refers to two interrelated processes. First, it concerns the achievement of separateness from the environment and the important objects in it; it involves the establishment of a reasonably intact ego boundary, necessary for the individual to distinguish between those impulses arising from within and those stimuli that impinge from the environment. Second, it concerns the development of specialized functioning. Special skills emerge, involving various components of the personality. Along with these skills must come an awareness of the specific situations for which they are appropriate. Characteristically, the schizophrenic shows a disturbance in both types of differentiation. He has little sense of his own identity; his repertoire of adaptive behavior is often both limited and inappropriately applied, to the point of being bizarre.

Integration is required to provide some consistency and continuity to the individual's functioning. The patient's various abilities must be brought together so that they can operate in a coordinated fashion. The integrated ego is capable of identifying internal stimuli with a reasonably accurate ideational construct; the affect experienced is appropriate; and suitable action (or, if necessary, delay of action) can be taken.

We are seriously limited in our ability to generalize about the precise conditions needed for the ego to achieve adequate differentiation and integration. An enormous amount of material has been accumulated concerning the quality of early object relations in families that produce a schizophrenic. I want, here, to stress my conviction that disturbances in the early object relation can interfere with differentiation and integration, leaving the patient with a serious defect in ego functioning.

The early life experiences of Eileen, the patient just mentioned, certainly were fraught with conflict and inconsistency. Two years before the patient's birth, an older sister died in infancy of an obscure nutritional disturbance. It was feared that Eileen might suffer the same fate, and from her birth the parents were preoccupied with her eating. Her parents separated when she was about six, and a few years later were divorced. Her father, a successful contractor, was so absorbed in his work that he took little interest in the family, even in the years before the separation. The patient and a sister, younger by three years, grew up with the mother, who was extremely dependent on both of her children, especially Eileen, and did everything she could to keep them from becoming independent. She regularly conveyed to her children that her marriage had been blissfully happy prior to their birth, indicating that the patient and her sister were responsible for the divorce and, therefore, obligated to make this up to her in some way.

Eileen, being older, bore the brunt of the family turmoil and the pathologic needs of both parents. The mother seemed to be completely taken up with her criticisms of the father, and was predominantly concerned with convincing the world that she was a good woman shamefully wronged by a bad husband. The father found it convenient to register complaints against the mother through criticisms of the patient. During Eileen's illness, he monotonously told her at every contact that all she had to do was to stop thinking about herself and see more people. Both parents were lacking in any deep concern for the patient; yet they were both intrusive and controlling in a way that stifled ego growth.

Consequences

Determining the causes of the need-fear dilemma poses all the familiar problems involved in making reconstructions from anamnestic data. The consequences of the dilemma are easier to study because they are susceptible to direct observation as they unfold before the therapist. In brief, the schizophrenic's reaction to the need-fear dilemma falls into three major patterns. *1. Object avoidance.* If the fear is dominant, he avoids objects. This can range from mild aloofness to profound catatonic withdrawal. *2. Object clinging.* If the need is dominant, he clings to objects. This can involve seeking a dependency relationship that provides an auxiliary ego; in the extreme, it can include such phenomena as the automatonlike behavior of echolalia and echopraxia. *3. Object redefinition.* He may seek a compromise solution through a redefinition of the object; he overlooks or actually distorts various features of his relationship to the object. This solution represents an attempt to maintain the belief that the object will always be reliable and available.

The three reactions—object avoidance, object clinging, object redefinition—are rarely seen in pure form in a particular patient. One pattern may predominate for a long period and then give way to another. This was true of my patient, as we shall see. Frequently we see sudden shifts between the poles of object clinging and object avoidance—the characteristic ambivalence of the schizophrenic's object relations.

OBJECT AVOIDANCE

Eileen, who was unmarried, began intensive psychotherapy at the age of 36 after some 25 years of disturbed behavior. Her overt symptoms had begun when she was 12. She felt panicky in school, and complained that she could not understand what was being said. She had attacks characterized by headaches, dizziness, and anesthesia of various parts of her mouth and tongue. Because contact with other children intensified these symptoms, she was withdrawn from school. She never returned, and developed severe phobias that forced her to lead a restricted life. There were long periods when she refused to eat, wasted away to as little as 65 pounds, and had to be tube fed. Over the years, these symptoms gradually gave way to a more frankly schizophrenic picture. She experienced auditory hallucinations, usually derogating. She was extremely hostile toward her immediate family, partially on realistic grounds but also with pronounced delusional ideas. At times she showed disorganized thinking and regressed behavior. She spent all of her time in psychiatric hospitals or nursing homes, and consequently had very little contact with anyone other than her doctors and nurses. Even these contacts she could tolerate only so long as they remained strictly impersonal.

As Eileen's symptoms progressed, the therapies became correspondingly more drastic. A hysterectomy was strongly recommended, but never performed. She was given repeated courses of electroshock and insulin coma therapy, both separately and in combination. Hormonal treatments of various types were attempted. A lobotomy was strongly recommended, but not done. Psychotherapy was never attempted, not once.

When Eileen first arrived at my office, she walked unsteadily, with the assistance of two nurses. She looked like a teen-ager, not a 36-year-old woman. She was thin, weighing 85 pounds. Her clothes were drab, she wore no makeup, and her appearance was lifeless, like her conversation. In a monotonous voice, she explained that she was stupid, insane, and completely hopeless. She saw no purpose in living, never had, and was waiting to die. She did not wish contact with people, just to be alone. She apologized for wasting my time, but explained that she had been forced to come. She understood that she was to be subjected to some new form of treatment, but was convinced that this would be as useless as all the previous efforts.

During the first year, she repeatedly told me that she was hopeless and that I could not possibly be of any value or mean anything to her. I tried all the things that therapists try when a patient drives them to the depths of discouragement and exasperation. Mainly, I tried to let her know that I was there, would continue to be there, and did not believe the situation hopeless, not yet at least. There were occasional flashes of life. For a few moments in one hour she actually behaved flirtatiously toward me. Another time she flared into anger as she recalled her father's desertion of the family and his second marriage. Once she dropped her stereotyped complaints to say, fearfully, that if she lost her illness there would be nothing left, that nurses and doctors are interested only in sick people, and that she had had no one else for years. No one would want her if she were not a sick patient.

Object avoidance was the patient's predominant response during the first 25 years of her illness. The initial overt symptoms were precipitated by the emergence of erotic feelings at puberty. The affects involved might have been assimilated, or at least handled, by neurotic defenses had there not been serious limitations of ego development. She experienced a longing for primitive closeness, but the very intensity of the affects was intolerable. Avoidance of objects provided the closest thing to a workable solution.

I believe, to recapitulate, that this schizophrenic patient had an inordinate need for objects to compensate for an ego defect. That need was so great that it liberated a complex of painful feelings arising from the fear of losing such a valued object, from the threat of engulfment by the object, and from a perception of herself as insatiable and destructive. One way to handle this, of course, was to avoid objects and the painful experiences they evoked.

Unfortunately, the avoidance of objects brings its own problems. It forces on the patient a life of isolation that can rarely be maintained in society as it is now organized. It tends to cut off the most effective sources for ego support and growth. It serves to perpetuate and accentuate faulty reality testing, because the opportunity for consensual validation is eliminated.

Quite often, the patient who avoids human objects substitutes a delusional system or hallucinations. My patient recalled that shock therapies were administered to get rid of her "voices." Her last thoughts before losing consciousness involved a determination to keep her "voices," and on awakening she immediately tried to recapture them. As she put it: "What would I have without the voices? I'd be nothing." Her hallucinations had become a substitute object, a substitute for human relationships.

OBJECT CLINGING

After about a year of psychotherapy, Eileen began to change in her response to objects. She talked at length about a former psychiatrist who had managed her treatment for some five years, until he died of leukemia. She showed me a letter that he had written to her shortly before he died. For the first time, she felt the full impact of his death, intense grief. She began to show an interest in some of the other patients, and often talked about them. She acquired some pets, which became topics of conversation in the cottage where she lived. She talked about becoming an outpatient and, after a few months, persuaded her clinical administrator to let her make the move. This was the first time in 25 years that she had lived outside an institution. She showed enthusiasm as she furnished her home and revealed that this had been her lifelong ambition. She was fearful about her ability to live alone, but each time some problem arose she mastered it. She had few human contacts, but instead related to her house as a substitute object. Gradually, she dissociated herself from the hospital and within a few months had no further contact except her intensive psychotherapy.

Despite these indications of improved functioning, Eileen recurrently threatened to stop treatment, always following the same pattern. She would complain, just as she had throughout the first year of therapy, that everything was hopeless, a waste of time. She would say, finally, that she was through, but would return after having missed one or two appointments. On her return she would be less defensive, express some hopefulness, and openly acknowledge that her relationship to me had become extremely important.

I first thought of this sequence as a method of defending against the emergence of erotic feelings in the transference. Although she had never discussed sex directly, there had been allusions to it when her finch laid an egg, when her yard man planted the grass seed, and when she named her dog Cleo after learning that I had a dog named Caesar. Then, quite suddenly, she began to experience intense physical sensations throughout her body.

She reported several dreams: "You had a baby—your wife was there—she was pretty—I don't know if your children were there—I think I was taking care of the baby—I don't know—I woke up feeling worried and remembered how I took care of my sister's baby." A few days later she reported: "Eloise (her father's second wife) was having a baby—everybody was afraid that I would be jealous—actually I was very happy—I did feel sorry for the way Father had left Mother." A few days later: "You were at a picnic—other doctors were there—their wives were there—we were all having a good time." She recalled that the wife of one of the doctors in the dream had just recently been pregnant. Again, a few days later: "I was going to have a baby—can you believe that? I wasn't even ashamed." She then wondered whether it would be possible for her to have a baby by artificial insemination.

The Oedipal quality of these dreams was apparent. They occurred during the emergence of erotic feelings within the transference relationship. Libidinal strivings toward the father and infantile fantasies of being impregnated by him appeared in almost undisguised form. At a later time, I came to consider these dreams as having strong pre-Oedipal determinants. They were indicative of the archaic quality of the patient's object relations. There was the wish to be my child, the wish to share in the oral pleasures of the picnic, the wish to have her father's child, to have my child. The dreams revealed a yearning for objects, but through a primitive fusion by incorporation and introjection.

During the period when these dreams were occurring, Eileen repeatedly experienced sensations similar to those at the onset of her illness. Several times she had difficulty in walking, and often her legs trembled. She recalled the previously repressed memory of having masturbated as a child. As she became conscious of this memory, the generalized feelings gave way to genital sexual feelings, the first she had experienced in her adult life. At the time, she was quite frightened by these feelings, because of their intensity and her inability to control them. Later, she seemed to go through a belated adolescence: she read books about what every young girl should know, became interested in her clothing, and took a course to improve her figure. She had her greying hair tinted an auburn color.

These changes were encouraging. The patient's symptoms appeared to be a defense against Oedipal sexual strivings toward her father, which had emerged in the transference and been worked through. Although an immediate change in a lifelong pattern of isolation could hardly be expected, I did anticipate a gradual expansion of her activities, that she might acquire some friends, and that she might even do some work. But no: the remarkable changes in Eileen's relationship to me did not seem to extend into other aspects of her life. She lived by herself and had only minimal contacts with people—in stores, delivery men, and such. These were often pleasant and comfortable, but were brief and sharply defined in terms of the specific service being rendered. At times, her prevailing feeling was one of extreme gratitude to me, and she took pleasure in our relationship. But, quite regularly, she felt threatened by the thought that she might lose it. At other times, she resented the enormous power over her that this gave me. She also feared that she would have to satisfy my dependency needs just as she had those of her parents. Nevertheless, she could take no steps to develop other relationships. The only possible alternative that she could see was to break off altogether and return to the old pattern of object avoidance.

The inevitable vicissitudes of object clinging are illustrated by this sequence of events. Object clinging occurs as a response to the need-fear dilemma in the schizophrenic when the need is dominant. An effort is made to compensate for the ego defect through fusion with an object. The object becomes an auxiliary ego that shares the responsibility for organizing behavior, managing and controlling drives, and testing reality. This device may work remarkably well. Superficially, at least, patients may seem fully intact so long as this kind of relationship to an object is maintained.

But like object avoidance, such a solution to the need-fear dilemma has its problems. The demands placed on the person who is the object can be so taxing that he will break off the relationship. Even when this does not happen, the patient is constantly reminded, directly and indirectly, that he does not have total control and possession of the object, and this becomes threatening. The patient must contend with the rage evoked by his state of helplessness, and he may live in fear that this rage will lead him to destroy the object.

For a vast number of patients an institution becomes the object to which they cling. A hospital offers much greater promise that it can meet the patient's needs than an individual. It is always there; it has a visible structure; it provides a vast array of routines, policies, regulations, and traditions. Schizophrenic patients functioning with reasonable adequacy within a hospital setting number in the scores of thousands. They have solved their need-fear dilemma by clinging to the institution and in so doing compensate for a defect in ego function.

My patient further illustrates the impact of psychotherapy on the need-fear dilemma. The psychotherapist, regardless of his theoretical orientation or technical approach, will at least see his patient with some regularity and make a concerted effort to understand his communications. This in itself will activate the need-fear dilemma. The patient will see in the therapist an object to which he can cling to strengthen his weakened ego, but this can rouse all of the fears I have just described. In addition, the therapist may be seen as a controlling agent that will threaten the patient's autonomy.

It has often been reported that first-year psychiatric residents do well with schizophrenic patients. Although this observation has probably not been subjected to a controlled study, all psychiatrists know of instances when a chronically ill schizophrenic patient responded dramatically to an inexperienced therapist. This phenomenon can be explained by the concept of the need-fear dilemma: the resident approaches the patient with eagerness, the need-fear dilemma is activated, and this may lead to drastic alterations in the patient's behavior. More important, it opens the way for a different resolution of the dilemma. New object relations can be formed that may lead to further ego growth. If the resident is gifted and the circumstances favorable, enduring changes can occur.

OBJECT REDEFINITION

Thus far I have described how my patient dealt with her need-fear dilemma through avoiding objects or through clinging to them. At times Eileen sought still another solution to the dilemma. During the early phases of treatment, while she was still in the hospital, many decisions about her life situation were made by the administrative psychiatrist. I participated in these decisions and quite openly acknowledged to the patient my role in them, but she directed any criticisms only toward the administrative psychiatrist. For example, she felt that it was the administrator who had to be persuaded that she was well enough for trial visits from the hospital, and eventually for discharge. In actuality, he was less reluctant about these moves than I was, but my patient still viewed me as her champion and the administrator as her enemy.

Later, she directed her negative feelings toward her general physician. She felt that he made light of her symptoms, that he ridiculed her, and that he was not sufficiently supportive. Invariably such criticisms were displacements of feelings that she was experiencing in the therapeutic relationship. I regularly confronted her with the distortions in her views, but she was remarkably resistant to efforts at clarification and interpretation of this issue.

Eileen required a fair degree of selective inattention to maintain the idealized view of me as an entirely benevolent helper. Dynamically, this made it possible for her to tolerate some of the fears aroused by the therapeutic relationship. By always displacing negative transference feelings onto someone other than the therapist, she was able to avoid any feeling of hostility toward the therapist that might have led to thoughts of terminating treatment. Such thoughts were intolerable to Eileen when she had to rely completely on me to serve as an auxiliary ego. By directing her negative feelings toward other persons, she could account for and deal with the affective experience and at the same time preserve the therapist as an object to whom she could cling for support.

In some patients, this reaction to the need-fear dilemma requires more serious distortions of reality. The paranoid patient is perhaps the classic example. He may displace his negative feelings onto some mysterious person or group that is responsible for all the ill that befalls him. Within the hospital setting, even the most paranoid patient usually manages to retain some person whom he can picture as good and willing to help.

Unfortunately, such relationships are so highly conflictual that they seldom last.

The hostility of the schizophrenic is an outgrowth of the need-fear dilemma. He feels bound to the object for the support that he needs; yet he tries to free himself from the object to escape the fear it creates. This state of conflict creates a rage in the patient that can be like that of the helpless infant. In other words, hostility is not the primary problem in the schizophrenic; rather, it is a secondary consequence.

Object redefinition is a resistance. It is used in the service of denying hostility. But it is something more: it is a way of maintaining an object relation and, as such, should be treated with care. Eventually it must be dealt with but only after a great deal of work has been done on the core issue—the need-fear dilemma.

Orality and Object Relations

The primitive quality of the schizophrenic's object relations makes him especially prone to oral disturbances. The first reality is known by what can be swallowed, perception in terms of what can be taken into the mouth. Disturbances in differentiation and integration during this early period of oral introjection may, in the adult schizophrenic, lead to a variety of autoerotic activities as well as feeding difficulties.

As an infant, Eileen showed feeding difficulties that became the focus of much of the interaction between her and her parents. As a child she had been literally tormented by thumb-sucking. She had thought of it as a terrible sin, and had repeatedly tried to stop, but could not because it was the only way she could get to sleep at night as she lay listening to her parents arguing.

From an early age, she had been criticized by her father for her poor eating, to the point that she felt that he was not interested in anything else about her. During her many hospitalizations, her father had continued to focus on her poor appetite and weight loss. Once he offered her a Cadillac as a birthday present if she could reach 100 pounds, and as a consolation prize offered a mink coat of one pelt for each pound that she weighed. She never got the Cadillac, but did settle for a 97-pelt mink coat.

There was a kernel of truth in the father's emphasis on the patient's eating. Variations in oral activity closely paralleled the state of her object relations and, as such, were a rather good index to the state of her ego functioning. For example, she revealed that her periods of literal starvation had been an attempt to control diffuse sensations that verged on panic. Starvation, she believed, might control the feelings and further served to reassure her that she was not insatiable.

As therapy progressed, she again began to suck her thumb at night and reexperienced the terrible torment that she had felt as a child. She began to crave sweets and on occasion gorged herself on candy bars. She broke the 100-pound mark with ease, though she never became actually obese. The increase in appetite itself became extremely threatening because it was something else that might get out of control. Her underlying voracity was revealed by her acquiring a collection of over 100 cook books. For the first time her teeth were visible as she talked and smiled instead of being concealed by tightly drawn lips. The emergence of oral strivings had its counterpart in daily living. She was freer about making purchases and initiated more contact with people. She wanted and expected more from her life.

The whole constellation of the need-fear dilemma was condensed and represented in the patient's oral activity. For years her characteristic response had been object avoidance, not eating. In therapy the dilemma was activated, and she reexperienced the hungering for objects along with the fears that she was insatiable. As her relationship to the psychotherapist deepened, she felt strengthened. Gradually she learned to tolerate her oral strivings, and finally she could even indulge them without threat of ego dissolution.

Conclusion

In this chapter, I have drawn heavily on psychotherapeutic work with schizophrenic patients, and presented the concepts which I have found most helpful in treating them. Briefly, the major thesis runs as follows: the schizophrenic is confronted by the dilemma of a need for objects and a fear of them. This dilemma arises out of a defect in ego function which has as its origin disturbances in the processes of differentiation and integration. The ego functioning is characterized by *1.* a vulnerability to disorganization, *2.* a relative lack of autonomy from internal drives and external stimuli, and *3.* a disturbance in reality testing. Three major patterns of response are available to the schizophrenic as he attempts to solve the dilemma of his object relations: *1.* he may avoid objects, *2.* he may cling to objects, *3.* he may try to redefine objects to achieve the illusion that a benevolent protector is always available.

The psychotherapist of the schizophrenic patient inevitably activates the need-fear dilemma. This in itself may open the way to new object relations and offer an opportunity for a different resolution of the dilemma. Within the context of the transference relationship, the therapist opens himself to the patient and lets him experience the therapist as both a threatening and a need-fulfilling object. This willingness of the therapist to open himself provides a model that gives the patient the courage to expose himself to the hazards of object relations. The therapist helps the patient to identify and become thoroughly familiar with both poles of the need-fear dilemma. He helps him to discover the origins of early conflictual object relations. Perhaps most of all, the psychotherapist shares in the need–fear dilemma, and in so doing establishes a new kind of relationship for the patient—a relationship that nurtures ego growth.

Stuart M. Finch, MD
Michigan, Children's Psychiatric Hospital

9

Childhood Schizophrenia

PROBABLY THE ONLY SYNDROME IN PSYCHIATRY MORE CONFUSING THAN adult schizophrenia is childhood schizophrenia. This is a condition variously labeled by many authors: the atypical child, early infantile autism, symbiotic psychosis of childhood, many others. A long and serious debate has contended whether "functional" psychoses of children really are schizophrenia or some entirely different syndrome. Is the 40-year-old man with paranoid delusions suffering from the same kind of malignant personality disintegration that the two- or three-year old may manifest?

Someone facetiously remarked that all two-year olds are ambulatory psychotics with a good prognosis. Certainly it has taken man a long time to recognize that there are deviant young children with severe problems in adapting to reality and that these youngsters are quite different from normal children proceeding along a rather rocky pathway toward reality adjustment. It has not been too many years since we considered childhood psychosis a relatively rare event. Today's literature, however, is replete with illustrations of bizarre, peculiar children whose attempts at adjustment are fragmentary or almost nonexistent. In spite of our intensive study of such children, we are still not clear why these malignant processes take place; some blame heredity, some constitution, some psychological factors, and others a blend of these.

What we can do for these children is, however, of tremendous importance. At the moment, our methods of treating the psychotic child are limited, expensive, lengthy and, usually, only partially successful. Some feel that a schizophrenic, child or adult, will always remain a schizophrenic and that his core personality will continue to be psychotic. Others feel that although under considerable stress a child or adult may lose his contact with reality, subsequently he may restore it and be not much worse for the process. Certainly it would seem that if the adult psychiatrist cannot define schizophrenia clearly, child psychiatrists should not be criticized for a similar disability. Children, particularly the youngest ones, are in some sense psychotic anyway. It becomes a problem when and how we determine which will remain psychotic and which develop out of this chaotic primeval adjustment. Is it factors inherent in the central nervous system, or psychological environment acting on the child? Or, perhaps, both?

History

The history of our study of childhood psychosis is brief. Until Leo Kanner[4, 11] described early infantile autism in 1943, cases of childhood schizophrenia were thought to be relatively rare. We have tended to think of all children as idiosyncratically peculiar and, therefore, have hesitated to label any of them psychotic. Anyone who has ever watched a three-year old, with his unpredictability, his emotional instability, his fantasy magical world, realizes that a determination of psychosis is not easily made. It was only when youngsters reached grade-school age that a few of the most pronounced deviants forced the psychiatrist to call them psychotic. Kanner, however, recognized that a small group of children, often previously labeled as either deaf or mentally retarded, really suffered from severe ego-growth inhibition. It may have been the fact that his early series was overweighted with the middle-class high intellectual group led him to believe that the parents of these youngsters had certain characteristics more typical of this class. He described them as intellectual, emotionally cold and uninvolved with the infant. As time passed, we learned that parents from any socioeconomic group may produce this particular type of atypical or autistic child. Lauretta Bender,[1] with her wealth of clinical material, felt that these youngsters suffered from a neurologic developmental lag, which led to a difficulty in adjusting to their environment. She put the main emphasis on the neurophysiologic aspects. A third noteworthy contributor was Margaret Mahler,[10] who from her psychoanalytic orientation delineated the "symbiotic psychosis of childhood." Many writers, including Mahler and Kanner, have postulated the presence of constitutional factors which, in combination with certain environmental problems, create these malignant syndromes of childhood.

The literature that has appeared since the formulations of these three authors has largely concerned the psychological problems. We still remain relatively ignorant of physiologic difficulties, at least the measurable factors. There are indications that some youngsters come into the world with a tendency to use one or more of the receptive senses, such as sight, hearing, touch, whereas their mother may emphasize another. These findings, however, are difficult to measure. If there is some hidden physiologic defect, we do not know it either in adult or in childhood schizophrenia. It would seem most appropriate, therefore, to hold an open mind and to assume the possibility that various factors contribute.

Types of Childhood Schizophrenia

Childhood schizophrenia can produce a variety of syndromes, depending on several factors. The first is the age at which the psychotic process manifests itself and whether this is a result of a lack of ego growth or of a regression from a more advanced level. The second is the degree of ego impairment, which, of course, may range from minimal to marked. The third is the ego defense systems that the child has available to him. Kaufman[5] has divided childhood schizophrenia into five subtypes: schizophrenic children with 1. *minimal ego development*, 2. *fragmented ego development*, 3. *pseudodelinquent schizophrenia*, 4. *pseudopsychosomatic schizophrenia*, and 5. *pseudoneurotic schizophrenia*. In our work, we have used a somewhat simpler classification but one which in part overlaps Kaufman's.

Kanner's description of early infantile autism corresponds generally to Kaufman's subtype 1. These are youngsters whose ego growth has been minimal. They remain fixated in the autistic phase of development normally characteristic of the first three months of life. It would be inaccurate to say that there is a total absence of ego development, since these children do manifest evidences of autonomous, conflict-free ego growth. Their development of motor skills is often age-appropriate, and they have often been described as graceful youngsters. They do, however, remain isolated in a world almost totally of their own design. They erect a barrier against object relationships and seem unable even to differentiate animate from inanimate. To some extent, this barrier also stands in the way of messages coming from within the child. For example, these youngsters are usually unresponsive to pain. What would appear to be a painful cut may be only glanced at by the child. The diagnosis of early autism becomes progressively more difficult the younger the patient. At less than one year of age, it is almost impossible, and between 12 and 18 months subject to many errors. Deafness and mental retardation are considerations usually presenting themselves. As the child grows older, the typical symptoms of early infantile autism become more readily discernible. The three-year-old does not either talk or, if he has learned words, use them to communicate. At times, one sees an idiot savant type of development, the child showing a precocious memory for music, numbers, automobiles or some other category, yet maturing in a chaotic, uneven and inefficient pattern. By five years, he is usually easily recognizable as grossly abnormal, although the proper diagnosis may still not be easy. Kanner and probably others, also, feel that the label of early infantile autism is used too often and inaccurately. For example, children with brain damage or mental retardation are often erroneously labeled autistic. A brief case history may serve to illustrate some of the features common to autistic youngsters.

Case history: autism. Ethel was 32-months old when the pediatrician first referred her for psychiatric evaluation. He was concerned about her lack of speech and apparent inability to relate to anyone. She was the seventh of seven children, all of whom were under nine. Her parents, overwhelmed by the rapid arrival of so many children, were exhausted by the burden, and readily agreed that Ethel was an unplanned child and that by the time she arrived they had little energy to spend on her. She had been a quiet baby, undemanding and unresponsive. She had walked late and had begun to use one or two words only by 32 months. When seen for evaluation, she came with the physician willingly but really paid little attention to him. She wandered around the playroom picking up various objects, feeling them, sometimes putting them in her mouth or smelling them, and then dropping them and moving on. She seemed most pleased by hard, shiny objects, which she stroked rhythmically with her fingers. She did not respond to directions, although her parents reported that she did understand conversation and would "obey" if their request coincided with her desires. Only once during the interview was there any eye contact with the examiner, and this occurred when he took a toy that she seemed interested in holding onto. The eye contact was only brief, however; she quickly gave up her attempts to get the toy back and went on with her aimless wandering. She was untestable by the usual psychological instruments appropriate for her age, but during her examination did respond with a few reactions indicative of potential intelligence. These were times when her fleeting attention could be focused briefly and she would follow a simple order, such as handing the examiner a particular toy of a specific color.

Another type of childhood schizophrenic is the symbiotic psychotic as described by Mahler.[10] Such children correspond to Kaufman's subtype 2, those with fragmentary ego development. They have been unsuccessful in passing from the symbiotic phase of development to the separation-individuation phase. They may have a history of superficially adequate adjustment for the first two or three years of life, only to go through a period of ego disintegration following some traumatic event such as the birth of a sibling, a family move, or a hospitalization. Actually, of course, the child has not been given the proper kind of mothering to allow him to separate and individuate himself when the proper time comes. Mahler and others have described these mothers as overprotective and infantalizing the child, having trouble allowing the youngster to grow up. They mention that these children seem also handicapped by a constitutional predisposition to the psychosis. Clinically, the children present evidences of more advanced ego function than the autistic children, but also of a psychotic process. If untreated, these children may eventually become more autistic. A short case history will illustrate this type of child.

Case history: symbiotic psychosis. Donna was five when she was referred for evaluation by the school officers because they had been unable to keep her in kindergarten. She had been aggressive, profane, exhibitionistic, and unable or unwilling to conform to routines or regulations. She would wander about the room and, if interrupted or restrained, scream at the teacher and, on occasion, become physically aggressive. She often said illogical or irrelevant things. Admitted to the hospital, she showed much the same behavior. She was, sometimes, echolalic and would repetitiously repeat television commercials. She often asked anyone near her questions, such as "Am I a girl?" "Are you a boy?" "Am I going to die?" "Will the hospital be here tomorrow?" She paid little attention to the answers she received and would continue her questions. The history revealed that she was the elder of two daughters of a very disturbed couple. The father was distant, passive, uninvolved; the mother insecure, subject to intermittent depressions and, alternately, overprotecting and rejecting toward Donna. Donna had seemed to develop fairly well until, when she was 2½-years old, her sister was born. Then she began to show periods of excessive crying and marked anxiety. Over the next few months, there was a gradual disintegration of her ego functions and her ability to communicate meaningfully. Both the history and direct observation of Donna indicated that she was symbiotically psychotic.

A third type of psychotic child we have preferred to call the borderline psychotic. This group encompasses subtypes 3, 4, and 5 of Kaufman. They are children who, to some extent, mask the basic psychotic process —sometimes with what appears to be a character problem, at others with a neurotic-like appearance, and occasionally with psychosomatic symptoms. We prefer the term borderline because these children seem less disturbed and closer to the normal than the two previous types and because they have more ego functions. They have periods when they are in contact with reality and are able to relate on at least a marginal basis, and other periods when they are more clearly psychotic.

In our hospital, we often find staff mentioning that one of these patients "had a good day" or "had a bad day," by which they refer to the degree of relatability and contact with reality that the children exhibited. These children show an interesting phenomenon described by Cain[2] as "playing crazy": they experiment at times with acting psychotic but are actually in control of what they are doing. At other times, they actually are psychotic and are not able to use secondary process thinking. The "playing crazy" is, in part at least, an attempt to master the psychotic episodes by seeming to turn them off and on at will. The following is an abbreviated case history of a borderline child.

Case history: borderline psychosis. David was a seven-year old referred for treatment by the school because of disruptive classroom behavior, academic underachievement, exaggerated fears, and occasional aggressive behavior toward other children. He was the only child of middle-aged, unintuitive parents, who had little knowledge of the basic needs of a young child. In the hospital, David seemed at first a severely neurotic child whose numerous phobias almost totally incapacitated him. He was at best only a fringe member of the group and seemed unable to relate comfortably to either peers or staff. He resisted any kind of change and tried to set up a constricted, inhibited routine for himself. He mentioned bizarre worries—about therapists killing patients—and elaborated a multitude of fantasies about death. On some days, he seemed fairly comfortable and able to perform, in school as well as in other areas. On other days, usually coinciding with some unexpected event, such as a field trip, a letter from a relative or the admission of a new child, David was preoccupied and uncommunicative. He would prefer to sit in his room daydreaming, and seemed oblivious to his surroundings. If another child teased him, he might strike out viciously. On his "good days" David verbalized superficial insight about his difficulties, which he referred to as his "problems." On his "bad days," he seemed almost totally lacking in any insight.

Summary of Types

One obvious question occurs at this point: Are all of these children described here suffering from different degrees of severity of the same disorder, or are they really afflicted with different conditions with different etiologies? At the present time, our feeling is that no one could answer this question to the satisfaction of all, nor could any answer be supported by sufficient evidence to be conclusive. We can only offer our ideas supported by our own impressions and hope that more clear-cut data will eventually follow.

First of all, we believe that these three (or, if you use Kaufman's classification, five) categories of childhood schizophrenia are all on a continuum, are all part of the same general process. It is highly probable that, with varying degrees of the "biologic factor" and the "emotional factor" interacting, we could postulate different degrees of illness and of "health." Some infants with a heavy biologic predisposition and a heavy dose of family psychopathology could become autistic and almost totally untreatable by present methods. Another infant with lesser biologic and emotional handicap might become borderline psychotic.

We have arrived at this working hypothesis for several reasons. The first is that these children, especially with treatment or with adverse situations, may move up or down the "scale"—from autistic up through symbiosis on to borderline, or the reverse. If the conditions were really separate, such movement would seem unlikely. A second phenomenon that strengthens our view is the overlap of symptoms seen in these children as individuals. A child may seem partially autistic and partially symbiotic: he does not fit a classical description of either of these syndromes but, like most clinical patients, chooses a middle ground. A third is the various similarities in all of these patients: the poor object relationships, the tendency to a fantasy world, the primitive impulses, the weak ego and other such factors. They all tend to retain a basic oversensitivity to others and a need to retreat from human closeness.

Someday we may be able to differentiate and prognosticate more accurately with these children, but this would seem beyond our capabilities now. We still cannot be sure which child will respond best and which will remain almost unchanged with treatment. This is despite our best efforts to evaluate family psychopathology, type of treatment, astuteness of the therapist and innumerable other factors.

Families

The families of children with schizophrenia have been studied by a number of authors. The psychopathology in them seems undeniable. The mothers tend to be narcissistic and either overtly rejecting or markedly overprotective. The fathers tend to be passive and either withdrawn from the family or overcompensatingly tyrannical. It has been our experience that these are extremely difficult families with which to work. The most disappointing have been those in which we discovered signs of psychosis in a very young child and yet were unable to effect sufficient change in parental attitudes to prevent the further development of psychosis. If, for example, one diagnoses a child as psychotic at 16 months, it is essential that remedial action be prompt and thorough. More often than not, we have been unable to produce rapid changes in these mothers nor have we been particularly successful in having them hire warm, competent nursemaids to serve as a mother surrogate. By the time our treatment measures have begun to take hold, the child is close to three years of age and the psychosis is more fully developed.

We agree with Escalona[3] that it is difficult to "blame" parents alone for the creation of psychosis in their child. Nevertheless, it would seem to us that the psychotic children whom we have seen all have disturbed parents. We have seen self-involvement and narcissism as routine qualities, whether the parents were highly intellectual middle-class people or immature, acting out lower-class parents. Not infrequently, we have felt that these are people who either should not have married or certainly should not have had children. They may have had other children who were nonpsychotic, but the vast majority were disturbed in some way. Usually the psychotic child was born early in the marriage (or before it), when the parent was unready to take on these responsibilities, or was born late in the unhappy marriage, when there was little affection or time for the child. In addition to this, it seems to us, many of these infants came into the world poorly endowed with a capacity to build an ego and they did not stimulate a maternal response as well as the normal infant does. The two factors seem to go together, the infant's lessened responsiveness and the parental problems. We strongly suspect that either infant predisposition, or powerful parental psychopathology, or any intermediate combination, can produce childhood psychosis.

Case history[9] family. Jennie was 19-months old when she was first seen for evaluation, having been referred by an ophthalmologist. He had seen her for a strabismus and was concerned about her peculiar behavior. She was a typically autistic child whose visual problem was mild and whose physical development was otherwise normal. The mother was a youthful 25-year-old woman, extremely attractive but extremely immature. She had three other children, all of them problems for her. She ran a highly disorganized household with little discipline for the children. The father was a wealthy young executive who prided himself on all his accomplishments and all his acquisitions, including his beautiful wife. He boasted of his four children as if they were stock dividends, yet he could only guess at their birthdays. He gave his wife only a small amount of money to run their large home and resented that she did not perform up to his standards. He did not accept the idea that there were any emotional problems in anyone in the family, and would not participate in any treatment program. He agreed to have his wife seen at whatever interval the psychiatrist chose but then resented the beginning changes she showed toward maturation. The mother was a high-school girl when she married, and came from a large family of low income. She was a naive, hysterical girl not only narcissistic but totally unequipped to marry and to raise a family. She gave every indication of a potential to respond to therapy, but discontinued after four months because her husband made her life more miserable with sarcastic remarks about the process.

Here was a not untypical case in which we could see many of the factors contributing to the child's illness, but were unsuccessful in our attempts to change them. The father was distant, autocratic and unavailable for treatment. The mother, though potentially treatable, could not continue. When last seen, the child continued to present a picture of early infantile autism.

Etiology

We have been hesitant to adopt any single theory of etiology. Over the years, we have come gradually to view these children in a manner somewhat akin to our concept of children with psychophysiologic disorders. For example, the vast majority of children with ulcerative colitis have a brittle, intellectual, obsessive type of personality. In many ways, they resemble children with ordinary obsessional character disorders, but they have the important added problem of colitis. There would appear to be a biologic factor, possibly autoimmunologic, which when combined with certain types of environmental and emotional problems leads to the development of the colitis. Is it not possible also that psychotic children may have some type of "biologic weakness" which, when combined with certain family dynamics leading to specific emotional difficulties, may result in a psychosis? Whether such biologic difficulty is genetic in nature is, of course, not known, but that is entirely possible. One can also postulate varying degrees of such biologic weakness that would then require greater or less degrees of environmental trauma to produce a psychosis. It might also help explain why childhood psychosis appears in such differing degrees of severity.

We are cognizant of the fact, of course, that genetic and biochemic studies have yet proved inconclusive in regard to the etiology of schizophrenia. It does remain possible that we may eventually find that causative factors lie almost totally in the environmental area. It is also possible that we may eventually discover some biologic factor that strongly predisposes the child to psychosis and that may be activated with the minimum of emotional trauma. As we view the situation now, it would appear that both factors probably contribute.

Treatment

Almost everyone who has had experience in the treatment of childhood schizophrenia retains a rather pessimistic attitude about the eventual prognosis. This includes all forms of treatment, whether in or out of an institution, with or without psychopharmacologic agents, and with or without concomitant family treatment. From time to time, one sees in the literature reports of children who apparently respond much better than most and who achieve a vastly improved adjustment. Even in these children, however, there tends to be a residual of the earlier psychosis. Their entire adjustment remains marginal; they lack the warm, comfortable spontaneity of a healthy individual.

Our experience in the treatment of these children has been in a large center that provides outpatient and inpatient, as well as day-care, service. We have over the past several years experimented with various treatment procedures for them and their families. We have tried to find ways and means by which we could recognize certain children or their families as those who would respond most favorably. One factor of favorable prognostic importance is the age of the child. The earlier we can begin treatment, other things being equal, the better the outlook, even though early treatment has the difficulties already mentioned. Another favorable factor is the level of ego function. The more ego skills a child has developed, the better he will fare in therapy. Finally, modifiability of family patterns is an important prognostic factor. If we cannot change the family and must leave the child in it, our treatment efforts are usually futile.

We have also tried to delineate the most efficient methods of treatment. Our residential treatment unit is part of the University teaching center. This has meant that we have had students from many disciplines rotating through our hospital, and that we have tried to keep a caseload with a representative variety of disturbed children. Initially, we were concerned that contact with students from various disciplines might well jeopardize any chances of success in the treatment of these psychotic children. This concern would seem to have been unjustified. We have, however, tried to give each of these children a psychotherapist who would remain with him over an extended period of time. It would appear that one can change occupational therapist, recreational therapist, or nurse without producing a severe regression in the patient, although this concept can be invalidated if there is a close attachment between the youngster and a particular staff member. Nevertheless, if the psychotherapeutic relationship is developed properly, the child's other relationships may be broken and restarted without major disaster.

Another point is worth mention. In our work, in both day care and inpatient treatment, we have found the mixing of psychotic with non-psychotic children useful and effective. This is true from the standpoint of not only the psychotic children but also the staff. During some periods, one particular ward may have become "overloaded" with psychotic or borderline children. The staff then begins to feel strong concerns about their own abilities to treat disturbed children effectively. The treatment of psychotic and borderline children is obviously slow, tedious and demanding. Staff nurses, teachers, occupational therapists, recreational therapists, and even psychotherapists cannot comfortably spend their entire days treating this group of relatively unresponsive children without developing certain negative or even nihilistic views. The foregoing statement is true for both the university students and the career workers on our staff.

It is, in our view, also to the advantage of the psychotic and borderline child to be placed with youngsters of less serious disturbances. For example, several psychotic children were on one of our wards for three to four years. Each of them improved so considerably that it became advisable to move them to a more advanced ward. This move was debated at length, because of staff feelings on the old as well as the new ward, and because of concerns about the children's eventual adjustment. Staff on the old ward were attached to the children and fearful that they couldn't adjust to "all those bigger, healthier children." Staff on the new ward were worried that these children were "too sick" and would disrupt their ward routine. Yet the moves were made without incident; the transfers, exposed to children of more mature development, continued to improve.

Our impression is that the overall treatment process for psychotic children can be divided into three general phases.[9, 6, 7] The first is that of breaking through the autistic barrier to establish contact, the second that of enhancing ego functions, and the third that of treating intrapsychic and interpersonal conflicts. Treatment, of course, begins at whatever level one finds the child. In severely autistic children, for example, the first phase is essential and is a major undertaking. In less seriously psychotic children, this phase may be unnecessary and only the second and the third phases required.

In the first phase of treatment, the goal is to intrude oneself into the child's awareness as a useful object. This requires a great deal of time and patience and produces minimal ego gratification for the therapist. As Weiland[12] has mentioned, the responsibility for initiating and carrying through this process is totally the therapist's, and in this first phase of treatment he gives a great deal of himself. He attempts to gratify the child's needs in almost any way he finds effective. Not infrequently, the child first begins to recognize only parts of the therapist as being useful to him.

Early in her hospitalization, five-year-old Louise showed a fascination with, but fear of, gloves. She would play with them endlessly and draw pictures of them, but she could not put a glove on her hand, nor could she allow anyone to do it for her. She became intrigued when she watched the therapist put a glove on his own hand and gradually she learned to enjoy putting it on and taking it off his hand. One had the impression that she was so unsure of her own body boundaries and integrity that she did not know where her hand really went when it was inside a glove. She was unwilling to risk the disappearance of her own hand, but could experiment with that of the therapist. At this point in her treatment, the therapist as a person was not important to her but she could and did become interested in a part of him.

It is not uncommon for these children to fear performing a number of relatively simple acts. The therapist then can become of some importance to them by doing these things for the child. At one point in her treatment, Louise was afraid to open the therapist's desk drawer to reach the candy supply. She would take the therapist's hand and open the drawer with it. Here the therapist himself was not a total person to her, but once again she did utilize a part of him. Another aspect of this first phase of treatment is a sort of parallel play akin to that indulged in by very small children. The therapist literally plays alongside of rather than with the youngster, with the goal of leading the child to become more aware of him. For example, many of these children enjoy spinning things. The therapist may experiment with bringing into the play situation objects which spin better than those that the patient has chosen or in some other way catch the child's attention.

In summary, then, during this first phase of treatment we are dealing with a child whose tendency is to remain hidden and protected by the autistic barrier. He has little, if any, motivation to change, and only through the therapist's persistent and active giving can he slowly be enticed out of his shell. One of the greatest difficulties is the feeling of discouragement or even of negative countertransference aroused in the therapist. As one might expect, some therapists can tolerate this one-sided relationship much better than others. The autistic child is surprisingly sensitive to the therapist's discouragement or hostility, and will easily retreat further into his autistic world. As one observes these children, he might assume that they are relatively oblivious to much that is going on around them. Yet they are not. One is often surprised, as a child improves, to have him refer to minor events that occurred when he was apparently most autistic. These are often incidents that no one else at the time felt had any importance to the child, since he had showed no outward reaction to them. Yet when the child mentions them months or even several years later, it is evident that they were important: the therapist must be continuously on guard in his work with such children. He cannot assume that they are not paying attention to him or that they are not listening to whatever he says. A main reason for this remarkable memory in these children is the almost complete absence of any repression.

The second phase of treatment of psychotic youngsters deals primarily with helping them to develop ego functions. We agree with Weiland[12] that the essential ingredients of this phase are gratification and frustration, in the proper proportions. Once the youngster breaks through his autistic barrier and begins to relate to the therapist as a person, one still should maintain an overall giving and permissive attitude, but also begin to inject small doses of frustration. The child is now, as Mahler[10] has said, in a symbiotic type of relationship.

Louise, the child described above, entered the hospital at the age of five presenting a classic picture of early infantile autism. She was an attractive, graceful, blue-eyed blonde girl who had almost no vocabulary. She would dart from one place to another on the ward and paid little attention to staff or peers. If frustrated, she would occasionally bite and scratch, but generally preferred to ignore everyone. Gradually, over two years, she began to come out of her autistic shell and develop new abilities. Her vocabulary improved remarkably and, although she spoke in a peculiar sing-song fashion, she did learn to express many of her likes and dislikes. In the beginning, she had the typical difficulty with pronouns, but eventually she managed to use them appropriately. She had co-therapists with whom she developed specific individual relationships. During the second phase of her treatment, the slow introduction of various frustrations became an important ingredient. As the patient achieved this more advanced level of maturation, she began experimenting with teasing other children and staff. She would not infrequently rip her clothing, particularly when she was irritated. She soon became aware that this was an action that the staff disapproved and teased them with it. About the same time, she developed a strong preference for seeing one of her therapists in her regular office rather than in the playroom. The therapist made it quite plain to Louise that the office was used for seeing older people and youngsters who could behave reasonably well. Louise was told that as long as she acted in an acceptable fashion, she could be seen in the office, but that continuation of her "silly" behavior would result in her being seen in the playroom.

There followed a period of struggle, with the girl sometimes curtailing her bizarre behavior but at other times being unable to do so.

Another aspect of this phase of treatment concerns itself with the child's confusion about his own feelings as well as those of others. Louise, for example, had great difficulty in conceptualizing her own anger or that of staff or peers. It is necessary, for example, to tell such a youngster not only *that* she is angry, but *why* she is angry. It is necessary to spell out for her when the therapist becomes irritated and why. This is equally true of other affects. For instance, such a simple phrase as "I like you" is, initially, beyond the comprehension of these children. It is true that they can learn to say it, but much therapeutic work is required before it becomes meaningful to them.

Still another aspect of this second phase of treatment is helping the child to gain a better concept of such abstract things as time. During her struggles to learn the meaning of time, Louise became preoccupied with "8:30". This was originally associated with the hour at which she ate breakfast, and for a while she confused it with breakfast itself. Various and sundry things and events became to her "8:30". She made most progress in the area of time when she began having occasional home visits. These were extremely pleasurable to her, and she anticipated them. It became possible for her therapist to introduce calendars as well as clocks on a more meaningful level. She began to be aware of how long it would be before her next home visit, and also how long she would remain at home. She began to ask for longer visits. All of these factors enabled the therapist to help her with this abstract concept of time.

One of the potential pitfalls of the second phase of treatment is the emergence of the child's powerful ambivalent feelings and oral incorporative impulses as the symbiotic relationship with the therapist develops. The child both loves and hates, and struggles with, impulses to devour and fears of being devoured. The closeness that the youngster desires also means annihilation. During this phase of treatment, the child will often seek physical closeness with the therapist only to bite or hit him; will look forward to treatment sessions but fly into a rage at their termination. These violent emotional storms are frightening to the patient and, if not properly handled in therapy, may lead him to regress to a more autistic but presumably safer level of development. It is as if coming out of his shell and attempting to relate become too painful and too threatening and the youngster gives up. It is during this phase of treatment, also, that even brief separations from the therapist—because of illness, vacations, or whatever—are traumatic to the child.

In summary, during the second or symbiotic phase of treatment, we are attempting to help the child improve his object relations through a gratification-frustration approach, to gain a better understanding of his own and others' emotional responses, and to master various abstract concepts. The child needs help in understanding that the therapist will not allow his ambivalent feelings or oral incorporative impulses to destroy either himself or the therapist.

The third phase of treatment is concerned primarily with working through various conflicts in the intrapsychic and interpersonal spheres. Some youngsters never reach this level of treatment, while others, particularly the borderline group, often require more work in this area than in any other.

David, referred to earlier as a borderline child, is a good example. During one period of his therapy, David became extremely attached to and sexually curious about his female therapist. He made many crude advances toward her, using and misusing a hodgepodge of oral, anal, and phallic words he had picked up from other youngsters. He revealed his chaotic misconceptions about sexual differences and procreative functions. Gradually, he was able to sort out some of his feelings, and learned to deal with them more effectively. He also was able slowly to allow himself to learn some of the facts about sexuality that he had previously been so fearful of and confused about.

It has been our impression that it is extremely difficult, if not impossible, to cure the psychotic child completely. Many of them do improve in most areas of their living. We still find, however, in even our most successful cases, a basic residual of the psychotic process. These youngsters have tended to develop a veneer of socially acceptable behavior, which, on superficial evaluation, seems fairly adequate. Closer observation, however, shows that they do not relate spontaneously and comfortably either to adults or to other children. They remain somewhat isolated and can, at times, behave in a bizarre or inappropriate fashion. They do not tolerate change well and prefer to lead constricted lives with little variation.

One of our most successful cases was Barbara, who came into the hospital at the age of six, with a history of a classic symbiotic psychosis of childhood. She came from an extremely pathologic background and had every environmental reason to be psychotic. She did respond favorably, however, over a period of three years, to an extremely intuitive, adept therapy. It became possible eventually to place her in a good foster home and continue her treatment on an outpatient basis. She was able to enter public school only one year behind her chronologic age, and made a marginal adjustment. She learned to say the right things in many everyday social situations, but could really put little of herself into any relationship: she was a peripheral member of her peer group and had no close friends. In her treatment sessions, she could describe various events that had taken place at home and in school, but continued to have great difficulty in really understanding other people or their feelings. She had learned to suppress most of her fantasies, but when encouraged to express them revealed them to be almost as distorted and unrealistic as they had been previously. She was, in other words, a much more socialized, but certainly not a cured, child.

As we have worked over the years with the various types of psychotic children, certain broad principles about their treatment, particularly residential treatment, have become increasingly evident. Each mental health discipline has something to offer such youngsters, and an effectively functioning team requires that all therapeutic personnel contribute to the process. The special educator cannot be effective unless the psychotherapy moves satisfactorily. On the other hand, the psychotherapist cannot be expected to be an educator in the sense of giving the child academic skills. In all areas, however, the child gets more than he gives.

One of the biggest problems in the treatment of these youngsters is the development of a negative or indifferent attitude on the part of one or another staff member. Once this happens, the children slow their progress or may even regress. Since they are easily capable of withdrawal, we often found evidence of this phenomenon—the staff was paying progressively less attention to a patient, and a progress conference would reveal that few people had noticed any progress, change or, for that matter, had invested the child with much real interest. As a result, following such progress conferences, there would be a resurgence of interest in the child and some progress would occur. We finally organized regular weekly team meetings to discuss work with these psychotic patients.[8] They proved invaluable in our work with the psychotic children. They allowed the staff to ventilate their feelings about the child's actions and behavior, and to learn more about why the child was behaving in a particular way and how he could best be handled. The group ego seemed better able to cope with the difficult psychotic youngster than the individual staff member.

Summary

Here, then, is a brief outline of our current knowledge of childhood psychosis and its treatment, of individual aspects of which the literature is replete. Presently, our knowledge of the etiology and treatment of childhood schizophrenia is fragmentary. One school still presents a biologic, another a psychological, etiology. In our work, we have come to assume, in the majority of cases, the presence of both factors. We recognize that the families of these children are disturbed but, like Escalona,[3] cannot place all blame on the parents. We assume that these children as infants have had more than their share of difficulty in adapting to their environments and in developing adequately functioning egos.

We have discussed the treatment of these children as divided into three phases: *1.* breaking through the autistic barrier, *2.* developing additional ego functions, and *3.* working through various inter- and intrapersonal conflicts. Therapy begins for each child at the emotional stage where he is. Some proceed rapidly and successfully; others seem unable to move forward. The factors determining such progress are not all known. The skill of the therapist is one important, but by no means the only, factor in the child's response. In the treatment of these children, the initiative is the therapist's: the child gives relatively little; the therapist must give much. This often leads to the therapist's withdrawal from emotional involvement or to the development of negative feelings. In either instance, the child reacts negatively, and treatment progress ceases. We have attempted to ameliorate this, at least in part, by regular team meetings of all disciplines involved with such youngsters. This allows for ventilation of negative feelings and better understanding of what is occurring in the treatment process.

It is our impression that few if any of these children are really cured. Some of them reach a much better socialized type of adjustment, but still retain their psychotic core. They tend to be resistant to change. They lack spontaneity. Their relationships continue superficial and without intuitiveness.

REFERENCES

1. Bender, Lauretta: Childhood schizophrenia, Psychiat Quart *27*:663–681, 1953.

2. Cain, Albert: On the meaning of "playing crazy" in borderline children, Psychiatry *27*:279–289, 1964.

3. Escalona, Sibylle: Some considerations regarding psychotherapy with psychotic children, *in*: Haworth, Mary, ed.: *Child Psychotherapy*, New York, Basic, 1964.

4. Kanner, Leo: Autistic disturbances of affective contact, The Nervous Child *2*: 217–250, 1943.

5. Kaufman, Irving, *et al.*: Adaptation of treatment techniques to a new classification of schizophrenic children. Treatment of Schizophrenic Children, J Amer Acad Child Psychiat *2*:460–483, 1963.

6. Kemph, John: Communicating with the psychotic child, Int Psychiat Clin *1*:53–72, 1964.

7. ———: The treatment of psychotic children, Cur Psychiat Ther *4*:74–78, 1964.

8. Kemph, John, *et al.*: New directions in the inpatient treatment of children in a training center, Amer J Psychiat *119*:934–939, 1963.

9. ———: Promoting the development of ego functions in the middle phase of treatment of psychotic children, J Amer Acad Child Psychiat *4* (No. 3):401–412, 1965.

10. Mahler, Margaret: On childhood psychosis and schizophrenia, *in*: *The Psychoanalytic Study of the Child*, vol. 7, New York, Internat Univ Press, 1952.

11. Rimland, Bernard: *Infantile Autism*, New York, Appleton, 1964.

12. Weiland, I. H., and Rudnik, R.: Considerations of the development and treatment of autistic childhood psychosis, *in: op. cit.* (ref. 10). vol. 16, 1961.

Hilde Bruch, MD
Baylor, Columbia

10

Eating Disorders and Schizophrenic Development

SOMETIME AGO A RESIDENT TOLD ME THAT HE HAD HEARD MY NAME IN medical school, that I had been quoted as saying: "Inside every fat man is a skinny schizophrenic." I was sorry that I could not tell him: "I wish I had said so," because, even though a relationship does exist between certain types of fatness and schizophrenia, the statement is not true. It is a distortion of the sentence: "Imprisoned in every fat man, a thin one is wildly signaling to be let out." And that is not mine but Cyril Connelly's, the British author who expresses the fat man's inner awareness that his creative potentialities are locked within him.

When I first read his sentence, it seemed to express the essence of the obesity problem. Gradually, a new question formulated itself: "Why does the thin self not succeed in breaking out of his prison?" It appears that he does not dare to come forth because he would be expected to fulfill the magnificent dreams of unheard achievement that seem to fill the fat person's idle hours, and he dreads the possibility of failure—great because of the grandiosity of his expectations. In this dilemma, usually the "fat" personality wins out. If reducing is pursued and failure becomes a reality, then a schizophrenic psychosis may become manifest. From the study of many obese patients, I have gained the impression that the large physical size gives at least a symbolic feeling of strength, and the untested daydreams provide a sense of potential power and achievement.

The discovery of this flourishing, often bizarre, fantasy life in indolent, apparently unambitious obese adolescents, and even more the potential for schizophrenic development, was completely unexpected—at least to me, who, when I began my studies of obesity more than 25 years ago, operated within the traditional concepts of schizophrenia. According to Kretschmer's widely accepted scheme of the relationship between body build, character and mental illness, schizophrenics are of leptosomic build, that is, they are thin and tall. Large-scale statistics demonstrate that this is the common relationship. It was also borne out in the twin studies of Kallman,[10] who, however, at the same time observed that in identical twins who had become schizophrenic, greater weight and strength were favorable signs; in a few cases, the heavier twin who maintained his excess weight did not become psychotic. It was old clinical knowledge that chronic schizophrenics occasionally became obese. Since it was also known that certain diseases of the brain were accompanied by obesity, this was cited, in the older literature, as one more point in support of the organic origin of mental illness.

Fat Children Grown Up

By the time I became concerned with the relationship of obesity to schizophrenia, and with the question of "What is schizophrenia?", my clinical observations, on a large group of obese children, had led to the conclusion that whatever the organic factors, inherited or acquired, powerful processes were at work, within the individual families, that drove these youngsters into a way of life, with overeating and marked inactivity as leading symptoms, that resulted in a state of self-perpetuating obesity. Much more appeared to be involved than a simple imitation of family food patterns and habits. Many areas of behavior were recognized as abnormal, with intense involvement of the parents. This was so compelling that it led to a detailed survey of 40 families.[7] No other studies of the families of psychiatric patients were then available for comparison.

By following these children into adulthood, one could recognize various patterns of development and adult adaptation. If the data are analyzed according to absence or persistence of overweight, and to good or poor psychological adjustment, four different combinations can be observed: *1.* slenderness with good adjustment (the always hoped for outgrowing of the condition), *2.* slenderness with poor adjustment (usually severe obsessive compulsive behavior), *3.* continued obesity, usually of moderate degree, with good adjustment, and *4.* continued obesity with severe maladjustment. It is this last group which potentially becomes schizophrenic; also some previously slim children who react to puberty and the demands of adolescence with an acute increase in weight.

It is of practical importance that the long-range outcome can be predicted during childhood, with a fair degree of accuracy, through a comprehensive evaluation of the intrafamilial problems and their effect on the obese child. Among the psychological findings, poor performance on the Draw-A-Person test, indicating disturbances in body image, and marked discrepancies between verbal and performance tests, are indicative of serious difficulties later in life.

Such severe personality and adjustment problems were observed in approximately a third of the group which was reexamined. This figure may indicate too high an incidence, since not all former patients appeared for reexamination. It is possible that a larger percentage of the more troubled ones responded to the follow-up invitation. Only a few had been hospitalized; many led the indolent life of the ambulatory schizophrenic.

Case 1. The development of a man 25-years old on reexamination may serve as an example. He had been known to the clinic since age 10, when he was approximately 90% overweight. He had been sent from the school with additional complaints about his restless behavior: he played the role of the clown and constantly drew attention to himself. The boy was a voracious eater and had no friends. He spent all his free time at the movies, or just sitting around at home—eating. His mother was also markedly overweight; she nibbled constantly, which she attributed to her nervousness. She was overpowering in anything she did or said in relation to the boy. "I cannot trust him" was the leit-motif of all her complaints. She would not permit her son to do anything because it made her nervous to see him so slow and awkward. The father was more affectionate, but he too was overanxious about letting him play with other boys.

The need for psychiatric help was recognized, but the mother refused to come to the clinic, "just to be talked to." She wanted something concrete done for her boy and she would shop around until she found a physician who would give him endocrine injections, "to alter him."

At 16, he left school and tried to find work as a messenger boy or in similar unskilled positions. When 18, he made one sustained effort at losing weight: his older brother came back from the army and expressed disgust over his bloated appearance. The expected rewards not forthcoming, he regained the weight, at first gradually and then rapidly. During the preceding year, after he had lost his last job, he had gained more than 40 pounds, and now weighed nearly 300 pounds.

When asked details about his lack of plans, he suddenly admitted that he had plans, and that they were "immense." "Someday my boat is going to come in and then I'm going to buy my folks a house in the country," he said. He dreamed of becoming a comedian and appearing on television. He spent hours in front of the TV set, watching fat comedians, memorizing their lines and jokes, and waiting for the day when he would be discovered, become a success—and be rich and slim. "Then I'm going to have one woman for every night of the week."

Daydreams Unlimited

Many fat young people with dull, complaisant surface behavior engage in daydreams of their unlimited potential achievements, the fulfillment of which depends on their becoming thin. The inability to follow a diet acts as a safeguard against putting these fantasies into realistic action. Such people are often convinced that no diet will work. The discovery that a diet is effective becomes emotionally disturbing because they fear they must prove their specialness.

Depressive reactions during reducing regimes are not uncommon, but mainly in adults and middle-aged people. Obese adolescents, particularly those who have been fat since early life and for whom being fat has been the core of their whole growth and development, are apt to become frankly schizophrenic. They no longer are aware of the unreal quality of their magnificent daydreams and aspirations. It is not easy, sometimes impossible, even in cases that are studied in detail, to determine why in one situation the fantasies remain fantasies, clearly recognized as such and guarded as precious secrets, and why in another the border between fantasy and reality becomes vague and disappears.

This is apt to occur when reducing is enforced, or self-imposed, in a misguided effort to do away with all the difficulties of living by changing the outer appearance. When reducing is successful and their looks as desirable as possible, such patients become overpowered by their inner difficulties and by feeling psychologically different from others. There is no longer the face-saving device of blaming their difficulties on the ugly weight, and there is no longer the hope of being able to correct things by losing it. In many obese youngsters, the psychological problems come into full awareness only after their secret power has been exhausted through effective reducing. As long as they are fat, they feel they have it in their power, now or in the future, to set everything right by losing weight. By becoming thin, having made this choice, they face the bare facts of serious mental problems.

While in many fat adolescents the fatness itself serves as protection, a psychotic breakthrough may occur even while a patient stays fat. This may happen when the inner struggles are more severe, the interpersonal situation more frustrating, or when the overeating is fought with more harshness and arouses more guilt and counter-aggression than in other obese adolescents who do not become manifestly psychotic as long as they stay fat.

Case 2. I have chosen as an example the story of a 16-year-old girl from a socially prominent and cultured home whose mother had fought against her daughter being fat throughout her life. Now the girl had given in, weighed more than 200 pounds. No longer able to differentiate between her fantasies and the realities of life, she was unable to attend school or to maintain even the slightest social façade, and would spend hours in what she called "trances." She was preoccupied with dreams of the prince who would come and release her from her ugliness; or of spending her time on a beautiful mountainside covered with bushes which produced the most delicious food, of which she could eat as much as she wanted without becoming fat, and without having the compulsive hateful feeling that she had when she ate sweets and other foods forbidden to her. Gradually, she imagined a whole secret world of her own, with language, laws, religion and mores of her own creation.

The outer manifestation of her breakdown was her becoming extremely careless of her appearance and her eating inedible material. As far back as she could remember, her mother had been "phobic" about her figure and had tried to supervise every bite she ate. She had some vague memories that when she was little, she was permitted to eat such "forbidden" things as chocolate pudding or cake. But she was sure that since age six or seven these things had never been allowed, and her whole life had been a struggle to feast on them. When all food was locked away, with a lock even on the refrigerator, she commenced to eat the staples—unprepared jello or uncooked cereals and spaghetti. She also would chew pieces of string and eat concert tickets and programs. Her behavior became so disturbed that hospitalization became necessary.

She was sufficiently in contact to give a picture of her family life. She felt that her mother's slimness and smartness were the result of eternal denial of food, and that her anxiety over her daughter's figure was an effort to exercise complete control over her. Although the family had given her a great deal of cultural stimulation, she felt that they had not been really interested in her, only in her appearance and brilliance. The father had only two absorbing interests: his business, in which he was very successful, and a complete devotion to mother. His concern about his daughter's queer behavior was also, in her feeling, only an expression of his devotion to the mother and, of course, anger that his daughter, one of his possessions, was not as perfect as she was supposed to be.

The relationship to the mother had been very close, but entirely in terms of the mother's wishes and needs. They had a great common interest, music. The daughter received a good musical education, but there was an exhausting struggle to make her conform to traditional standards. Her ambition was to compose unconventional works. This meant to her that she was expressing her own individuality through her artistic development. She wanted and needed an accomplishment of her own, and despite the self-belittling terms in which she talked about herself, she was also convinced of her essential greatness. She wanted to achieve something quite extraordinary that would be recognized by everybody. She compared herself to great composers of the past who had achieved fame at an early age. She felt her life would be wasted unless she accomplished something that would be on the genius level. This demand for recognition on the superlative level is frequent in obese adolescents. Characteristically, it must be an innate gift and it must fulfill itself without effort on their own part. This very special talent must be so outstanding that the whole world will admire their genius, and thus serve as a compensation for the sense of essential worthlessness from which they suffer.

At this stage in her development, she no longer cared about being fat. To be sure, she still dreamt of having the fatness taken away by the magic prince, but actually it would not help. It would not change the fact that she was inwardly mean, filthy and dirty. When she dropped some ashes on her dress during the interview, she became panicky: "That's me! I'm always filthy and I fill the chair and I flow all over it. It's just my meanness coming out."

It seemed that when she could hide no longer behind her fatness as a cause of dissatisfaction and failure and became convinced that even reducing could not change her problem, reality checks broke down. The deep problems of the schizophrenic became manifest: the desperate search for her own identity, physical and psychological, for effective means of orienting herself about her own behavior and interaction with other people and of facing the world with an adequate sense of mastery and self-respect.

Obesity and Schizophrenia

These two examples may suffice to illustrate that young people in whom, for many years, abnormal weight and overeating had been considered the leading pathology, carry the potential for schizophrenic development. I shall try to discuss the question of the possible common features in the background of those suffering from developmental obesity and schizophrenics-to-be. There are certain similarities in the professional approach. During the past century there has been a nearly consistent search for an organic factor as cause of the disorder. The patient was conceived as *having* an illness that, if removed, would restore him to normal. Though a new line of investigation proved disappointing, hope was always rekindled that a breakthrough would occur in another area. There were many isolated discoveries of abnormal functioning; many were soon recognized to be the consequence of the abnormal way of life.

In a recent paper on the theory of schizophrenia, Lidz and his coworkers state: "Schizophrenia is an illness of unknown etiology: indeed the phrase 'of unknown etiology', has, by now, almost become an integral part of the definition of schizophrenia. We question, however, the extent of the 'unknown', for a great deal concerning the etiology of schizophrenia seems reasonably well established. Might not the preconceptions that some biochemical dysfunction or anatomic anomaly must form the basis of the aberration, keep us from recognizing the obvious? Schizophrenia is a disorder of personality disintegration, of psychosocial competence, of symbolic function." In obesity research, too, there has been the tendency to relegate disturbances in the psychosocial field to a secondary position. It is only quite recently that it has become possible and acceptable to view the organic and psychological disturbances as closely interrelated.

In comparing the background of the two disorders, it is easy to demonstrate parallels and similarities on the descriptive biographical level. Maladaptation is often apparent as an overall passivity and immaturity. Defects in social relations are described with words like "withdrawn," "seclusive." In obesity this is usually "explained" as being due to the condition, hence the pressure to reduce. Like schizophrenics, obese people have an exceedingly low frustration tolerance and will react with sudden withdrawal or undermining hostility to what they perceive as a slight or an unjustified demand. They have a sense of helplessness, a conviction of inadequacy and ugliness, and daydream of magic transformation into glamorous appearance, change of sex and unlimited power over and admiration from everybody, counteracting their derogatory and self-destructive attitudes. Theirs is an all-or-nothing attitude towards life; when the unlimited knowledge or power is not obtainable, when there is no way of achieving the unrealistic goals, they are apt to give up in sullen despair. Instead of suffering a schizophrenic break, most of them will resort to more avid overeating and grow still fatter. Others may identify with the demands to reduce their food intake in an exaggerated way and anorexia nervosa may develop.

Quite often in anorexia, the previous behavior appears less disturbed. These patients succeed through automaton-like compliance in being a "perfect child" until the underlying malfunction breaks through as a relentless preoccupation with weight and a delusional body concept of what they should be.

Family Constellation

Great similarities can also be recognized in the family constellation in obesity and in that considered conducive to the development of schizophrenia. Since the first report in 1940, the picture has been modified and elaborated in many ways. Outstanding among the many disturbing features is the fact that the child is used by one or the other parent, sometimes by both, as a thing, an object whose function it is to fulfill the parents' needs, to compensate them for the failures and frustrations of their own lives, in particular in their disappointment in each other. Many parents openly express dissatisfaction with the sex of the child because the other sex would have better fulfilled *their* hopes and wishes. Confusion about sexual identity appears to be related to these misguiding parental attitudes, and so seems the child's fantastic misinterpretation of his importance in the world; nothing he achieves ever matches the exaggerated expectation of what he feels he could or is expected to do.

The studies of the intrafamilial environment of schizophrenics that have been conducted during the last decade deal with the problem in more detail and, recently, with clearer delineation of basic questions.[11] Many conclusions are encouragingly similar, whether one talks with Lidz about the "transmission of irrationality" and failure in observing generation and sex boundaries, with Wynne[13, 14] of "pseudo-mutuality" in the family interaction, or with Bowen[2] of the "over-adequate parent" who needs to maintain the child in a position of helplessness. Specific for the obese family is the distortion of the eating function: food is used as an unspecific means of appeasing all the dissatisfactions manifest in later life, as a fat person indiscriminately "feels hungry" whenever there is a disturbance in his interpersonal or intrapsychic equilibrium.

Common to the various family studies is the effort to recognize the forces in the environment that interfere with the patient's becoming a distinct individual, with needs and impulses clearly differentiated from those of his parents. In this quest, psychoanalytic thinking has played an important role through elucidating the psychodynamic and emotional significance of the various interacting forces. The exciting development of recent years is the way new questions are raised, beyond the range of psychoanalytic theory, dealing with the formation and development of perceptual and conceptual mental tools. Independently, several investigators began to focus on the cognitive disturbances. There is a decided change in the tone of recent studies, with greater definiteness of what is looked for. It began with Bateson's[1] report on the "double bind," his recognition that the disturbed language and thought processes of schizophrenics could be related to contradictory influences from the environment, which made it impossible, even dangerous, for a child to learn to discriminate various levels of abstraction in messages from his parents. Lidz has expanded his considerations to the wide range of experiences in which the disturbed intrafamiliar environment deprives the schizophrenic-to-be of needed and appropriate guideposts. Wynne and Singer[13, 14] have been able to outline a relationship between the parental style of communication and the severity of a patient's illness.

Disturbed Hunger Awareness

In my own work,[3–7] focused on the faulty eating function, the direction of my questions changed from trying to understand the *why*, the unconscious symbolic motivation of the disturbed eating patterns, to *how* it is possible for a body function to be transformed in such a way that it can be misused in the service of nonnutritional needs. In simpler words: How does the organism learn this trick, or what has gone wrong in the whole interpersonal processes surrounding the satisfaction of nutritional needs? If the early learning is incorrect, the outcome will be an inability to recognize hunger and its satiation, and to differentiate "hunger," the need to eat, from signals of bodily discomfort that have nothing whatsoever to do with "food deprivation."

Psychoanalysts used to speak of fixation of inherent drives, with special emphasis on the sexual drive, and explain deviations in character and personality as caused by the instinctual disturbances. The term "orality" has been worked to death, and has been used to explain and account for anything and everything. I am afraid I hold the distinction of having written a book on obesity without using the term "oral." The whole concept has always been too general for my thinking; it simply did not fit my own observations. To arrive at an independent understanding of how bodily tensions can be transformed and then used in the service of other needs, I felt it necessary to approach the whole problem without preconceived convictions.

Clinical discussions usually proceed on the assumption that the way bodily sensations are experienced is founded in innate biologic factors. This is undoubtedly true, but it is not the whole truth. The ability to recognize bodily needs, and the behavior that the organism develops for the appropriate satisfaction, depend to a large extent on learning, from earliest infancy on. The subcortical centers that regulate our viscera and emotional behavior must receive "information" how to satisfy these needs during the early developmental phases.

This problem has been studied by a neurophysiologist. Hebb[9] writes that lack of food, the state of nutritional deprivation, is apt to be disruptive of behavior. The first effect of lack of food is not an increased directedness, and, even in an animal as low as a rat, certain learned knowledge must be acquired for appropriate behavior. He emphasizes the learning factors that must be considered when "hunger" and also the sensation of "satiation" are studied in the mature animal.

In man, with his much more complex cerebral structure, the ways of learning are also more complex. Hebb feels that the nonnutritional aspects of our desire for food are so familiar that we are apt to overlook them, because they do not fit into the concept of hunger as an innate drive. Hunger, defined as the excitation of a neuromechanism that controls eating, is not a simple direct product of the need for food. My clinical observations are in good agreement with Hebb's conclusions.

By evaluating the early feeding history of obese people, and also of anorexic patients, in a factual noninterpretative way, one will find invariably that "food" has been used in a grossly inappropriate way, whether as the great pacifier, a cure-all for whatever makes a baby cry, or as an imposed duty to fulfill a mother's concept of her own perfection, or moralistically as reward and punishment. Traces of such concomitant attitudes can be recognized, of course, in every early feeding history. In cases of eating disorders, the characteristic aspect is the *absence* of the appropriate pattern, and the overpowering and often contradictory determinants coming from the mother.

Personality Development and Learning of Bodily Sensations

In an effort to visualize how environmental attitudes can be transformed into early learning experiences, and trying to think in terms of observable behavior (instead of introducing adult motivations and emotional concepts), I felt it necessary to assume that there are *two* basic forms of behavior that must be differentiated: behavior that is *1. initiated* in the organism and *2. in response* to stimuli from the outside. This distinction applies both to the biologic and the socioemotional field and to pleasure or pain producing states.

Behavior in relation to the child can be classified as *stimulating* and *responsive.* The interaction between the infant and environment can be rated as *appropriate* or *inappropriate*, depending on whether it serves the survival and development of the organism or is handicapping or destructive. These elementary distinctions permit the dynamic analysis, irrespective of the specific area of content, of an amazingly large variety of clinical problems.

Similar subdivisions are made in experimental psychology, where a subdivision is made between *emitted* and *elicited* behavior; and in learning theory, between *operative* and *respondent.* Piaget speaks of *assimilation* and *accommodation* as basic modes of integrating experiences. Escalona, in her detailed observations of early infantile behavior, uses similar concepts. She considers it a milestone in the course of personality development when outgoing behavior on the part of the infant, directed toward a person or object in the outer world, finds a response. In my opinion, the environmental responses to clues or signals from the biologic field, emitted from the infant from birth on, are even earlier manifestations of this all-important interpersonal transaction.

For healthy development, experiences in both modalities are essential. *Appropriate responses to clues coming from the infant*, initially in the biologic field and subsequently in the social and emotional field, are *significant building stones for the development of self-awareness and self-effectiveness.* If confirmation and reinforcement of his own initially rather undifferentiated needs and impulses have been absent, or confusing and inaccurate, then the child will grow up perplexed when trying to differentiate between disturbances in his biologic field and emotional and interpersonal experiences, and be apt to misinterpret deformities in his self-body concept as externally induced. Thus he will become an individual deficient in his sense of separateness, with "diffuse ego boundaries," and feel helpless under the influence of external forces.

An interplay of this type, with confirmation of clues originating in the child, as well as the child responding to outside stimuli, must be assumed for all areas of development. How it operates can be observed rather concretely in the eating function. When a mother offers food in response to signals indicating nutritional need, the infant will gradually develop the engram of "hunger" as a sensation distinct from other tensions or needs. If, on the other hand, a mother's reaction is continuously inappropriate—

neglectful, oversolicitous, inhibiting or indiscriminately permissive—the outcome for the child will be a perplexing confusion in his efforts to identify biologic clues and to recognize stimuli from other areas. When he is older, he will not be able to discriminate between being hungry or sated, or suffering from some other discomfort. At the extremes of eating disorders, one finds the grotesquely obese person who is haunted by the fear of starvation, and the emaciated anorexic who is oblivious to the pangs of hunger and to the weakness, fatigue and other symptoms characteristic of chronic under-nutrition.

Rarely, if ever, is nutrition the only function that is misperceived in this way, and thus becomes liable to being misused in the service of other tensions and conflicts.

The learning process is not restricted to infancy but is continuous through childhood. The content of this learning relates to the whole range of experiences that characterize human life. The broader the area of appropriate responses to the various expressions of a child's needs and impulses, the more competent he will become in identifying his bodily needs and sensations, thoughts and feelings as arising within him, and as distinct from the human or nonhuman environment. In other words, he will grow into a person who, regardless of difficulties of living, feels essentially self-directive in his experiences. Failure of a regular and persistent sequence of events—namely, that of discomfort, appropriate response and relief—*deprives* the developing child of the essential groundwork for the perceptual and conceptual awareness of his own needs and impulses, and for correct perception and awareness of the functioning and behavior of others.

Robot-like submission to the environmental demands may convey a façade of adequate functioning. The gross deficit in initiative and active self-expression will become manifest when such a person is confronted with new situations and demands for which the misleading routines of his early life have left him unprepared. Not having developed an integrated body concept, he will feel helpless under the impact of his bodily urges, as if he is controlled from the outside or does not "own" his own sensations and body.

This theoretical frame goes beyond, or avoids, the traditional dichotomy of somatic and psychological aspects of development. An infant handicapped by "genetic factors," or suffering from unrecognized paranatal injuries or confusing earliest experiences, is apt to give clues to his needs that are weak, indistinct and contradictory. It would be a difficult task for any mother to satisfy them appropriately, and will be completely confusing to a mother who herself is emotionally disturbed, preoccupied with her own problems, and impervious to expressions of a child's needs.

It may sound too sweeping to consider the absence of confirmation of child-initiated behavior of such crucial importance. Unexpected support for this view came from Harlow's observations in monkeys.[3] Giving infant monkeys free access to cloth-covered dummies, referred to in his work as "mothers," to whom they could cling without restriction, he expected that they would grow up more "secure" than monkeys given access only to wire dummies. This expectation was not fulfilled. On the contrary, when fully grown, both groups of monkeys were grossly abnormal, apathetic, stereotyped, incapable of grooming, inadequate in their sexual behavior, and suffering from an abiding affectionate deficiency. This "nonsocial syndrome" of the monkey offers many parallels to human schizophrenia. In my opinion, the crucial defect in the experimental design was the *absence* of responses, confirming or inhibiting, from live mother monkeys to the behavior initiated by the infants, thus depriving them of learning essential for the organization of usable adaptive behavior.

These considerations, the result of my efforts to understand why in juvenile obesity schizophrenic behavior may occur, are in good agreement with some recent developments in schizophrenia research.

Lidz and his co-workers, after expanding the study of schizophrenic families to the problem of how symbolic meanings are transmitted, have begun to consider the possibility of schizophrenia's being a *deficiency disease* rather than the result of noxious or traumatic influences. This deficiency can be recognized in inadequate parental nurture and guidance, and in failure to transmit the basic adaptive technics that a child must acquire within his family if he is to become able to direct his own life as a reasonably independent adult. The falsified learning of essential bodily functions and the ensuing distorted body concept, which I have described here, may be considered essential precursors of the later developmental phases, in which deficiencies have been recognized by many other authors.

Therapeutic Implications

Otto Will,[15–16] elaborating on my concepts, applies them to a wider group of schizophrenics who fail to identify or respond to their *needs* and *desires*. He feels that the formation of need patterns in harmony with both the culture and the biologic requirement of the organism are essential for successful adaptation, and that their normal organization depends on the mother's giving appropriate, satisfying responses to the nonverbal gestures of the infant. Failure to form such need patterns or distortion of these patterns will result in a form of presentation of the need that is so deviant from cultural norms that recognition and response are inadequate or lacking. If there is only a loose organization of such patterns and associated desires, then they may readily disintegrate in periods of stress. In delineating the psychotherapeutic field for chronic and regressed schizophrenics, he spells out in detail how to help a patient to identify his needs and to learn behavior that is need-satisfying and anxiety-reducing, and states that this is a necessary step in the growth of the organism that is in the process of recovery.

In my own work, these new theoretical formulations were also the result of a changed therapeutic approach, away from the conventional psychoanalytic interpretative technic to a *fact-finding one.* The conventional approach had been therapeutically ineffective. I gradually recognized that *giving insight* to these patients, through motivational interpretations, was not only *useless* but reinforced a basic defect in their personality structure, namely, the inability to know what they themselves felt, since it has always been mother who "knew" how they felt. As my approach changed, many thus far inaccessible patients began to respond. For many, it was the first consistent experience in which someone listened to what they had to say and did not tell them how to feel. An essential therapeutic task in dealing with such patients is to evoke awareness that there are feelings and impulses that originate in themselves and that they can learn to recognize them. In my experience, this approach has been useful for obese and anorexic patients, and also for schizophrenics without manifest eating disorder.

REFERENCES

1. Bateson, G., *et al.*: Toward a theory of schizophrenia, Behav Sci *1*:251, 1956.
2. Bowen, M.: A family concept of schizophrenia, *in* Jackson, D. D., ed.: *The Etiology of Schizophrenia*, New York, Basic, 1960, pp. 346–372.
3. Bruch, H.: Fat children grown-up, Amer J Dis Child *90*:201, 1955.
4. ———: Transformation of oral impulses in eating disorders: a conceptual approach, Psychiat Quart *35*:458, 1961.
5. ———: *The Importance of Overweight*, New York, Norton, 1957.
6. ———: Developmental obesity and schizophrenia, Psychiatry *21*:65, 1958.
7. Bruch, H., and Touraine, G.: The family frame of obese children, Psychosom Med *2*:141, 1940.
8. Harlow, H. F.: The Development of Patterns of Affection, Thomas William Salmon Lectures, Dec. 5, 1960.
9. Hebb, D. O.: *Organization of Behavior*, New York, Wiley, 1949.
10. Kallman, F. J.: *Heredity in Health and Mental Disorders*, New York, Norton, 1953.
11. Lidz, T.: *The Family and Human Adaptation*, New York, Internat Univ Press, 1963.
12. Lidz, T., *et al.*: Transmission of irrationality, Arch Neur Psychiat *79*:305, 1953.
13. Wynne, L., and Singer, M.: Thought disorders and family relations of schizophrenics, Arch Gen Psychiat (Chicago) *9*:191, 199, 1963.
14. Wynne, L., *et al.*: Pseudo-mutuality in the family relations of schizophrenics, Psychiatry *21*:205, 1958.
15. Will, O. A.: The awareness of need and the schizophrenic reaction, presented at 40th An'l Mtg Amer Orthopsychiat Ass, Mar 6, 1963.
16. ———: Schizophrenia and the psychotherapeutic field, Contemp Psychoanal *1*: 1, 1964.

Charles Shagass, MD
Iowa

11

Drugs in Treatment of Schizophrenia

ALTHOUGH DRUGS HAVE ALWAYS PLAYED A ROLE IN THE MANAGEMENT OF disturbed behavior, the treatment of schizophrenia was revolutionized by the introduction of compounds with specific ameliorating effects on psychotic symptoms, such as delusions and hallucinations. In the decade or so since chlorpromazine has been available in America, it has been administered to over 18 million patients in the US and the subject of over 10,000 reports in the world literature.[28] Pharmaceutical manufacturers have produced a host of similar agents, and "tranquilizer" has become an everyday word. Heinz Lehmann, one of the first to use these agents on this continent, could say in 1964:

> Pharmacotherapy is today the treatment of choice for schizophrenia. No other single therapeutic measure can compete with it in terms of rapid effectiveness, sustained action, general availability and ease of application, while it compares at least favorably with the shock therapies as far as incidence of side-effects, complications and serious risks is concerned.[21]

The enthusiastic acceptance of drug therapy has not changed schizophrenia as a major unsolved problem of psychiatry and public health. We still do not know whether it is one disease or many, there are no proved etiologies, and, in the absence of specific objective tests, diagnostic criteria tend to vary from time to time, physician to physician, and place to place. Thus, although the concept of drug "cures" has gripped public imagination since the sulfonamides and antibiotics, pharmacotherapy of schizophrenia is properly discussed within the conceptual framework not of "cure" but of "management."

Management implies a variety of therapeutic measures. Assessment of pharmacotherapy in the management of schizophrenia, the purpose of this chapter, must take into account other therapeutic factors, with which drugs may interact. The newer drugs were introduced during a period of rapid growth in psychiatric thinking, therapeutic optimism, and psychiatric services. The evidence reviewed suggests that, against this background, the drugs had a catalytic effect, speeding a therapeutic revolution already in progress and turning its impact on, particularly, the schizophrenic patient. They seem to have made it easier for psychiatrists to accept at least the optimism, if not the therapeutic humility, in Bleuler's statement of 1911, that "the therapy of schizophrenia is one of the most rewarding for the physician who does not ascribe the results of the natural healing processes of psychosis to his own intervention."[1]

This chapter is a review of selected studies bearing on various aspects of drugs and schizophrenia. It is not "comprehensive," nor does it consider all the newer drugs or combinations of them.

Criteria of Therapeutic Effect

The new drugs have created a new problem for drug research[31]: the objective, scientific determination of the chemical agents' effects on human behavior and experience. Scientists from nearly all disciplines, now involved in this area, are producing a mountain of literature. Nevertheless, criteria with clinical face-validity still provide the only useful basis for evaluating clinical usefulness. Investigators have become sophisticated in the application of such clinical criteria. Numerous rating-scale procedures and experimental designs, such as the double-blind, have come into use to distinguish pharmacologic effects from those of suggestion and other factors. A valuable by-product has been the increased attention given to the placebo effect.[19] Unfortunately, there is still no uniformity in clinical criteria, and findings of different investigators can be compared only generally, not specifically.

In addition to the therapeutic criteria based on appraisals of symptomatology by interview or rating-scale methods, the public health criterion of hospital-release rate is prominent. Governmental optimism, accompanied by financial support of the new mental health measures, was undoubtedly facilitated by evidence that more patients are being discharged from mental hospitals than before. The increased rates of release are attributed often to the newer drugs, which has given rise to controversy.

Treatment of Acute Schizophrenia in Hospital

The definitive study of the effect of phenothiazines in the treatment of acute schizophrenia is that of the NIMH Psychopharmacology Service Center.[29] Initiated in 1961, it involved the collaboration of nine institutions. They included an appropriate range of psychiatric treatment settings: state hospitals, psychiatric departments of general hospitals and private psychiatric hospitals. Acute schizophrenia was selected as the focus of investigation, because there was a paucity of controlled, double-blind studies of phenothiazines in such cases, whereas considerable information on chronic patients had already been accumulated. The design of the study involved the administration of three phenothiazines and a placebo. The drugs were chlorpromazine (Thorazine), fluphenazine (Prolixin) and thioridazine (Mellaril).

There were 344 patients, divided into 4 groups on a random basis. These were between 16 and 45 years of age and exhibited 2 or more of the following symptoms or behaviors: thinking or speech disturbances, catatonic motor behavior, paranoid ideation, hallucination, delusional thinking other than paranoid, blunted or inappropriate emotion, disturbance of social behavior and interpersonal relations. To complete the study, patients had to be treated for 6 weeks. The residual group of 344 remained after 119 dropouts. The placebo group had more than twice as many dropouts, mainly for treatment failure, as any drug group.

The dosage schedule was flexible. Standard pink capsules were prepared with either 100 mg of chlorpromazine, 100 mg of thioridazine, 1 mg of fluphenazine or a lactose placebo. Standard ampoules for intramuscular injections were also available, but used in relatively few cases. The average daily dose of oral medication was about 650 mg of chlorpromazine, 6 mg of fluphenazine, or 700 mg of thioridazine.

Clinical assessments were of 2 kinds: *1.* global judgments, *2.* judgment of the presence and intensity of specific symptoms and behaviors. The doctor and nurse rated the severity of the patient's illness on a 7-point scale; they also rated improvement in comparison to condition at the time of admission. The Inpatient Multidimensional Psychiatric Scale (IMPS), developed by Lorr, and the Burdock Ward Behavior Rating Scale (WBRS), were used for symptom and behavior assessments. The pretreatment scores on both of these instruments were subjected to factor analysis. The IMPS resulted in 14 independent subscales, the WBRS in 7 independent factors.

The global clinical ratings of improvement showed that 95% of patients on drug improved, and that 75% were either "much improved" or "very much improved." Placebo patients showed significantly less improvement. With respect to degree of residual illness, the data showed that almost half of the drug-improved patients did not manifest enough residual symptoms to be judged even "mildly" ill after 6 weeks' treatment. It also appeared that, if the period of treatment had been longer than 6 weeks, there would have been an even more favorable drug effect.

To examine the differences between drugs and the placebo in improvement of specific symptoms, the 21 subscales obtained by factor analysis of the IMPS and WBRS were studied. Significant differences between drug and placebo patients emerged in 13 of these 21 measures. The findings are charted in Figure 1. Almost all symptoms or behaviors that can be characterized as schizophrenic in nature were affected by active drug treatment, whereas others, such as guilt and memory deficit, were not. As Figure 1 indicates, the drugs had a rather varied action. For example, they reduced not only hostility but also apathy, made movements less retarded, reduced hebephrenic symptoms, and so on. The authors point out that these data show that the word *tranquilizer* is a misnomer, since these drugs have many actions.

There were no significant differences between the three phenothiazines employed in the study with respect to beneficial effects. A good deal of promotional literature suggests that drugs like fluphenazine are stimulating in nature, whereas chlorpromazine is more sedative. The finding that the drugs were of equal effect in controlling such symptoms as slowed speech and movements, social participation, hostility, and agitation suggests that these purported interdrug differences are largely mythical.

A large number of side-effects were reported, most of which represented patient discomfort rather than serious complication, as only 11 dropouts occurred because of them. Among the three drugs the pattern of side-effects was significantly different, a finding in striking contrast to the absence of difference in effects on symptoms. This suggests that thera-

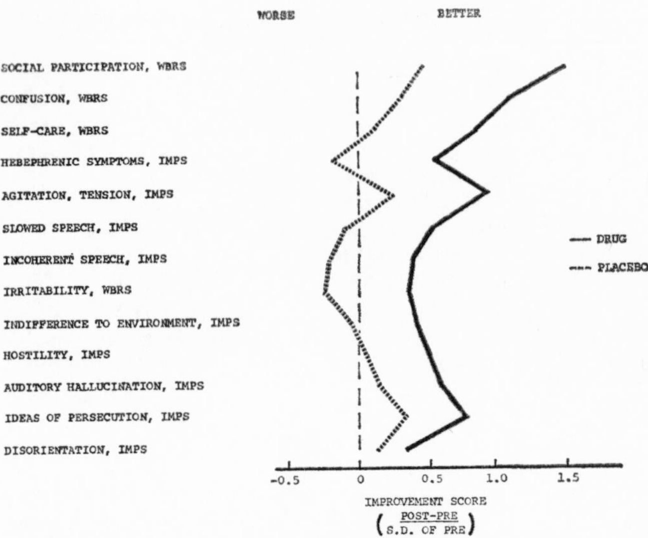

Fig. 1. Comparison of changes with drug and placebo on subscales of WBRS and IMPS in NIMH study.[29] Only scales with significant differences are plotted.

peutic properties of these drugs may be quite independent of their tendency to produce specific side-effects. Hypotheses concerning the possible relation between the therapeutic benefits of drugs and their tendency to produce extrapyramidal dysfunctions were not supported by the findings. As in other studies, there was in the placebo group a significant incidence of side-effects, such as restlessness, constipation and headache.

The NIMH study clearly demonstrated that, in acute schizophrenic patients, the phenothiazines reduce or abolish schizophrenic symptoms and behavior, and that the drug effects were superior to the changes observed with nonspecific milieu therapy in placebo-treated patients. These results should reduce or dispel doubts about the specific action of the drugs, which arise from the consideration of hospital-release rates and which will be discussed later. However, such additional questions as duration of effects, need for maintenance therapy, and subsequent relapse rates require answer.

Large-scale collaborative studies were also conducted by the Veterans Administration. In one VA study, 640 newly admitted schizophrenic men, with an average of 3 previous hospitalizations, comprised the subject population.[6] The drugs used were chlorpromazine (Thorazine), triflupromazine (Vesprin), mepazine (Pacatal), prochlorperazine (Compazine), perphenazine (Trilafon), and phenobarbital. Treatment followed a double-blind procedure for 12 weeks. Clinical evaluations with 2 rating scales provided multiple criteria of change. The results showed that all 5 phenothiazine derivatives were therapeutically more effective than phenobarbital, and that mepazine was less effective than the other 4 drugs. Favorable clinical effects were noted on such behavioral manifestations as resistiveness, belligerence, thinking disturbance, motor disturbance, paranoid projection, perceptual distortion and withdrawal.

Another VA study compared the clinical effectiveness of several drugs: chlorpromazine, chlorprothixene (Taractan), fluphenazine, reserpine, thioridazine and triflupromazine.[20] These agents were administered, in a randomized double-blind design, to 512 male schizophrenic patients for 24 weeks after admission to 32 VA hospitals. At the end of the treatment period, the drugs were found to have the following rank-order of effectiveness: chlorpromazine, thioridazine, fluphenazine, chlorprothixene, triflupromazine, and reserpine. However, only the differences between reserpine and the 3 most effective drugs were statistically significant.

The results of the VA studies are thus in substantial agreement with the more recent NIMH study, even though the patient population was restricted to males and contained a high proportion of previously hospitalized individuals. The 2 drugs found to give significantly poorer therapeutic results, namely mepazine and reserpine, have dropped from favor in treatment of schizophrenia.

Outpatient Therapy of Schizophrenia

Granted that the phenothiazines are effective in reducing or removing the symptoms of newly hospitalized schizophrenic patients, one would like to know how effective they are in those who are not hospitalized. Several investigations have been directed toward this question, although they have not been as well controlled as the hospital studies. Relevant information provided by two major studies will be reviewed here.

Engelhardt and his associates in New York City followed 445 chronically schizophrenic outpatients admitted to their research clinic between March 1958 and the end of 1961. The patients were between the ages of 18 and 44, had a primary diagnosis of schizophrenia, and showed evidence of mental illness existing at least 1 year prior to their admission. They were randomly assigned to 1 of 3 treatment conditions: chlorpromazine, promazine (Sparine), or placebo. The double-blind method was used and the treating physician was able to vary the dose of the standard capsule. The mean dose of the phenothiazines was 200 mg daily. In an initial report of 173 patients, with treatment exposure ranging from 1 to 18 months, the investigators found that hospitalization rates were significantly lower in the group treated with chlorpromazine, being only 5% compared with 18% in the promazine treated group and 29% in the placebo group.[9] Subsequent follow-up of this initial sample, which now had a treatment exposure ranging from 43 to 61 months, revealed shrinkage in the differences between the 3 treatment conditions.[7] Only the difference between chlorpromazine and placebo was significant, the respective hospitalization measures now being 15% and 32%. The hospitalization rates for the larger sample of 455 patients showed no significant overall difference, with treatment exposure ranging from 15 to 61 months; the rates were, for chlorpromazine 19%, promazine 28%, and placebo 30%.

In their most recent report, Engelhardt *et al.*[8] provided the graph reproduced in Figure 2. This shows that, as treatment exposure continued, the hospitalization rates for the phenothiazines kept on increasing, whereas the placebo curve reached a plateau at about a year. Projecting their curves, the authors estimated that the chlorpromazine-treated group would

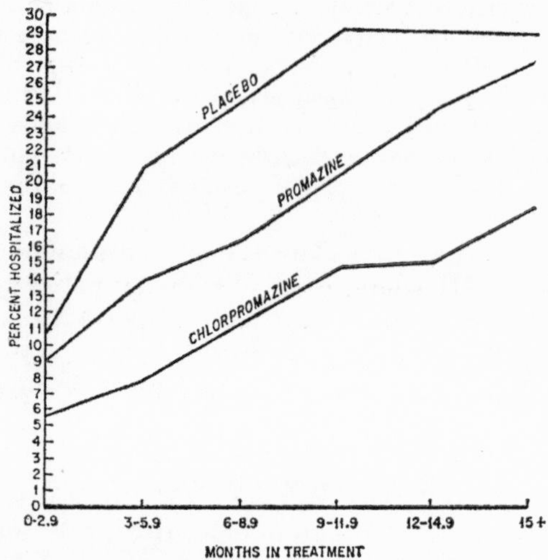

Fig. 2. Cumulative hospitalization rates by drug treatment in study of Engelhardt *et al.*[7-9]

reach the placebo plateau at 30 months' treatment exposure. They interpreted their findings to indicate that the phenothiazines *delayed* rather than *prevented* hospitalization.

The interpretation of hospitalization under the conditions of the Engelhardt study is difficult. It is most striking that the maximal rate of hospitalization of the placebo group was no more than 30%. Chlorpromazine was used in the relatively low average dose of 200 mg per day, and one may ask whether larger doses would have effected a lower rate of hospitalization. As the authors point out, delay of hospitalization must not be interpreted as a meaningless outcome. Chlorpromazine treatment kept the patient in the community, and available for outpatient treatment, for substantially longer times than placebo treatment. The study lacks the kind of rating-scale data that would picture the symptom and behavior areas affected by the drugs in the treated group. However, in a subsample of 85 patients treated for a minimum of 6 months, a check list of 15 items, describing clearly dysfunctional social behavior, was filled in from information provided by a relative.[10] The results showed that the family perceived more improvement in behavior in chlorpromazine-treated than in placebo-treated patients. In addition, and agreeing with the findings of the NIMH study, improved behavior occurred in the areas of both aggression and withdrawal.

Another study[24] of outpatient drug treatment was unique insofar as all the subjects were considered to have schizophrenia of sufficient severity to require hospitalization, and its aim was to determine whether the patient could be cared for at home as a substitute for hospitalization. All patients committed to a state hospital were screened to determine their eligibility for the study, which, in addition to diagnosis, involved absence of homicidal or suicidal tendencies, age 18 to 60 years, residence within a radius of 60 miles from downtown Louisville, and family members willing to supervise the patient in the home. The patients were randomly placed in 3 groups: drug, placebo and hospitalized, the latter being returned to the hospital. A regimen of home care, including regular visits by the PH nurse and the availability of a 24-hour answering service, was instituted. Seventy % of patients had experienced at least 1 previous hospitalization for psychiatric illness, and many came from multiproblem families.

The results indicate that the drug patients were significantly more successful in staying out of hospital than the placebo patients. Of those given drugs, 83% remained continuously in the community, compared with 55% of the placebo patients. The differences between drug and placebo groups were small for the first 6 months, whereas comparison of those patients who had been treated for 6 to 18 months revealed a striking difference in favor of the drug group. Both of the groups treated in the home spent significantly more time out of hospital than those who were allowed to enter hospital immediately. Percentages of days at home for the placebo and hospital groups were 82% and 60%, respectively.

The results of the Pasamanick study differed from those obtained by Engelhardt *et al.* in that the difference between drug and placebo was accentuated with time, rather than diminished. It seems likely that the populations were not comparable. Apart from demonstrating superiority of drug over placebo in seriously ill patients treated at home, the findings of the Pasamanick study showed that a treatment policy that favors keeping the patient in the home will result in shorter periods of hospitalization.

Treatment of the Hospitalized Chronic Patient

From the time of their first use in mental hospitals, the phenothiazines and reserpine were found to reduce behavioral disturbance. Employing such measures as the number of restraints and broken windows, it was easy to demonstrate that drug-treated patients were indeed "tranquilized." The special effectiveness of the drugs on specific symptoms of psychosis was discovered only after they had been administered for relatively prolonged periods. Numerous studies have now established the value of the drugs in reducing schizophrenic symptomatology amongst hospitalized patients, resulting in improved ward adjustment and permitting discharge of a significant, though small, proportion of patients previously considered destined for lifelong hospitalization. However, the special role of the drugs in bringing about the currently reduced resident population of state mental hospitals has been a matter of controversy, as so many other developments that could affect the therapeutic climate of the hospitals were taking place. It seemed worthwhile, therefore, to examine evidence bearing on this issue, in the hope of developing perspective on drugs in treatment programs in relation to other therapeutic approaches.

The questions being raised about hospital treatment today are not new. Bockoven's papers on "Moral Treatment in American Psychiatry,"[2,3] which deal mainly with 19th century events, provide a fascinating analysis of the ways in which physician attitudes and social factors may interact to influence the rates for release from a mental hospital. Bockoven presents data from a follow-up study carried out between 1881 and 1892 by Dr. Park, superintendent of Worcester State Hospital. The study dealt with the fate of patients admitted to the hospital from its opening in 1833. Although dealing with all admissions, rather than with schizophrenics alone, Bockoven's graph of release rates from 1833 until 1950 is worth scrutiny (see Fig. 3). About 45% of patients were discharged as recovered from 1833 to 1862; the rate then decreased to a low of less than 10%

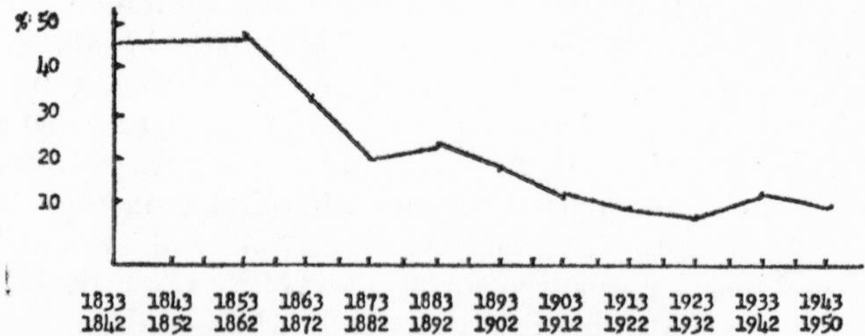

Fig. 3. Per cent of admissions discharged as recovered from Worcester State Hospital by decades for 120 years.[2, 3] (Reproduced with permission from Bockoven, J. S.: Moral Treatment in American Psychiatry, New York, Springer, 1963.)

between 1923 and 1932. Yet the follow-up study showed that, of 1,173 patients admitted between 1833 and 1846, 48% had no relapse after discharge and only about 20% again became a burden to the state.

Bockoven's view is that the ideas of one influential psychiatrist, Dr. Pliny Earle, had an important impact on the recovery rate. Earle apparently had puristic criteria of recovery, which seemed to preclude the occurrence of an attack of mental illness at any subsequent time in the life of the patient.

> By this means he could always defend a pessimistic view with the argument that lifetime follow-ups would inevitably disclose many relapses of mental illness. Whatever Dr. Earle's underlying purpose was, he succeeded in convincing the psychiatric profession that the prognosis of mental illness was extremely poor and thus exonerated its members for poor recovery rates. The idea that mental illness was incurable became more and more popular. By the turn of the century recovery rates acceptable even to Earle (approximately 30 per cent) seemed preposterous. By the 1920's few medical officers were inclined to discharge more than four or five per cent as recovered. Progressive tightening of criteria for recovery and concomitant deterioration in standards of care were equally potent factors underlying this decrease in recoveries. Belief in the incurability of mental illness, which Dr. Earle had sold the medical profession, was a barrier to the adoption of much needed corrective measures which has not yet been torn down.[3]

In comparison to the United States, Bleuler's figures on the outcome of schizophrenia in 515 patients hospitalized at Burghölzli between 1898 and 1905 are remarkably good. Bleuler so defined schizophrenia—it "does not permit a full *restitutio ad integrum*"—that he found, not surprisingly, no fully recovered cases. He therefore spoke of the course of illness in terms of degree of deterioration. Those capable of earning a living displayed "mild deterioration", those completely incapable of living outside a hospital "severe deterioration", those intermediate "medium deterioration." Sixty % exhibited "mild" and 22% "severe deterioration." Bleuler also pointed out that "few of those with a good remission, have had to be returned to the hospital for permanent commitment because of a later exacerbation of the disease."[1]

Bleuler's optimism concerning therapeutic outcome has been quoted earlier in this chapter. Much in his monograph could have been written today. He advised against hospitalization, which he viewed as an educational process, except when necessary because of danger to self or others. He recommended release as soon as possible, provided that the patient's family would not exert a destructive influence. In essence, Bleuler used the "moral treatment." Apparently, in Switzerland it was possible for a physician to believe in the incurability of a disease and simultaneously to carry out optimal therapeutic management.

It appears that in the United States the hospital release rates for schizophrenia were not actually so gloomy as depicted in the recovery figures for Worcester State Hospital. In 1956, Israel and Johnson[16] presented the results of a study of discharge and readmission rates in over 4,000 consecutive first admissions of schizophrenics between 1913 and 1952. Using a 10-year follow-up, the rate of discharge in the total group was 64% over the 40 years. The lowest discharge rate, 54%, occurred for patients admitted during the decade 1923 to 1932. The readmission rates averaged 24% for the group as a whole. The release rates varied with age. In cases of schizophrenia under age 20 on admission, they were never less than 75% and were close to 90% for a decade. Patients aged 20 to 34 had discharge rates ranging between 63% and 77%. The rates for patients between 35 and 49 years of age were about 40% between 1913 and 1932, increased to 57% in the next decade, and were over 70% in the most recent group. Even the patients aged 50 and over, who had a discharge rate ranging between 20% and 32% in the first 3 decades of the follow-up, were being discharged at a 50% rate in the last decade. Israel and Johnson concluded that the old pessimism about schizophrenia was not justified, that 3 of 4 schizophrenics currently coming to the hospital were being discharged, and that only 25% to 30% of patients being discharged at the time of their report would require permanent readmission. These latter figures are similar to Bleuler's 22% with "severe deterioration."

These data were recently utilized by Peterson and Olson[25] to make comparisons with their own cohort of schizophrenic patients treated with drugs between 1956 and 1958 (see Fig. 4). The patients from Warren State Hospital were those reported on by Israel and Johnson. The curves are astonishingly parallel after a year. More patients than previously were released during the first year of the drug era. However, the difference between the first and second Warren cohorts was just as great as that between the second Warren cohort and the Anoka drug cohort. The

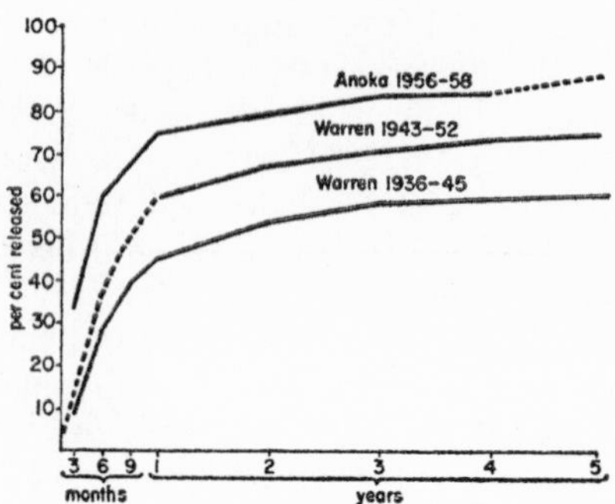

Fig. 4. Cumulative % of first admission schizophrenics released within specified periods of time for 1 drug and 2 predrug cohorts (from Peterson and Olson[25]).

authors, however, also compared the readmission probabilities in their sample with those obtained at Warren between 1943 and 1952; this showed that the higher Anoka release rate was associated with a higher readmission rate. An additional analysis reviewed the schizophrenic patients hospitalized on successive anniversaries of their first admission; this varied between 21% and 28%. They concluded that a population of hospitalized chronic schizophrenic patients, comprising about 24% of first admissions, was being developed even with modern treatment methods.

A position more favorable to the importance of the drugs was taken by Brill and Patton,[4,5] who reported on the population statistics of the New York State mental hospitals. The resident population had reached a high of 93,600 on June 30, 1955, and had increased by 2,400 in the previous year, this being a continuation of the long-term trend that had doubled mental hospital cases since 1929. Then, between 1955 and 1956, the population began to fall: at a rate of about 1.5% per year between 1955 and 1962. The fall in the schizophrenics was the most impressive of all groups. Although the authors acknowledged that attributing this trend to drug therapy remains open to debate, they could find no other explanation for a change of such magnitude, beginning quite abruptly, both in the New York hospitals and elsewhere, in 1956, the year when psychiatric drug therapy first began to be applied on a large scale. About 60% of the population of various mental hospitals have actually been receiving drugs, regardless of theoretical views about the effectiveness of the drug being used. It may be noted, however, that the New York State hospital population differed in important respects from that of the remaining states.[17]

In California,[11] in a cohort of 421 male, white schizophrenics aged 25 to 44 and committed in 1949, between 60% and 70% had attained discharge status in 4 years. More patients admitted in 1956 and 1957 were released than in 1950, but during 1956 fewer patients who received drugs were actually released. The findings were similar in hospitals with high and low drug usage. The investigators conclude that the increased rate of discharge was not a function of drug usage, and suggest that it could be attributed more directly to treatment policies resulting in an altered hospital environment. Similar conclusions, that drugs had little effect on population changes, were reached for an English county mental hospital.[27]

Odegard[23] reveals no impressive impact of the drugs in Norway. Comparing patients admitted 1948 to 1952 with those admitted 1955 to 1959, he found the slightest increase in the discharge rates in the later period: 47% in the predrug era, 49% in the drug era, and a tendency for shorter hospital stay. Far greater improvement of therapeutic results occurred between 1936 and 1950, indicating that the somatic therapies and therapeutic orientations previously introduced had already exerted a large effect.

The extent to which therapeutic attitude amongst physicians and hospital personnel affect hospital-release statistics is a dominant consideration in these reports. Linn,[22] selecting patients admitted to St. Elizabeth's Hospital (Washington, DC) between 1953 and 1956, provided provocative data on this issue. Although he included all functional psychoses, about 90% were diagnosed as schizophrenic. Release—the first time the patient went into the community for a trial period of living away from the hospital—was the criterion. The release rates were strikingly higher for 1955 and 1956 than for 1953 and 1954, rising from 40% to 70%. Those patients who received chlorpromazine or reserpine and those who did not showed the increased release rates: the untreated patients were somewhat higher.

Linn considered the influence of various factors on the release rate—social history before hospitalization, diagnosis, symptoms, hospital-admission policies, and the use of treatments other than drugs—and was unable to establish any relationships. Nor could he find that hospital policies had changed regarding release or the standards of behavior required. He did find that patients who changed from hyperactivity, in the sense of agitation or destructiveness, to nonhyperactivity, had a better chance for release than those who remained nonhyperactive, i.e., were continuously withdrawn. He suggested that the change from hyperactivity connotes an improvement to the staff. The staff is thus led to expect further improvement, which is probably communicated to the patients who have changed, and this has therapeutic value toward decreasing other symptoms of mental illness.

Linn concluded that the behavioral changes produced by the drugs induced an increasingly optimistic expectation of staff that patients would recover, and that this altered therapeutic attitude increased the probability that all patients, hyperactive or not, treated with drugs or not, would recover. He felt that the optimism did not necessarily derive from the results of drug therapy with patients admitted for the first time during the study years, but may have been based on previous success with the

use of drugs in chronic patients. He also found that there was a greater probability of return to the hospital among the patients released in 1955 and 1956, and speculated that the return rate may have been due to the failure of optimism within hospital to be extended to the community environment of the discharged patients.

The available evidence obviously fails to clarify the role of drugs in reducing hospital stay, except to make it clear that they alone are not responsible. Since it also appears undeniable that the drugs modify behavior of schizophrenic patients in a direction considered desirable by those responsible for their care, the hypothesis that drugs induce an attitude of general therapeutic optimism seems attractive. However, it seems likely that they do more than this. By reducing disturbed behavior, they render the patients more amenable to psychotherapeutic, educational and rehabilitative intervention. By controlling manifest behavior disturbances outside the hospital, they make it easier for relatives to tolerate the patient in the home setting. The drugs thus appear to qualify for a catalytic role in a wide range of therapeutic events, which can facilitate the natural healing processes in schizophrenia spoken of by Bleuler.

Maintenance Therapy

Successful treatment of schizophrenia with drugs, in or out of hospital, raises some difficult questions. How long should the drugs be continued, and in what doses? What clinical guidelines should be used for reducing or removing medication? Does the situation change after drugs are removed, so that there are special difficulties in reinstituting therapy? These and similar questions, of vital interest to the practitioner, remain largely unanswered. They are particularly important with respect to the patient who is having his first episode of schizophrenic illness. In such cases, the probability of remission is at least 2:3, but the statistics suggest that the probability of relapse is also high. According to the Anoka figures,[25] the chance of readmission within a year following release is approximately 1:4, and this increases year by year until it is 1:2 within 5 years. A policy of maintaining all patients on drugs for an indefinite period of time seems impractical. Furthermore, the data[8] suggest that hospitalization would not thereby be prevented, although their conclusion might perhaps be altered if higher dose-levels were employed. We sorely need methods for identifying the patients with a high probability of relapse, so that maintenance medication may be instituted. In the absence of such methods, it appears that regular visits to the physician over a long period of time may be the most efficient currently available means for preventing rehospitalization in schizophrenic patients. Certainly the data of Vaillant, Semrad, and Ewalt[32] support this suggestion.

The situation appears to be somewhat clearer with respect to chronic patients discharged from hospital. These patients present complex problems of rehabilitation, not considered here. From the drug standpoint alone, a number of workers have provided reasonably consistent data to show that when chronic patients discontinue their medication, or receive an inadequate dosage, they tend to relapse and require rehospitalization. Before treatment, a group of women patients at Elgin State Hospital[30] were incontinent, combative, destructive, noisy and denudative. After five years of study, 273 of the 913 treated had been discharged conditionally, and were followed by systematic treatment with chlorpromazine. At the time of the report, 73% of the discharged patients remained out of hospital, the majority for two years or more. Many were gainfully employed. Unwillingness of the patient to take the drug or to attend the clinic, or unwillingness of the family to provide necessary cooperation, were responsible for some, but not all, relapses. Among the discharged group, 72 patients were placed on placebo; of these 52 (72%) relapsed, even though the placebo patients were selected from those who had been away from the institution for at least 10 months and were considered to have a consolidated social recovery. The results with placebo suggest that the previously regressed patient needs the drug for a lengthy, if not indefinite, time.

A double-blind study of withdrawal from maintenance therapy in an outpatient clinic, carried out by Gross *et al.*,[14] supports this view. Subjects were 144 chronically psychotic patients (127 schizophrenic) who had improved under drug treatment, been released from the hospital, and referred to the clinic. The average monthly relapse rates were 4% for a control period on stabilized medication, 11.7% for a phase of withdrawal from medication, and 13% for a phase in which placebo was administered. Gross *et al.* suggested that the optimum time to attempt drug withdrawal was during the second year of treatment. Because the increased rate of relapse continued undiminished for at least six months after withdrawal was completed, they recommended that the patient should be observed closely for at least six months. The investigators also searched for factors predictive of drug relapse. In their sample, relapse was more frequent in the patient who, under 30 or over 50 years of age and treated exclusively with drugs, within the previous year had failed in attempts to live outside the hospital, had a family critical or only tolerant toward him, and had failed to assume responsibilities in the life of the family. There was some evidence that patients with a better work adjustment had less tendency to relapse.

Others[18, 26, 33, 34] have also reported a high incidence of relapse after withdrawal of medication in previously controlled chronic patients. Some of Kris's observations[18] highlight the benefits of maintenance therapy, since many of her patients were able to return to previous occupations, respond favorably to new training, and develop satisfying home life. She also found that the children born to mothers kept on drugs during pregnancy showed normal development. A plea for avoidance of what they termed the current dosage "merry-go-round" was recently made by Forrest *et al.*[12] They recommended that chronic patients who had been rehabilitated on drug therapy, especially when previously refractory to other treatments, should stay on their optimum dosage indefinitely. In their view, efforts to reduce the maintenance dose should be made only during hospitalization and side-effects should be corrected not by reducing the optimum phenothiazine dose but by administering other drugs appropriately. Although the available evidence seems to warrant this kind of recommendation, one can only agree with the conclusion of others[13] that we still lack precise knowledge of the specific long-range effects of chemotherapy.

Discussion

The evidence reviewed here supports the conclusion that the phenothiazines exert normalizing effects on schizophrenic symptoms and that these effects are achieved more readily in acute than in chronic patients. Considerable room for doubt exists that the pharmacologic properties of the drugs influence the long-term course of a schizophrenic illness more favorably than optimal management without drugs. However, there is also no reason to doubt that, without drugs, a large number of patients would not receive such optimal management, would spend much more time in mental hospitals, and would be exposed to the risk of serious complications from such hospitalization.

The outcome of untreated schizophrenic illness can be considered a function of individual recovery potential (natural healing processes), providing no injurious influences are introduced. The data concerning release from mental hospitals indicate that, until recently, overall effects of hospital treatment may well have been injurious, since not enough patients with sufficient recovery potential were released. This has been attributed to professional and public pessimism regarding possibilities of recovery, with consequent failure to provide adequate treatment facilities. The importance of such attitudinal factors is a matter no longer of opinion but of fact. For example, a recent multihospital study in the VA system[15] showed that more patients were released earlier in smaller and better staffed hospitals whose atmosphere was considered "nontraditional." "Nontraditionalism" involved a number of variables, including more open wards, less custodial atmosphere and social restrictiveness, a greater amount of ongoing research and training.

By providing a means of controlling psychopathologic manifestations of schizophrenia, the newer drugs appear at least to have reduced the injurious influences acting on the schizophrenic patient and, probably, to have facilitated favorable influences. Outcome is affected, of course, by complicated interactions of multiple factors. Many of the serious complications of mental illness arise from what may be referred to as its self-perpetuating tendency: for example, a disturbed person finds it hard to learn new skills. This is tremendously important for the young patient: he may lose his adolescence in schizophrenic illness, fail to acquire the social and vocational skills he needs for future adjustment, and thereby increase the probability of subsequent episodes of illness. It seems reasonable to expect that the drugs can reduce such self-perpetuating complications. Avoidance of them is, of course, a basic aim guiding the move toward treating mental illness in the community.

It is difficult not to be impressed by the figure, which recurs in study after study, that 20% to 25% of schizophrenic patients require prolonged hospitalization, even with modern treatment methods. It seems likely that entirely new therapeutic approaches may be required to keep this population, with exceptionally low recovery potential, functioning in the community. However, the results—with acute patients and with maintenance therapy of released chronic patients taken together—suggest that systematic continued care, including optimal use of drugs, may reduce the number needing indefinite hospitalization. Furthermore, although the need for new rehabilitation facilities and procedures for the chronic schizophrenic patient was recognized soon after introduction of the drugs, these have not yet been adequately developed. One hopes that advances in the area of rehabilitation will help to reduce chronicity.

The effect of the drugs has been described here as catalytic in treatment. They have had an even greater catalytic effect in research. They have stimulated psychiatrists to reexamine concepts of treatment, to attempt to distinguish the relevant from the nonrelevant, to look for objective methods of assessment and, in general, to develop greater awareness of behavioral science and research methods. The drugs have also helped to bring into the broad arena of psychiatric research a large number of investigators from basic disciplines, such as neurophysiology, biochemistry, pharmacology, and psychology. In addition to their specific contributions, these scientists, with their emphasis on the clearly conceptualized, answerable research question, have fostered a more critical, scientific attitude among psychiatrists.

REFERENCES

1. Bleuler, E.: *Dementia Praecox or the Group of Schizophrenias*, New York, Internat Univ Press, 1950.

2. Bockoven, J. S.: Moral treatment in American psychiatry, J Nerv Ment Dis *124*:167–194, 1956.

3. ———: *Ibid.*, 292–321.

4. Brill, H., and Patton, R.: Analysis of population reduction in NY State mental hospitals during the first 4 years of large-scale therapy with psychotropic drugs, Amer J Psychiat *116*:495–509, 1959.

5. ———: Clinical-statistical analysis of population changes in NY mental hospitals since introduction of psychotropic drugs, Amer J Psychiat *119*:20–35, 1962.

6. Casey, J., *et al.*: Treatment of schizophrenic reactions with phenothiazine derivatives, Amer J Psychiat *117*:97–105, 1960.

7. Engelhardt, D., *et al.*: Phenothiazines in prevention of psychiatric hospitalization. II. Duration of treatment exposure, JAMA *186*:981–983, 1963.

8. ———: Phenothiazines in prevention of psychiatric hospitalization. III. Delay or prevention of hospitalization, Arch Gen Psychiat (Chicago) *11*:162–169, 1964.

9. Engelhardt, D., *et al.*: Prevention of psychiatric hospitalization with use of psychopharmacological agents, JAMA *173*:97–149, 1960.

10. Engelhardt, D., *et al.*: Changes of social behavior in chronic schizophrenic outpatients under phenothiazine treatment, J Comp Psychiat *1*:313–316, 1960.

11. Epstein, L., Morgan, R., and Reynolds, L.: An approach to the effects of ataraxic drugs on hospital release rates, Amer J Psychiat *119*:36–47, 1962.

12. Forrest, F., *et al.*: Drug maintenance problems of rehabilitated mental patients: the current drug dosage "Merry-Go-Round," Amer J Psychiat *121*:33–40, 1964.

13. Gittelman, R. K., Klein, D. F., and Pollack, M.: Effects of psychotropic drugs on long-term adjustment, a review, Psychopharmacologia (Berlin) *5*:317–338, 1964.

14. Gross, M., *et al.*: Discontinuation of treatment with ataractic drugs, *in* Wortis, J., ed.: *Recent Advances in Biological Psychiatry*, vol. 3, New York, Plenum, 1961, pp. 44–63.

15. Gurol, L.: Correlates of psychiatric hospital effectiveness. Presented at Symposium, "An Assessment of Psychiatric Hospital Effectiveness," Amer Psychol Ass Mtg, Los Angeles, Sep, 1964.

16. Israel, R., and Johnson, N.: Discharge and readmission rates in 4,254 consecutive first admissions of schizophrenia, Amer J Psychiat *112*:903–909, 1956.

17. Kramer, M., and Pollack, E.: Problems in the interpretation of trends in the population movement of the public mental hospitals, Amer J Public Health *48*:1003–1019, 1958.

18. Kris, E. B.: Effects of pharmacotherapy on work and learning ability—a 5 year follow-up study, *in* Wortis, J., ed.: *op. cit.* (ref 14), pp. 30–34.

19. Kurland, A. A.: Placebo effect, *in* Uhr, L., and Miller, J. G., eds.: *Drugs and Behavior*, New York, Wiley, 1960.

20. Lasky, J., *et al.*: Drug treatment of schizophrenic patients, Dis Nerv Syst *23*: 698–706, 1962.

21. Lehmann, H.: Pharmacotherapy of schizophrenia. Presented at 1964 An'l Mtg Amer Psychopathological Ass, New York City.

22. Linn, E. L.: Drug therapy, milieu change, and release from a mental hospital, Arch Neurol Psychiat *81*:785–795, 1959.

23. Odegard, O.: Pattern of discharge from Norwegian psychiatric hospitals before and after the introduction of the psychotropic drugs, Amer J Psychiat *120*:772–778, 1964.

24. Pasamanick, B., *et al.*: Home vs. hospital care for schizophrenics, JAMA *187*: 177–181, 1964.

25. Peterson, D., and Olson, G.: First admitted schizophrenics in drug era, Arch Gen Psychiat (Chicago) *11*:137–144, 1964.

26. Pollack, B.: The effect of chlorpromazine in reducing the relapse rate in 716 released patients: study 3, Amer J Psychiat *114*:749–751, 1958.

27. Shepherd, M., Goodman, N., and Watt, D.: The application of hospital statistics in the evaluation of pharmacotherapy in a psychiatric population, J Comp Psychiat *2*: 11–19, 1961.

28. Smith, Kline and French Laboratories: *Ten Years' Experience with Thorazine*, Reference Manual, ed. 5, Philadelphia, 1964.

29. The Nat'l Institute of Mental Health Psychopharmacology Service Center Collaborative Study Group: Phenothiazine treatment in acute schizophrenia: effectiveness, Arch Gen Psychiat (Chicago) *10*:246–261, 1964.

30. Tuteur, W., Stiller, R., and Glotzer, J.: Chlorpromazine—5 years later. Fifth of a series—a 5 year study, *in* Wortis, J., ed.: *op. cit.* (ref 14), pp. 35–43.

31. Uhr, L., and Miller, J. G.: Prologue, *in* Uhr, L., and Miller, J. G., eds.: *op. cit.* (ref 19).

32. Vaillant, G. E., Semrad, E. V., and Ewalt, J. R.: Current therapeutic results in schizophrenia, New Eng J Med *271*:280–283, 1964.

33. Winkelman, N. W.: A clinical and socio-cultural study of 200 psychiatric patients started on chlorpromazine 10½ years ago, Amer J Psychiat *120*:861–869, 1964.

34. Wright, G.: The treatment of non-hospitalized schizophrenics, Amer J Psychiat *119*:261–262, 1962.

John Donnelly, MD
Institute of Living, Yale

12

Short-Term Therapy of Schizophrenia

LEAVING ASIDE THE DEFINITION OF PSYCHOTHERAPY, THE TERMS "BRIEF" and "short-term" may describe a variety of time relations episodically occurring in the course of the therapist-patient relationship. Some authors utilize them to denote interviews of as few as 5 to 15 minutes' duration, while others refer to the total duration of treatment with individual psychotherapeutic contacts of up to an hour.[1–5] Moreover, "brief" is variously applied to indicate frequency rather than duration.[6–9] As contrasted with intensive psychotherapy, brief interviews may be scheduled from twice a week to once a month. The most useful definition is derived by exclusion or comparison; thus, brief or short-term refers to therapy that is less than the stereotype of the ideal, namely, that publicized by Fromm-Reichman and others under the name of "intensive psychoanalytically oriented psychotherapy." *Brief* or *short-term* implies that the "amount of therapy" is limited in relation to the degree of severity of the pathology, the guardedness of prognosis, and the potential for improvement.

Definitions

The use of the phrase "psychoanalytically oriented psychotherapy" has in turn provoked disagreement.[10] Generally, it is understood to define the therapeutic process utilized by a physician who uses as his frame of reference his interpretation of Freud's psychodynamic formulations, with or without modifications made by a number of investigators. The contributions of Sullivan,[11, 12] Fromm-Reichman,[13, 14] Arieti,[15] Rado,[10] and others[16–18] have presented important observations and interpretations of etiologic, pathologic, dynamic and therapeutic factors. Each has developed theoretical viewpoints that each advocates and teaches. Nevertheless, there is a consensus that the individual is born with a specific, personal, physiologic endowment, that between birth and maturity he passes through a number of stages related to psychological and physiologic development, and that at these stages the interaction between the individual and his environment is of major significance in his psychological functioning and growth. Because the psychological changes and the length of the stages are common to all relatively mature human beings, and despite the fact that there are different ways of observing, interpreting and describing the subject at those stages, certain generalizations can be made despite vigorous arguments of the adherents of the conflicting schools about the scientific merit of each particular set of theoretical assertions. Mental illness may arise because of failure to bring into operation satisfactory methods of coping with a variety of stresses, or by failure of later developed patterns to deal adequately with current stress leading to a return to earlier and less satisfactory, less mature patterns.

The picture is complicated by the adherents of those viewpoints that maintain that mental illnesses, in particular schizophrenia, are organic diseases.[19, 20] Within this group are those who hold that the schizophrenic process is the result of inborn errors of metabolic functioning, genetically determined, and not amenable to psychological intervention, and others who maintain that schizophrenia is essentially a syndrome, a subcortical syndrome with a number of different causations. Still others hold that the combination of organic or metabolic deficits, perhaps genetically determined, together with the stress-inducing environmental experiences, results in a personality or characterologic dynamic structure; that the symptoms appearing under stress represent attempts to cope with the anxiety and its causes and that they are restitutive in nature.

Indeed, excepting those who believe in the purely organic etiology, the majority hold that the symptoms are restitutive in nature. If it be accepted that the symptomatology is the representation of the efforts of the individual to overcome the results of stress, intervention that succeeds in reducing stress or in reinforcing the restitutive efforts is therapeutically desirable. For the purposes of this chapter, short-term psychotherapy is defined as intervention that utilizes the patient-doctor relationship with the intention of so modifying the balance of forces that restitution functions more normally. The type of intervention is determined by the frame of reference in which the theoretical beliefs of the therapist are cast. In general, short-term or brief psychotherapy will be used to denote intervention using as a framework the principles of psychodynamics based on successive stages of development, whether Freudian, adaptational, Sullivanian or other. Its practitioners do not claim to effect the fundamental changes in the personality attempted by advocates of the intensive, long-term, psychoanalytic treatment described by Fromm-Reichman and her disciples. Nor do they claim that large percentages of schizophrenic patients are amenable to these procedures. The objective is often restitution to a level of functioning at least as satisfactory as, and often far superior to, that existing prior to the onset of the episode. They hold that the patient's overcoming the fears, anxieties, and conflicts inherent in the illness itself adds to the strength of the more healthy defenses and enables him to operate more effectively.

There is a consensus that, in the schizophrenic patient, anxiety and rage of a particularly intense degree are present as characterologic features and as reactions to his perception of his environment. Feeling overwhelmed and inadequate, he endeavors, by withdrawal, to reduce the risks of emotional involvement. Thus, one may speak of the predisposed individual whose adjustment is schizoid in character, who breaks down into a more florid condition, and who may remit enough to return to his prior personality. Arguments whether he is still schizophrenic, or was prior to the onset of the more florid picture, are as yet largely academic, and are reflections of the theoretical positions of the contestants, reflecting in fact the inadequacy of present knowledge.

The important factor, therapeutically, is the pattern of withdrawal and isolation from involvement with anyone in the environment. This withdrawal represents a solution of the problems of ambivalence developmentally important and arising in the earliest years. The initial therapeutic problem is to establish a relationship that may provide the means of alleviating the patient's anxiety and enable him to recall and examine pertinent, unconscious memories in order to gain insight into important genetic experiences significant in the origin of patterns of behavior. This includes, of course, his beliefs about himself.

The rapid establishment of this initial relationship—Arieti has described it as relatedness—is fundamental to brief forms of psychotherapy. Because of the tendency of the patient not to become involved, it is necessary to take an active role from the beginning. The patient must be convinced that the interest of the therapist is based on attitudes that include respect for the patient and a belief that he himself can overcome the forces that have overwhelmed him. Of the utmost importance is the formulation which the psychiatrist uses in his own understanding of the etiology of the disorder. Equally important is the confidence of the therapist in the plausibility of his theory of personality development. Lacking conviction of the part that psychodynamic factors play in etiology, failure in establishing contact seems inevitable.

Yet conviction in the truth of a theory is often one indicator of the personality of the holder, and the degree to which the conviction is conveyed to others is often a reflection of the "powerfulness" of the individual vis-a-vis other individuals. The combination of the strength of the conviction and the relative "powerfulness" of the therapist in the relationship may be fundamental to the breach of the defenses of the patient against involvement. The importance of this aspect of the personality of the therapist lies in the incorporated images of the parents, which, in all schizophrenics, appear to be associated with rejecting, punitive and powerful authority figures. The therapist must appear, therefore, at least as powerful to the patient. There may thus be rapidly developed some elements of the transference relationship. The activity of the therapist must be, by normal standards, intense. The ambivalence of the patient is such that the arousal of negative and hostile reactions is always possible and is, indeed, frequent. The initial approach must vary according to circumstances. The technics to be used with the patient who himself comes to a therapist are initially different from those used with patients who, for example, are hospitalized against their will. The motivation for help present in the former must be aroused in the latter.

Therapist Activity

The hospitalized schizophrenic is not necessarily the most difficult patient in whom to arouse motivation. With the patient already suspicious and hostile, the therapist must identify himself immediately, state unequivocally the reasons he is seeing the patient, and hold out the prospect that the patient can get well. Moreover, an immediate approach that may be successful is to ally one's self with those elements not infrequently present, for example, the desire of the patient to be dependent on no one and his hope, usually present, that he himself can improve sufficiently to lead a life in which he makes all the decisions of importance to him. The success of the maneuver may turn on telling the patient directly that the long-term outlook depends entirely on him, that he must make the decision whether he wants to get well, that the alternatives are health and independence or sickness and, perhaps, hospitalization of indefinite duration. It must be conveyed to the patient that the therapist, knowledgeable in and understanding the significance of the experiences of the patient which have led to the present situation, can be of help and assistance to the patient but that the therapist cannot of himself make the patient well, even if the latter wished it. It may be desirable to point out that such a solution would be no solution at all, for either patient or therapist, because it would mean merely that the patient would be totally dependent on the therapist, whereas the objectives of both are the independence of the patient and the utilization by the patient of his own abilities and capacities to solve his problems. The therapist can help him understand the choices he may have to make, but that the patient has the same potentialities as other human beings for making the correct decisions.

It is important to convey to the patient that the therapist's sole purpose is to assist and to support him through the difficulties that lie ahead. At the same time, the therapist must communicate his belief in the right of the patient to have self-esteem as well as the respect of the therapist. All this must be communicated while maintaining a sufficient distance so as to be nonthreatening. Put in the right words and delivered in the correct manner and tone of voice, this combination can arouse hope and motivation to attempt the enterprise. During the course of therapy, it is of vital importance that the therapist maintain this attitude. The anger and hostility that may appear directed at the therapist must not have any justification insofar as an actual breach of faith, or any action that may be interpreted as attempted domination, is concerned. The realities of the patient's situation must always be pointed out, especially when misunderstandings arise based on fantasy. Should the therapist be at fault, by any chance, the error must be acknowledged, but it must be placed in the context of reality as must the reaction of the patient.

Placing the responsibility for therapy on the patient is helpful secondarily in a number of ways. The frequency of the interviews can be spaced at intervals longer than once a day. Indeed, by so spacing the interviews there is less tendency of the patient to develop excessive dependence on the therapist. The intervals between sessions must be at first of sufficiently short duration that the impact of the therapist is maintained. With time and after discussion with the patient, and after indicating the improved condition of the patient, the intervals may be lengthened.

From the beginning, the therapist must take an active role in encouraging the patient to recount his views of significant experiences. Starting with the problems leading to the need for treatment, it is important to gain as much information as possible to enable the therapist to conceptualize the important dynamics of the patient. This includes the life situation, the events leading up to the onset of the illness, the patient's customary patterns of behavior, his methods of handling anxiety-provoking events, his attitudes to his closest associates, peers, teachers, employer, supervisor, and so on. A key to success is the ability of the therapist to build rapidly this picture of the dynamic components of the patient's personality—his historical relationships with parents and siblings and his identifications with elements in the personalities of the parents as they appeared to the patient during his early years. The importance of this history-taking lies in the elucidation of data from which brief interpretative formulations can be made in the form of questions. The most useful appear those using direct analogy or comparison, always based on behavior, past and present, so that the patient is able to grasp the significant similarities and parallels. Interpretations based on formulations of deep dynamic significance are usually not understood and may, in fact, arouse resentment, because the patient feels a threat to the mutual agreement that he is to work out on a *cognitive* level the problems he has encountered. Whether such interpretations are valid and whether the anger is aroused because of the accuracy of the interpretations is beside the point. They are not useful. Despite the opinion often advanced that there is a close, if not complete, identity between the psychosis and dreaming states, the schizophrenic does not have ready access to all repressed material. It appears true that he may have more ready access than normal or neurotic persons. For this reason, it is imperative that interpretations are based largely on current situations and that developmental interpretations be limited to essential material. There is the danger of the patient rationalizing his past experiences as the cause of his illness. He may develop a scapegoat, with the conclusion that he participated not at all in the development of his condition.

There has been a tendency in recent years to divide psychiatrists into two groups, the directive-organic and the psychological-analytic, with the implication of personality characteristics which cluster discretely in the two sets of individuals. Clear-cut divisions of this nature may perhaps be illusory because such categorization obscures the middle group, who may fall into both of the other groups.

The label "directive" implies that such a therapist instructs the patient on what he shall do, projects to the patient a solution of conflict based on the personality structure and personal experience of the therapist, and scarcely considers the psychological conflicts of the patient. On the other hand, the terms "psychological" and "analytic" convey the stereotype of passivity on the part of the therapist, whose personality is removed from direct influence on the problem-solving functions of the patient.

Such categorization of therapists is of importance because of the values attached to stereotypes by psychotherapists, especially by psychiatrists in training. In the short-term treatment of schizophrenia, these stereotypes may lead to serious limitations in the therapeutic skill and potential of psychotherapists. Because this form of treatment calls for rapid evaluation of the personality structure and of the genesis of the conflicting forces within the patient, his patterns of resolution of conflicts, and the major factors in the situation that precipitated the psychosis, it is evident that passivity will be a self-limiting asset, if not a liability. It is important to elicit by questioning the nature of the early experiences of the patient, his images of the parental figures and how the latter were seen to exercise authority. This necessitates a degree of focusing on specific areas with some activity on the part of the therapist. For example, attention must be directed to the reactions of the patient to such exercise of authority and the fear and rage which developed in response to this; attention is directed to the counter-forces and the mechanisms with which the patient repressed such anger and hostility, and to the relationship of the real feelings of inadequacy to the habitual patterns of adjustment, especially that of withdrawal from environmental involvement.

The problem of therapist activity is not one of its presence or absence. The problem is making the patient feel that the therapist is allied with him, that the inquiries are part of the quest by both parties. Too often, active questioning is viewed by the psychological and analytic psychiatrist as an assault on the patient who must, in self-defense, react with measures that hinder and often prevent further therapeutic progress. Obviously, questioning conducted for the sake of knowledge only, or carried out in the manner of cross-examination by a hostile attorney, will have such effects. But the most successful attorneys do not conduct cross-examinations in this fashion. Rather by quiet, calm and apparently not penetrating examination, the witness may be led to admissions not advantageous to his position. Hostility of the witness develops only because the attorney is on "the other side." When the attorney for the party for whom the witness is testifying achieves, by the use of the same strategems, highly favorable admissions, the feelings aroused are positive and often associated with respect and admiration. In short-term psychotherapy, the conduct and effects of the interchange may be comparable. In long-term, intensive psychotherapy, there is little need to elicit information rapidly; activity is not called for, and the risks of adverse reactions to questions need not be taken.

Short-Term Psychotherapy

The technic of short-term psychotherapy, however, calls for a relatively rapid acquisition of knowledge of the major experiential factors in the development of the personality and of fitting the pieces into a conceptual model of dynamic relationships that account for or explain, even tentatively, the patterns of behavior and emotional response. Each therapist, therefore, must have an overall conceptual model of personality development and structure of which the details can be varied according to the dynamics of the particular patient. Flexibility of the therapist in modifying the structure of this model, as new information becomes available, is essential.

Information is derived in part from the content of the patient's verbal communications and in part from his patterns of behavior, both habitual and emergency in the face of particularly stressful situations. The speed at which pertinent information can be acquired can be accelerated by focusing questions in conformity with the therapist's private interpretations as the interviews proceed.

One important aspect of therapy is the evaluation of the stress that precipitated the acute episode or of the events that have modified, albeit slowly, the previous balance of forces. The therapist must interpret, for himself, the ways in which current forces have intensified or weakened the preexisting forces. He must identify the meaning of the symptoms in the context of the personality of the patient. For example, the birth of a baby may intensify feelings of inadequacy and may weaken the compensating forces of attention and support derived from the relationship with the husband; with the intensification of fears of diminished emotional support, there may be the arousal or the intensification of hostility to the husband, and secondarily the development of unacceptable hostility to the infant. These are but some of the changes in the dynamic structure of the patient; all, however, must be understood in terms of the preexisting ambivalent feelings towards the husband, which are usually primarily displaced from relationships with one or both parents, though usually the father.

One may argue that only a picture of the major psychodynamics is obtained, that the finer subtleties are missed and perhaps not appreciated. In part, this is correct, but the therapist realizes it. He is aware that he is painting with a broad sweep, that he is identifying the major forces operating in the illness. Needless to say, the sensitivity and the astuteness of the therapist determine his appreciation of the nuances. But the philosophy of short-term psychotherapy is based on the premise that the present psychotic picture is the consequence of the interaction of major forces within the dynamic structure, and that restitution of the preexisting dynamic relationship is the necessary prelude of further psychotherapy.

Essential to the concept of short-term or brief psychotherapy is the principle that, within the positive relationship of patient and therapist, the patient will confront the major problems that have led to his need for treatment. Because these have usually been repressed in the schizophrenic, often by the mechanism of avoidance, the therapist must introduce the topics of the true feelings and attitudes of the patient that are unacceptable to and unrecognized by him. He must make conscious the fear, rage, and guilt of the patient, in terms both of the present situation and of the traumatizing situations of the past. His skill is dependent in part on his capacity to conceptualize the parallels in the patient's experiences in a form in which the patient can also make the connections. Yet the pitfalls of intellectualization must be especially avoided.

The therapist, at the stage of elucidation of early emotional relationships, must be prepared to help the patient recognize his ambivalent feelings toward the parents. He must not be afraid to raise the issues of fear and hostility when he recognizes that the patient, who expresses strong, positive feelings towards a parent, is only verbalizing the effects of the defensive measures with which he compensated for the real feelings of being dominated and unloved. The therapist must provide the climate in which the patient can explore the possibilities of such feelings. For example, the statement that, given the history produced by the patient, it would be remarkable if the patient had not reacted in the same way that most individuals would react is most supportive in enabling the patient to consider the possibility of unacceptable feelings. This theme may have many variations. By such technics, a delicate process weakens the forces that have repressed anger and rage, and conveys to the patient that such feelings may have been understandable. The therapist recognizes that such justification occurs only in the sense that the reactions of the patient were in response to his own perception of these situations and of his interpretation of the relationship, an issue that must be raised at the appropriate moment. The therapist must keep in mind that the patient may have grossly distorted the real behavior and feelings of the parent and that such distortions are material for examination at a later stage of therapy. It is a common experience that when an individual, after reacting with hostility and anger to another person, observes that his feelings are shared by others or are regarded as understandable or justified, the intensity of the anger tends to abate and he is able to examine the occasion of his reactions in a calmer and more reasonable fashion. This is particularly applicable in the case of schizophrenic reactions, in which negative feelings are prominent.

Confrontation of the patient with the real emotions which he has repressed, then, is fundamental. In long-term therapy, this is not, though neccessary, so sharply defined a feature. The therapist must be reasonably certain, therefore, of his evaluation of the etiologic factors and their influences. He must be able to present in a simple, direct form his understanding of the conflict and to do so in a manner which, while it may initially be denied or even arouse anger or anxiety, nevertheless appears as a subject meriting thoughtful examination by the patient. To present to a disturbed woman, who speaks always of her absolute love of her husband, the possibility of her real desire to be parted from him and from the responsibilities that marriage to him entails, is no simple matter. The therapist must have convincing evidence that his position is valid. He must be prepared for intensification of already operating defenses; having made such an interpretation, he must be prepared to stand by his proposition. He must not become defensive under attack, remembering always that, as agreed with the patient, the latter must make all the decisions; then this possibility may become for the patient an acceptable topic for consideration. Moreover, when the therapist conveys, indirectly, that the matter is one worthy of consideration and is devoid of moralistic judgments as far as he is concerned, the patient will very quickly start to think about her real feelings.

It is imperative for the therapist to be identified, by the patient, with the ego of the patient. In the literature, one gathers that this is communicated to the patient by means of such "mechanisms" as kindness, supportiveness, and trust. Customarily, the possession of such qualities is taken to denote the positive feelings of the therapist. Yet, in brief psychotherapy in which confrontation of issues is developed, the meanings of the word "kind" may be narrow and restricted, or may encompass the type of interaction in which the therapist arouses great anxiety and may cause a considerable degree of pain, accepting this as a necessary part of the treatment program. This fact raises conflicts in some therapists, especially those whose psychological orientation leads them to see as sadistic any action that induces any kind of pain in another, irrespective of the purpose. This attitude may on occasion be of fundamental significance in helping the patient confront or avoid his present unclear problem. In psychotherapy of the schizophrenic patient, it is necessary to get to the heart of the matter. The shorter the time available, the more sharply focused the confrontation needs to be.

Success with Schizophrenic Patients

With regard to the ability to succeed in psychotherapy with schizophrenic patients, it is recognized that some therapists are more effective than others. The important attributes are still largely subjective; that is, they are listed according to the view of the person who specifies them. There is considerable agreement that the extrovert is more effective than the introvert. Most studies utilize psychiatric residents as subjects; experienced therapists are averse to exposing themselves and their technics to observations and judgments of others. The implications of this aversion are endless.

The studies that contribute most to the attempts to define characteristics making for a successful psychotherapist are those of Betz and Whitehorn.[21–26] Among the qualities investigated by these authors were the personal interest values based on the Strong Vocational Interest Inventory. A relatively large number of residents have been classified according to their ability to obtain a favorable outcome of treatment of schizophrenic patients. Both the most and the least successful groups scored high on physician, psychologist, and public administrator vocations. Analysis of the data, however, revealed that the *most* successful group scored high on lawyer and certified public accountant vocations and low on mathematics, physical science teacher, and printer. The *least* successful group of therapists scored high on the latter two but low on the lawyer and certified public accountant vocations.

These findings were then subjected to experimentation by predicting the high or low success of another group of resident therapists, utilizing the data derived from tests with the Strong Vocational Interest Inventory. The predictions of those who would be more successful therapists turned out to be 80% correct, while predictions regarding those who would be less successful in achieving a favorable outcome were 67% correct. Both groups, in both experiments, were equally successful with neurotic and depressed patients. Further screening procedures were developed with greater predictive value.

The inferences drawn included the possibility that the therapists with lawyer interests had a problem-solving approach, while those with printer or science teacher interests were more authoritative in their attitudes to the patients and were, at the same time, deferential to authority themselves. They tended to be passively permissive and "instructional" in their style of interpretation of behavior, whereas the successful therapists acted quite differently. The successful therapists expressed attitudes more freely on material arising in the interviews and did not hesitate to set limits when they believed they were indicated. They were able, to a far higher degree, to establish "trustful communications" with their patients.

One aspect of the schizophrenic patient generally agreed on is that he feels dominated by authority, especially external authority. The schizophrenic posture is one of withdrawal from others, often motivated, if not always, by the protective mechanism of avoidance of being dominated. His isolation secures a measure of security against being influenced against his will. If this concept of his basic problem is accurate, the implicit corollary is that his withdrawal is the manifestation of his basic resolution of the conflict between his positive feelings to the original authority and his hostility and anger aroused by domination of the same authority. Any effort to establish a positive response in him may be equally viewed as an attempt to dominate.

A characteristic of the schizophrenic patient is that he feels, in disagreements with his parents, that he was always defeated and was never able, by the use of his cognitive and intellectual powers, to win. Repeatedly, the feeling emerges that he was never listened to when he attempted to present his side of the conflict, that the parent, even when seeming to listen, was really too busy with his or her own thoughts to pay attention. The anger and rage in the schizophrenic arises out of the feelings of frustration and helplessness provoked by this failure of communication. Never has he experienced the success of persuading the parent in making decisions affecting him. From such origins spring the patient's often repeated assertions that he wants to be independent and lead his own life.

Those therapists with strong, lawyerlike interests may be attracted to this vocation because of similar types of struggle that were, however, successful. The intellectual objectivity of the law is highly esteemed by academic attorneys. The value placed on intellectual examination of both sides of an argument—the legal term—and on the winning of a contest through the cogency of intellectual logic is very close to the value placed by many schizophrenics on their intellectual powers. The "concrete thinking" of the schizophrenic bears some resemblance to the step-by-step presentation of the lawyer's brief. In other words, I am suggesting that the schizophrenic can follow, understand, and respond readily to interpretations made with the same step-by-step process, and associations between present and past situations are readily made, provided the concepts have "concreteness." The so-called concreteness of schizophrenic thinking is frequently nothing more than attempts to establish communication by using precise meanings at a very simple level of abstraction.

The concept is of merit in short-term psychotherapy, because the basic situations, which the patient has experienced daily, he appears to understand fully. When the therapist states in a quiet tone that he *feels* the patient's need for independence may be associated with the early experience of never having a say in decisions affecting himself, he can readily see the connection. Often this brings forth a series of memories from childhood, heavily charged with anger, rage, and helplessness. They may then be related, by the therapist, to situations and events occurring in the more recent past, which suggest the same type of experience; the patient is able to examine this possibility, and often to grasp the concordance.

The sense of utter rejection, and fear, which many of these patients express, seems to arise from the lack of communication rather than negative feelings of the parent. Parental indifference to their reasoning is far more traumatizing than the expression of parental anger. Those children who are able to arouse anger in the parent, thereby proving that there is communication, are, perhaps, more fortunate, by and large, than those who feel no response when a response is desperately needed.

The superego of the schizophrenic patient is, therefore, a hostile, domineering, controlling and irrational structure with corresponding emotional components of anger, rage and guilt. The anger is subdued by primitive intellectual reasoning, supplemented by avoidance of relationships in which repetition of past experiences would disturb the balance so delicately achieved. The superego is very much ego alien with the capacity to arouse intense guilt. In therapy, the therapist may attempt two approaches: one the reinforcement of the power of the tyrannical superego,[18] especially when the patient feels threatened by emerging pain; the other an alliance with the ego of the patient. This latter is on the level of cognitive functioning, so that emotional control is not disturbed. The irrationality of the superego is attacked by intellectual and seemingly objective examination of beliefs. The value system of the therapist is used as a counterforce to that of the patient, who is thus enabled to confront some of his current conflicts. The intensity of the need of the patient to be recognized as a real person with intellectual capacities becomes manifest in the transference, which can develop when the relationship of trust has been established. Another manifestation is the long period of time—years—during which the patient will periodically communicate with the therapist after the official termination of treatment. Such communications almost always center on the successes of the patient in his daily life.

A problem inherent in short-term psychotherapy is the avoidance of an intense transference relationship. Once trust has been established, this may develop rapidly. The objectives of treatment are limited, relatively, for reasons essentially outside the treatment process. It is important, therefore, that the therapist constantly refuse to give direction to courses of action to be followed. In this respect, there is no difference from the treatment process in intensive, long-term therapy. The interviews, however, are not scheduled so frequently, especially after the initial relationship of trust has been established. The focus is maintained on the solution of contemporary problems. The patient is encouraged to participate in everyday activities, a job, etc., as soon as possible. The therapist reassures the patient that he will always be available within the limits of the reality situation of the psychiatrist. The intervals between the interviews are lengthened as rapidly as practical, within the context of the patient's progress.

During therapy, efforts must be directed towards the avoidance of the patient's tendency to focus his attention too intently and minutely on his own psychical operations and especially on his psychological experiences in the past, lest he become preoccupied with the past to the exclusion of the present. Many schizophrenic patients volunteer the statement that they used to scrutinize constantly their experiences and their reactions.

Length

How long is short-term psychotherapy? The term is relative. The acute portion of treatment of some severely schizophrenic patients can be successfully completed in six months to one year, with intervals scheduled twice a week for about six months, followed by weekly interviews for a period of a few months, after which the intervals may be lengthened appropriately. Sometimes, the circumstances of the patient determine the duration of therapy. The patient who reintegrates relatively soon may maintain a tentative therapeutic contact for periods of weeks, months or even years, during which he is able to function reasonably well, but when decompensation threatens, he returns for more frequent interviews. When he reintegrates, he returns to the previous pattern.

One may argue that such patients make spontaneous remissions and that the psychotherapeutic encounter is an insignificant proportion of the factors that influence their recovery. Against this position, substantial evidence suggests that some therapists are more successful than others in securing a favorable outcome of treatment. Moreover, the level of functioning achieved after treatment is frequently at a much higher level than before the onset of the episode.

Some evidence exists that elapsed time plays a more significant role in the recovery of the patient than frequency of interviews. The constant testing, of what he has learned in therapy against the constant experiences of daily living, plays an important part in convincing the patient of his ability to meet stress in more rewarding ways.

The question may be raised: Why not persist with more intensive treatment over a long period of time so that maximum benefit might be attained? Often the therapist would welcome the opportunity, especially with patients who do so well. The demands of time, other obligations of both patient and therapist, the economic realities, often the satisfaction of the patient with his progress, and the ever-present need to prove his independence—all or any of these may be the crux in determining whether psychotherapy is short- or long-term.

REFERENCES

1. Zirkle, G. A.: Five-Minute Psychotherapy, *in* Masserman, J. H., ed.: *Current Psychiatric Therapies*, vol. 4, New York, Grune, 1964, pp. 222–229.
2. Miller, L. C.: Short-term therapy with adolescents, Amer J Orthopsychiat *29*: 772–779, 1959.
3. Brill, N. Q., Koegler, R. R., and Epstein, L. J.: Controlled study of psychiatric outpatient treatment, Arch Gen Psychiat *10*:581–595 (June), 1964.
4. Alexander, F., and French, T. M.: *Psychoanalytic Therapy; Principles and Application*, chap. 9, New York, Ronald, 1946, pp. 145–164.
5. ———: Principles and techniques of briefer psychotherapeutic procedures, Res Publ Ass Res Nerv Ment Dis *31*:16–20, 1953.
6. Walker, R. G., and Kelley, F. E.: Short-term psychotherapy with hospitalized schizophrenic patients, Acta Psychiat Scand *35*:34–56, 1960.
7. Taylor, J. W.: Relationship of success and length in psychotherapy, J Consult Psychol *20*:332 (Oct), 1956.
8. Tauber, L. E.: Motivational approach to psychotherapy with goal-symptom emphasis, Psychiatry *26*:273–280, 1963.
9. Lorr, M.: Relation of treatment frequency and duration to psychotherapeutic outcome, *in* Strupp, H. H., and Luborsky, L., eds.: *Research in Psychotherapy*, vol. 2, Washington, DC, Amer Psychol Ass, 1962, pp. 134–141.
10. Rado, S.: Theory and therapy: theory of schizotypal organization and its application to treatment of decompensated schizotypal behavior, *in* Sher, S. C., and Davis, H. R., eds.: *Out-Patient Treatment of Schizophrenia: Symposium*, New York, Grune, 1960, pp. 87–113.
11. Sullivan, H. S.: *Clinical Studies in Psychiatry*, New York, Norton, 1956.
12. ———: *The Interpersonal Theory of Psychiatry*, New York, Norton, 1953.
13. Fromm-Reichmann, Frieda: *Principles of Intensive Psychotherapy*, Chicago, Univ Chicago Press, 1950.
14. ———: The psychotherapy of schizophrenia, Amer J Psychiat *3*:410–419 (Dec), 1954.
15. Arieti, S.: *Interpretation of Schizophrenia*, New York, Bruner, 1955.
16. Federn, P.: *Ego Psychology and the Psychoses*, New York, Basic, 1952.
17. Rosen, J. N.: *Direct Analysis; Selected Papers*, New York, Grune, 1953.
18. Wexler, M.: Structural problem in schizophrenia: role of the internal object, *in* Brody, E. B., and Redlich, F. C., eds.: *Psychotherapy of Schizophrenia*, New York, Internat Univ Press, 1952, pp. 179–201.
19. Kallman, F. J.: *Heredity in Health and Mental Disorder; Principles of Psychiatric Genetics in the Light of Comparative Twin Studies*, New York, Norton, 1953.
20. Heath, R. G., *et al.*: Pharmacological and biological psychotherapy, Amer J Psychiat *114*:683–689 (Feb), 1958.
21. Whitehorn, J. C., and Betz, Barbara J.: Study of psychotherapeutic relationships between physicians and schizophrenic patients, Amer J Psychiat *111*:321–331 (Nov), 1954.

22. Betz, Barbara J., and Whitehorn, J. C.: Relationship of therapist to outcome of therapy in schizophrenia, *in Psychiatric Research Reports, #5*, Washington, DC, Amer Psychiat Ass, 1956, pp. 89–105.

23. Whitehorn, J. C.: Studies of the doctor as critical factor for prognosis of schizophrenic patients, Int J Soc Psychiat *6*:71–77, 1960.

24. ———, and Betz, Barbara, J.: Further studies of the doctor as crucial variable in outcome of treatment with schizophrenic patients, Amer J Psychiat *117*:215–223 (Sep), 1960.

25. Betz, Barbara J.: Experiences in research in psychotherapy with schizophrenic patients, *in* Strupp, H. H., and Luborsky, L., eds.: *Progress in Psychotherapy*, vol. 2, Washington, DC, Amer Psychol Ass, 1962, pp. 41–60.

26. ———: Strategic conditions in psychotherapy of persons with schizophrenia, Amer J Psychiat *107*:203–215 (June), 1950.

Elvin V. Semrad, MD
Harvard, Massachusetts Mental Health Center

13

Long-Term Therapy of Schizophrenia

FORMULATION OF THE CLINICAL APPROACH

PSYCHIATRY IN THE MID-SIXTIES BRINGS A CUMULATIVE EXPERIENCE TO the aid of the adult suffering "schizophrenic reactions." Consistent humanitarian care and scientific clinical study have developed since the 18th century despite oscillations between brutality and benevolence punctuated by neglect. A naturalistic understanding of human behavior characterized the thought of Plato and Hippocrates, who rejected demoniacal possession as a cause of mental illness. Their view of disturbed behavior as disease was abandoned until it reappeared in Coelius Aurelianus. It disappeared during the Dark Ages and was brought to light again in the 16th century by Paracelsus and John Weyer. Their influence resulted in partial acceptance of mental disorder as a province of medicine.

Towards Current Concepts

Psychological stresses were referred to as moral causes, and moral treatment—the first practical effort made to provide systematic, responsible care for the mentally ill—was successful in achieving recoveries. The innovations of Pinel, Tuke, Chiaruigi, Reil, and Rush dominated American psychiatry the first half of the nineteenth century, only to decline. From the writings of Earle, Brigham, Woodward, Butler, and Ray, it was clear that moral treatment was not a single technic, yet it had the goal of arousing the dormant faculties of the mind, the matrix of which was the communal life of patients and hospital personnel. The chief modalities used to awaken such feelings were the endeavors that required the patient to invest interest in something outside of himself in cooperation with others, such as manual or intellectual work, recreation or religious worship.[2] Psychotherapy as such was not mentioned, but it took the form of patients' sharing experiences and discussing them both in groups and with their physicians.

By 1910, American psychiatry was starting toward freedom from the physical disease theory of mental illness, inflicted on it by the materialistic science to which medicine was then beholden. With it came the transition from the concept of mental illness as disease-entity to that as reaction type. Gradually, its scope increased from that of a purely medical discipline, through that which included the psychological and social in mental illness, to our present theoretical framework of psychodynamic psychiatry and its extension into community psychiatry. The theoretical structure of psychoanalysis considered not only erotic drives as sources of motivation but also aggressive drives as determining factors in personality development. Freud's studies of transference and Sullivan's elaborations of the concept of interpersonal relationships added impetus to the growing knowledge and appreciation of the effects of personalities on each other, as factors in defective development as well as cues for therapeutic interventions.

Appreciation of the total life experience of the patient in the treatment of mental illness concentrated in developing technics of therapy to aid and allow patients to function at levels of optimum adaptation. Psychobiology,[18] psychoanalysis,[8, 9] social psychiatry,[2] interpersonal relationships,[37] and an appreciation of the dysfunctions of integrated personal functioning[40] have touched most of us today and added dimensions to communicating, understanding, treating and teaching in our extant theoretical frame of reference, dynamic psychiatry.[13]

Fortified by our analytic experiences, psychodynamics allowed the growth of a frame of reference for our mutual endeavors. Particular attention was given to the analysis of disturbances and disorganizations of the ego,[12] studying the functions that come from a person's experience, whether determined by accidental and/or current events. We were able to study regression and recovery profiles, and issues of emotional entanglement in the patient's life situation as they were repeated in the treatment situation. Particularly significant was the appreciation of the role of object anxiety and the ego's ontogenetic organization of its flights from it when overwhelmed, and to identify and classify them into ego executant patterns of behavior.[8, 14, 39] These enabled us to formulate some features of the schizophrenia-vulnerable ego and to study its function vicissitudes under variant conditions of emotional entanglement with another person, the therapist.

ASSUMPTIONS

Data thus assessed, drawn primarily from observing the schizophrenic person in the interaction of therapy, with the patient's recovery in view, allowed us to make the following assumptions, from the clinical laboratory:

1. That the way the patient negotiates his relationship with the therapist is habitual to him by virtue of his attitude; that is, his ego executant patterns of behavior can be so identified.
2. That this patient's ego executant acts can be classified into patterns of repetitive behavior, each pattern implying an object need, and suggesting to the therapist a course of action.
3. That these patterns are seen in everyday life and are normal for certain phases of child development—sick only if persevered in at the wrong time and place, or with the wrong person.
4. That a study of the purpose of these acts, of the patient's behavior, will give us some clues to what made them necessary, what inner message they convey.

5. That in the doctor-patient relationships, as the ego passes through the rhythm of disturbances and disorganization,[12] the clues relevant to functioning as a person will be suggested.

PSYCHOTHERAPY

My experience in the long-term therapy of schizophrenic persons is primarily psychotherapeutic. Medical treatments are adjunctive and used when recovery cannot be initiated or maintained on the basis of a relationship. Important in my studies was our staff's helping each other and our resident to maintain therapeutic relationships with schizophrenic patients. Processes of sustaining, supporting, and at times perhaps even gratifying were studied. The clinical situation offers a laboratory allowing observation, since we do not hesitate to interview in each other's presence, in which two persons interact in order to help the patient return to his optimum functioning as a person. Burdens of life were the crucial issues, necessitating the patients' current level of functioning, and we had to find ways to help the patients with these, even though at times we could appreciate that their failures in their life undertakings had made them vulnerable to psychosis. The clinical situation allows study of content of a patient's productions not only as they flow spontaneously from him, but as they are evoked, provoked, obstructed, and/or facilitated in this attempt of one person to understand another person, although both may have uncertainties.

The responsible physician serves as a resource, a support and a gratification to all personnel involved with the patient as they take initiative to relate to a patient in a psychotherapeutic way. All personnel do so relate. The relationships are real; the symptoms and life events are also taken as real, with minimum concerns with unconscious fantasies. The purpose of treatment revolves around allowing the patient relief from suffering and equipping him better to live in peace, affection and stable equilibrium—with himself, his immediate objects, and the world.

The objective of therapy is to provide the patient with an opportunity to develop capacity for expression and/or sublimation of emotional needs and drives, to acknowledge, bear, and keep in perspective real life object experiences. Helping thus, individually, in groups, with or without the use of vehicles and/or activities, means *1.* providing a corrective ego experience for return to optimum ego functioning, and *2.* aiding and abetting continued personal growth as the patient's psychosis vulnerability is progressively studied. A corrective ego experience (Aichhorn[1]) implies an experience or experiences with an object, including the sensations that arise within the patient and those stimulated, leading hopefully to a relationship or relationships that are gratifying, rewarding, and growth-stimulating. In practice, what it amounts to is a trusting sharing of pain in efforts to acknowledge, bear, and put it in perspective. It means supplying the infantile object in reality: the unanalyzed transference; displacements: new symptoms and/or resistances; and stability: ego or superego building, or education, through reality events.

Details of technic vary with the physician's skill and training. Therapy is usually conducted face-to-face; it grows from the interview situation, conducted in an atmosphere of mutual understanding and rapport, and keeps in mind what help the patient needs, wants, and is willing to receive, as well as what help the physician has and is willing to give. Basic considerations of treatment center around a determination of the patient's personality structure, and, more important, of what in his current adaptation in the realms of his living and loving went askew, such as loss, frustration of object need, and/or organic structural change.

BASIC PRINCIPLES

Basic therapeutic principles applicable to all methods of psychotherapy —quite independent of ideology or theoretical system—are suggestion, emotional relief through abreaction, manipulation, clarification, and interpretation. The first three are usually employed in the service of fuller utilization of clarification and interpretation, and in themselves furnish very little in the way of the patient's self-understanding. Clarification and interpretation serve to extend his self-understanding. Influence through experience is what needs to be stressed. The patient learns from his experience with his therapist and the caretaking associates.

Therapy involves primarily the symptomatic relief of pain incident to what made the patient a patient, such as loss, frustration of object need, and/or organic structural change. Pain apropos of loss and frustration of object need is relieved in long-term gains by increasing the individual's tolerance. Long-term therapy of "schizophrenic persons" becomes essentially a character analysis, a long project. The immediate pain must be managed by specific therapeutic measures that ameliorate it in the overall integrative effort.

The therapist and patient retain each other as object. Varying aspects of the patient's life may have to remain uninterpreted and unanalyzed. Appropriateness in these judgments by the therapist is the essence of therapeutic strategy. The two have entered each other's lives, serving as infantile objects. The therapist actually intrudes into the life and personality of the patient and offers himself as a new symptom, a new experience. The transference manifestations and their substructure are a vehicle for cure in the sense of their being necessary building blocks for the patient's continued psychic functioning, introducing into the patient's mental economy a necessary and permanent factor.

The treatment of the psychotic patient is at best homologous[19] to that of the neurotic. In neurosis, as defensive processes are reversed and passage back into consciousness is found for the instinctual impulses and affects that have been warded off, the ego and superego are left to come to better terms with them. In psychosis, the ego is in a state of avoidance: functioning and providing an ego corrective experience are the primary objective. The patient is overwhelmed by object anxiety incident to his dread of the outside world. For success, treatment necessitates a reversal of the defensive process by helping the patient to acknowledge, bear, and keep in perspective the reality dreaded. Therapy unmasks this object anxiety, and may show it as a product of fantasy against which it is not worth while to assume defensive operations. More commonly and more usually, though the ego takes defense against affect for purposes of avoiding pain, the requirement is to help tolerate longer and larger quantities of pain without immediate recourse to defense mechanisms.

This in some measure is an educative process, a lesson to be learned, a corrective ego experience, which entails the patient's actual identification with the therapist for acknowledging, bearing, and keeping in perspective his life experience, painful or pleasurable. The homologous nature of therapeutic intervention with a schizophrenic patient reveals that it is not a matter of studying a patient's postponements and repressions, but a task of creating capacity to postpone and repress. It is a study of incapacity to deal with reality—by satisfying needs and providing sustenance, support and security, as long as the study of the patient's flights is in process. Manipulative procedures to try to influence reality—casework with relatives, family therapy—are of some value in allaying interpersonal tensions particularly. Sufficient ego-building may take place in short-term procedures to enable the patient to recognize that anxieties belonging to situations in the past led to the creation of defenses that are no longer needed to cope with situations in the present. Or, what appears to be objective anxiety may prove to have its sources in exaggerated and distorted notions of reality based on a primeval situation once but no longer existing. Some help may result from neurosis analysis in enabling the ego to adapt a less severe attitude toward the instincts, so that it does not have to make such great effort to ward them off.[16]

Much of the creative element that goes into structuring a helping situation is derived from the creative capacities of the people involved, from their ability to translate experience and principle into knowledge essentially through "experiential learning." The helping situation is really created anew each time with each patient. Styles vary so much that sometimes they may almost appear to be different technics. The essence of style and the principle involved are shared, in my opinion, by most psychotherapists. Yet I hope not to get involved in a discussion of style, and shall limit this chapter to those formulations that have impressed me as most useful:

a. The personal diagnostic processes
b. The ego compensation processes
c. The ego maintenance processes
d. The analysis of the psychosis-vulnerable ego

Personal Diagnostic Processes

A personal diagnostic summary, primarily to provide a grasp of considerations to guide therapy, is designed from the clinical picture and the ego patterns of negotiation that the patient uses with the therapist. A *regression profile* is plotted from the present illness and gives clues to the type of regressive course the patient has taken. This has implications for therapeutic procedure during the ego compensation phase. Identification of the life impasse which occasioned the ego decompensation is necessary. If acute and overwhelming, it implies a mourning type of therapeutic activity to enable the patient to integrate the overwhelming traumatic experience, usually a loss. If debilitating, frustrating of object needs and occasioning a chronic step-by-step regression, it implies accurate diagnosis of the frustration of object need and subsequent activity of replacement or substitution. If this is not possible in terms of giving it up realistically, mourning activity to integrate the loss becomes necessary.

An empathic diagnosis is crucial. It implies a capacity to feel oneself into the patient's dilemma and appreciate the painful experience, the idea and affects avoided, as well as the state of the patient's ego functioning in terms of need to avoid therapeutic helpfulness. Is the patient inviting the therapist to come forth to help him with his pain, or is he doing everything he can to avoid him in order to maintain a status quo of psychic and homeostatic constancy?

Leads to the emotional dependency factor, which must be supplied, can be derived from the clinical picture and the patterns of ego functioning. From the clinical pictures and their reaction patterns, one can see that the catatonic patient, in his ego patterns of negotiating with and his efforts "not to mind" the therapist, through denial turns his back on disagreeable reality and through imagination reverses the unwelcome facts and transforms them to suit his purposes and fulfill his wishes. This denial may be manifest in thought, fantasy, word, and act. Through projection patterns, the patient disposes of his own faults and unacceptable drives, even to the point of altruistic surrender, by laying responsibility for them at the door of external agents. Through distortion patterns, he changes himself by restricting his fields of interest and/or through the mechanisms of identifications with the aggressor. The ego's activities are governed by considerations of the tension produced by stimuli present in it, whatever the source; what clinically is felt as pleasure or unpleasure is not the absolute degree of tension, but something of the rhythm of its changes.

Our failure to respond by symptom signals is evidenced in our patients' behaviors and actions. The integrated adaptive response of anxiety manifest in and allayed by neurotic activity, as in situations of frustration, is denied by our patients and is expressed in seeking out objects for relief. So, first and foremost, an increase of unpleasure beyond the normal expected and foreseen, and met by a body response experienced as anxiety, is handled by our patients by activity. Because the object turned to cannot, or will not, respond in kind, occasions increase in unpleasure that is not expected and not foreseen, and that is met by a body response of helplessness experienced as depression, but resulting in manipulative responses manifested in and allayed by depressive activity without containment of the affect. Increase of unpleasure to the point of the ego's feeling overwhelmed is met by a body response of disintegration, terror, fear, panic and dread.

A survival response manifests itself in overuse of flight activities and is allayed by self-consoling activity that is tension-relieving in purpose only. An increase of unpleasure comes at periods of intensification. It requires getting rid and/or acceptance of an object in fact or fancy, especially the affect associated with the object. The unpleasure may be so intense, temporary or prolonged and catch the ego so unprepared that it is not able to organize itself for self-containment activity at any adaptive level; thus it must mobilize all its resources and methods of avoiding it through flight, through all its old habits of flight learned previously by happenstance. The struggle of wanting to stay versus wanting to flee is a very painful turmoil state, often occasioning debate concerning unacceptable issues that are projected, that is, sent back whence they came, relating to "object in" or "out." The ego can try to mobilize all its resources to meet it by sacrificing itself, that is, by trying to live in every new object relationship by imitating it. The result is an awkward, unstudied, very primitive kind of identification that represents a loss of personality and a consequent change in ego identification, that is, suiting self to other people's preferences and wishes as the only way to be sure of making them love and feel love.

Supplying the Patients' Needs

Patients who manifest *denial patterns* of "not minding" (usually those demonstrating catatonic features) call forth caring and demonstration of the fact that they matter to the therapist. In terms of technic, demonstration of the principle is the crucial matter, and style will vary by virtue of a therapist's personality.

Projection patterns (usually in paranoid patients), manifest clinically in blaming, call for responsibility-sharing on the part of the therapist via his awareness of and his capacity to bear and keep in perspective the painful ideas and affects, literally, the pain and the disquietude in his body, that the patient cannot bear by himself.

Distortion patterns (usually in deluded and hallucinated patients) are manifest clinically in megalomanic beliefs, hallucinatory experiences, and the need to act to keep other people from danger. Careful pursuit of the pain of the patient's own life dissatisfactions and failures enables him to face his future in its context and start from scratch as a failure, with awareness of the depressive component of his functioning. The more the patient progresses out of his narcissistic regressed position, the more he functions as a depressed patient.

Part of the diagnostic processes is the careful consideration of activity programs (and the worker's skill therein) that will have a specific place in total treatment planning. The most effective use of activity for the most integrated results of therapy depends on all workers' understanding clearly and using as much as possible the dynamic factors in the personal diagnosis. Dynamic concepts of importance are:

1. Activity and therapy activities serve as anxiety-relieving mechanisms.
2. An activity serves on a trial and error basis as a procedure for developing ego

skills that will contribute to the individual's total capacity to negotiate interpersonal relationships with due regard to himself and to those he cathexes.

3. Each therapeutic worker must appreciate himself as a tool, as an available object whom the patient can recathex as he progresses from his narcissistic state to use of his old capacity. Furthermore, the patient can increasingly add to his skills by his relationship with this therapeutic person.[35]

Special considerations of protective custody (for destructive trends in the patient or behavior leading from extravagant or dangerous errors of judgment) in terms of hospitalization and/or the many modifications of it have to be made. Usually full hospitalization is reserved for tiding the patient over a crisis and attaching him to a therapist. Such a plan has advantages: it saves patients the problems of separation from their own objects and spares their reputations by avoiding the stigma associated with persons no longer masters of their own destiny. Hospital facilities have been modified to aid and augment psychotherapeutic work by making helping objects available where needed. Emergency services to tide over crises, help in seeking resources, place people in helping situations without hospitalization, are provided by walk-in clinics, home treatment units, extension services and specialized organizations. Day and night hospitalization programs, half-way houses, patients' clubs, sheltered workshops—all are developments requiring careful timing and prescription to mitigate the iatrogenic aspects of patient care.

Supportive anaclitic methods, with or without adjunctive therapeutic aids, are indicated if relief cannot be achieved by a personal relationship that artificially enhances ego strength until strengthening through character analysis is possible. Libidinal attachment to love objects in the outer world, leading to subsequent attachment to internalized objects in the inner world, is the chief integrating force in the ego itself, which tends to neutralize aggressive destructiveness, sadism, excessive anxiety—forces that make for disintegration. Pain can be relieved by decreasing the environmental threat and thus mitigating the forces of disintegration inherent in the situation. Many spontaneous recoveries are effected by the experience of the psychosis itself and the change it effects in the patient's relationship with the "particular people" in his life.

The Compensation Process

The compensation process—return from regression to optimum ego functioning—begins with the initial step of supplying the patient's emotional needs. The patient has to experience the care-giving objects as sources of gratification and feel them as such. At this time, the use of anxiety-relieving procedures and activities and of object-providing procedures, such as occupational therapy or nursing, becomes an integral part of the team-planning activities. The therapist himself as a resource serves the patient as an object for ego identification. He allows and encourages the patient to experience his feelings in his presence and to mimic, and eventually internalize, the therapist's ways of dealing with such experience. The need to speak about what matters, especially the patient's pains, in doses tolerable to the patient, is the unique clinical task. Through candid, respectful interaction, a corrective ego experience is structured. The patient begins therapy with the therapist as a real object and gradually learns to deny himself the gratification and so to establish the necessary preconditioning for the development of a useful transference relationship. Mourning is a necessary part of treatment, and termination begins with the original working arrangement from the very first clarification or interpretation.* The principal therapy functions are to sustain support, deprive, and refuse in strategic manner until the patient can be himself and his problems are understood, integrated, and thus relieved and no longer pathogenic.

The patient who does not care (denial pattern) does not want to acknowledge, think, feel, strives only for internal peace, operates on the principle of "forgetting," "not minding," is often supported in this by his primary objects. The therapist's task is to demonstrate that he cares in a very active way by talking about what matters to the patient, noting very carefully the index of what matters, in terms of the patient's tears, emotional upheavals, protestations. Actively for and with the patient, he seeks the details of loss by asking details of the experience—when, where, under what conditions. He demonstrates that to master is to remember, to see, to look at, to hold in mind, and suggests and allows uncritical emotional relief through these actions. He thus aids the patient to re-

* Apropos of responses of object anxiety, we were impressed that the ego executant patterns of behavior considered so normal at certain stages of ego development could be so handicapping if persisted in, especially if in an exaggerated form at the wrong time, with the wrong person, or in the wrong place, or in the service of solving life issues calling for capabilities in which the schizophrenia-vulnerable ego is lacking, that is, in its capacity to acknowledge, bear, and put in perspective aloneness and loneliness as occasioned by loss, or capacity to acknowledge, bear, and put in perspective frustrations of object need inherent in progressive demands made on a person by his chronological maturation. These ego executant patterns were essentially in the service of conducting flights of an overwhelmed ego, and in this way had to be recognized as different from defensive organizations, effective primarily against the instincts. In these patients the latter are not proportionately developed, since they require initially and continuously an ego's being in a state of compensation, enabling successful postponement, a series of functions structured primarily around what we call repression. An ego developmentally altered we refer to as an ego changed by conversion processes,[17] that is, an ego that, in its efforts to avert the unbearable idea and associated affect, finally yields to the acceptance of the unbearable idea without contradiction. Thus, the ego in a sense has specialized in its alteration to become specialized in a secondary stage of defense. The purpose of the conversion is to avoid the unbearable ideas and feelings evoked or reevoked and associated with emotional entanglements with objects. The idea is that psychoses are adaptations to defects in the integration and efficiency of those functions essential to real relationships with people for pleasurable and egoistic reasons, and to those functions essential to the control of excessive infantile needs by either normal or neurotic mechanisms. That is, there is incapacity to acknowledge, bear, and put and keep in perspective, to control aloneness, depression and unchangeable sources of life dissatisfaction by either neurotic or normal mechanisms.

construct the details of the traumatic experience and to integrate it. He influences through, and helps the patient learn from, experience that to forget is not to get relief from intolerable life pain, and that mastery, remembering, reliving, acknowledging, bearing, and putting in perspective the reality of his pain go hand in hand. Ego capacities to think, tolerate loneliness, deal with life experience as it is rather than as one would like it to be—these become the patient's security.

The patient who cannot bear his pain and therefore assigns blame (*projection pattern*) wants somebody to share it. He asks the therapist to share responsibility unbearable to him, to be noncritical and nonpunishing, to try not to get too close too fast and thus to respect what he feels in his body, where, and his own interpretation of it. The patient's self-diagnosis, although a vehicle for frightening affects, is often the most important obstacle to tolerating the painful affects of the real traumatic event.

The deluded and hallucinated patient (*distortion pattern*) is in essence debating the pros and cons of his position and his inability to master his reality. He toys with the relevance of his hypotheses and utilizes them to bear his painful affect. The therapist's active pursuit of the reality details of the patient's dissatisfaction is the crucial technical activity. He helps the patient to give up reliance on infantile patterns of adaptation and to return to his optimum ego functioning. The process allows the patient to assess his reaction from the standpoint of the advantages and disadvantages it offers in his present life situation vis-a-vis the satisfaction of his emotional needs. He explores alternate possibilities by which he may resolve his situation more satisfactorily for himself, with due consideration for others. Analyzing fears of change[28] becomes a part of the therapeutic task. The patient-doctor relationship needs constant study. A positive relationship of trust, support, and confidence enables the two to do what the patient was not able to do for himself, whether to mourn, integrate trauma, or acknowledge, bear, and tolerate. A patient in loving trust with one person can function at his own optimum level, at least with that person. A return to optimum ego functioning is accompanied by a loss of symptoms.

Any regression is evidence of too much pain in the relationship, and means that the patient feels that you as therapist do not accept him as he is, as a real person in his own right, with and without his transference overloads. This immediately requires reevaluation of your role in the relationship. Has the patient picked up your impatience, your frustration, your anger with his demands, your dissatisfactions with his progress, your exhaustion, your allegiance to the relatives?

If all goes well, a patient returns to his optimum ego functioning, by giving up his exclusive reliance on infantile patterns of behavior, in about three months.

The Ego Maintenance Processes

After recompensation, there follows a period of nine to twelve months during which the patient works to reestablish his relationships with his own objects, aided and abetted by the pattern of his experience with his therapist. He is helped to recognize his own contributions to his maladjustments by analysis of his ego functioning in relation to the vital life issues with his objects. This period following the initial three to four months' regression is often referred to as the long haul. Longer periods of regression require a modification of the time table. In the hospital with the personnel and the therapist as "trustful objects," the patient attempts via trial and error to negotiate his interpersonal relationships more realistically and satisfactorily, primarily by thinking instead of acting, stopping, looking, listening, taking in data—especially cues from other people, but also those from within himself. Now, in essence, he tries to apply this lesson to unsolved relationships with the "particular people" in his life to achieve skill in social adaptation and success in self-expression and in great measure to "mend" violated relationships occasioned by his assault on them resulting from his regressive behavior. Aids to psychotherapy at this time come primarily from rehabilitation procedures, day or night programs, and the objects therein who serve as resources. Group psychotherapy and family therapy are still experimental possibilities.

For the patient in the acute regressive situation, this period is given essentially to the decathexis-recathexis process, i.e., making new investments and abandoning impossible ones. In the chronic situation, it is given essentially to the patient's becoming fully aware of what he wants for himself; he is aided and abetted in making arrangements for substitute supplies wherever possible or in accepting, doing without—that is, undergoing separations and weanings, accompanied by depression. In essence, he devotes himself to making changes, finding new ways of living and relating, and by trust relationships to the therapist and others; allows himself to be interested in new ways of thinking and doing, such as not going on alone, by making trials in the direction of interdependence. He tries to find conventional manners of living worth trying, and perhaps most of all to vitiate his psychotic value system and not rely on it, especially in his megalomanic aspects, thus devoting more attention to his society's current value system and managing a niche in it for himself. Often the patient must devote concern and effort to sizing up and learning to cope with his family, not in terms of defensive diagnosis but of the familiar isolations, the family scapegoating, the incongruities of in-the-house culture compared to the out-of-the-house expected culture, in essence giving up sick ways of life for healthier ones and adapting to the changes in the family produced by therapy.

Integration of the trauma of the regression—with its concomitant blows to self-esteem, the realizations that one's way is not the only way, that one's attitudes are wrong, and that reality bends for nobody—helps the patient tolerate the pain of failure. Integration of the trauma of the attempts at cure is no small task for the patient. He must undergo all the pains of realizing that his way was not adaptive, of trial and error change, of repeated failure, of the stupidity of wanting stubbornly to maintain "one's face," of missed opportunity, of time, patience, hospitalization, frustrated personnel and their behaviors, and perhaps most of all, of the narcissistic injury of being a patient and the necessary acceptance of the idea that one cannot go it alone, that other people know about life more than he, especially people he needs and often looks down on. Impersonal treatment procedures, the feeling of being abandoned, the terror of it, the eternal search for magic to avoid the real, and perhaps most of all the painful realization that psychosis is only a temporary respite, at best a self-deception, are all parts of the process.

The Analysis of the Psychosis-Vulnerable Ego

Experience in the analysis of the character disorder (its genetic development as well as the character structure extant as it has become modified by the homologous treatment procedure) is limited. The question whether it should be carried out by the same therapist who enabled the patient to come to his present point of ego stability, or by a new therapist, who could function more purely as a transference object, has not been answered. I believe that the better choice is the therapist who has long-term acquaintance with the patient's particular vulnerabilities, and familiarity with his mastery of them to this point, provided that he can make the transition.

OBJECT RELATIONS IN TRANSFERENCE

A few observations are relevant on the object relations of the schizophrenic patient in the transference situation. Transference[26, 36] elements are noted in the first contact with the patient when the relationship begins for good or for ill. In essence, what follows is a series of vicissitudes of presence and contact separations, all in the service of growth and development of the patient's capacity for taking objects into his life and letting them go as chronology and life events demand.

Infantile transference[22] interpretations are called for when infantile needs interfere with the patient's ego optimum functioning. They signify stress on the patient's integrative capacity, and mean to the therapist that in addition to interpretation, supporting measures of sustaining and/or gratifying may be called for to enable the patient to get a "good enough mother"[26, 41] to achieve some semblance of integrative capacity.

Delusional transference[22] serves especially as a valuable index of the patient's dissatisfaction with his therapist in the evolving program or the extant program of relationship. It indicates first and foremost the contact disquietude that the patient suffers in his therapist's presence as painful sensations in his body become unbearable. It immediately brings into focus the question how much "pain" the somatic conversion processes can handle[17] and the extent to which the ego must reundergo conversion by distortion, projection, and denial when called on to take the overload. Supporting conscious awareness of a patient's aggressive and libidinal identification is the procedure of choice at these times. It is particularly true of patients with blaming, paranoid tendencies that they find the therapist a persecutor in whom the delusions center and maintain the contradictions.

Ego change because of contradiction plays a big part in development and maintenance of infantile patterns of adaptation.[8, 17, 23] Rycroft feels that contradiction is not the same thing as denial,[23] and his patient, whose character defense showed a marked resemblance to clinical paranoia, did something more than deny and project the attachment to the mother, her hostility to men and her fear of death. She constructed an organized pattern of behavior and thought designed to replace her repressed wishes, feelings, and anxiety by a totally different order of experience. Transference may even appear lacking[26] because strong anxiety prevents the maintenance of any attitude; to reduce this anxiety, the therapist must interpret it.

By mobilizing the anxiety and aggression hidden behind the apparent indifferences, the analyst is able to convert this deficiency of awareness into open resistance and then analyze it. Analysis is fully effective only when the patient is able to recognize and endure reality brought about by analysis of fantasies and the transference situation. There is a distinction[26, 30] between the transference situation and the human relation to the analyst, and in some cases much longer time is required before patients make obvious any relation to the analyst personally, although transference was present from the beginning. The analyst is a persecutor in whom the delusions center. By analyzing from the very beginning the transference situation as well as the paranoid ideas, and by incorporating the persecution as anticipated punishment for the aggression, the analyst avoids damming the anxiety.

Projective identification,[22] as a typical transference phenomenon of the schizophrenic-vulnerable ego, is a secondary defensive mechanism. The patient utilizes an external object, the therapist, in order to alleviate the internal depressive anxiety that has to do particularly with lost objects, implying that identification by projection involves both splitting off parts of self and projecting them into another person, especially as painful, distressing and disturbing. Such alterations of ego boundaries produce increased anxiety, which fosters both regressive dependence and counteractive aggression.

Cameron[4] and Bychowski[3] observe that in the schizophrenic patient all relationships are based on the wish for possession of parental objects through fusion. Both believe that these primitive identifications through introjection must be isolated and the patient confronted with them in a therapeutic alliance that he trusts and respects. To do this, the therapist must be able to understand the primitive defenses and the primary process thinking, and finally to withstand the apathy and despair of an empty ego or the rage of one based on oral sadism. The observation and acceptance of both dependent and counterdependent attitudes is natural under the circumstances, and makes it possible to continue participation with some modicum of comfort and security for both the physician and the patient.

During treatment, as the patient becomes more aware of brief periods of depressive anxiety, he often tries to rid himself of these anxieties by projecting them into the analyst and by stage-managing the analysis, attempting thereby to provoke depressive feelings in the analyst. One must identify the time and circumstances in which the part of the ego capable of experiencing the depression has been projected and interpreted to the patient. Under conditions of stress within the capacity of the participants to endure, there is growth and development. When stress goes beyond the sum total of supports, especially from the therapist, the interactions and relationships take on a more disruptive, primitive, or disorganized character, often referred to as transference psychosis.[30]

Psychotic manifestations attach themselves to transference, and it is difficult to discover the coherent transference meaning, since the patient has regressed to an ego state with severe impairment in capacity to differentiate among, or to integrate, his experiences. Four varieties of transference psychosis[30] are described:

1. The therapist feels unrelated to the patient.
2. Clear-cut relatedness has been established, but is deeply ambivalent.
3. Within the context of the transference, the patient's psychosis represents an effort to complement the therapist's personality, or to help the therapist-parent become established as a separate and whole person.
4. The patient tries to perpetuate the symbiotic state with the therapist-parent and, alternately, tries to become a separate individual.

Parameters

The homologous quality of therapy process and the patient's relative inability to use free association* reveal that it is a matter of not only studying a patient's postponements and repressions alone, inadequate as

---

* Although in the period of compensation, we seldom are able to use free association as a tool of investigation, because of the patient's inability to comply (even in the periods of study of the psychosis-vulnerable ego, free association compliance is limited), we owe much to the tools of psychoanalytic research. For they make a specific contribution to society in its problem of dealing with the schizophrenic patient, not so much in direct application to the patient but to the investigator.[27] From every supervisor's experience (as he witnesses the therapist-investigator's increasing awareness of the misleading factors that accompany the processes of reading himself into the affective experience of another and consciously reading psychological qualities that exist therein), a progression can be charted, as consciousness of correctives enlarges from intellectual sympathy to emotional identification to empathic insight and, finally, to fruition in empathic understanding in therapeutic behalf of the patient, thus enabling appreciation of changing affect values as the participant-observer becomes able to make use of his own similar affective processes, shifting valuations and reduplicative memory experiences from his own psychological past, the latter revived by careful comparison with the experience under observation. Thus our psychoanalytic concepts, their associated mechanisms, and memory valuations are made as much as possible an exact duplicate of the patient's psychological state and of the processes we are seeking to understand.

they are, but making repeated efforts to create the capacity to postpone and repress. The reality problem with these patients always takes precedence over inner problems, as unawareness of them is manifested in a tendency towards temporary regressions. While giving needed sustenance, support, and security, the therapist, as long as the study of the patient's flight is in process, at the same time—gingerly, cautiously, always persistently, in tolerable amounts—deprives and denies complete satisfaction in their relationship, always for the purpose of enabling the patient to stay with it, to look, listen, to circulate his experience and put it in perspective. The effective use of the real and the transferred aspect in the relationship enables the patient to retroject the projected image and to reality-test it in the context and on the basis of analyzing and keeping clear the image of the therapist and differentiating himself from the therapist. Searles[31] feels that anxiety concerning change serves as a motive for resistance in schizophrenic patients. He warns that in prolonged and intensive treatment of schizophrenics, a sort of symbiotic relationship may develop between patient and therapist, that the therapist may unwittingly reinforce the fear of change, or experience it himself and contribute to retarding progress. He stresses that the therapist should respond casually to improvement: not urge the patient to change, instead help him to become aware of changes gradually. Finally, the therapist should acknowledge and reveal to the patient certain of the changes that occur in himself over the years that the treatment usually requires.

Searles suggests that, in addition to the active and intense intervention advocated by such authorities as Arieti and Jackson in the therapy of schizophrenics, there is a place also for the neutral response, for the therapist's being impassive or indifferent. He believes that the neutral response is essential to the resolution of the patient's basic ambivalence concerning his individuation, i.e., whether to cling to the autistic and symbiotic or move towards individuality and object relatedness. Freedom to choose impels the inner necessity to choose, and it behooves the therapist to provide the freedom. Furthermore, a neutral participation permits a neutral symbiotic relatedness in the transference, which, the author states, is the core phase in the therapy of schizophrenia.[31]

To summarize, eternal vigilance is required vis-a-vis the patient's tendency to return to negative therapeutic relationships, which characterizes the course of his study of himself as a psychosis-vulnerable person. Awareness is necessary of the manifestations of the therapist's contributions to the patient's overall ego. The patient first identifies with the therapist as an aggressor, in order to pursue conformity; i.e., he tries to achieve conformity by becoming a thinking organism, rather than acting in accord, or in contrast with his overdeveloped capacity to be a fleeing organism, thus making part of himself the therapist's capacity to stop, look, listen, and stop running.

In a negative therapeutic relationship, to which the patient constantly tends to return, the therapist repeatedly is experienced as an object anxiety experience. His significant usefulness to the patient depends on his capacity to be constantly different from the patient's past objects of anxiety, in that he neither punishes nor seduces, but is an emotional resource to be tested and retested until a basic security of affection comes through experientially. Hoedmaker[15] feels that the purpose of the close relationship of therapist with patient is to allow the patient to form a clear and consistent image of another person with whom to identify. This image, formed within the patient, is necessary for consistently effective ego functioning and success in the struggle against overwhelming instinctual impressions. The aggressive response that the patient is "hungry for" is a response of normal or appropriate aggressiveness, that is, to be shown how someone else meets as many divergent situations as possible.

Spotnitz[36] stresses that the self-hatred that has choked the ego must be unmasked and transformed into object hatred, and steadily siphoned off without endangering the patient's ego or his objects. Resistance is analyzed to mold the transference object in his own image, i.e., a person like himself, whom eventually he can love and hate. The first objective is to guide a narcissistic transference. On the surface, it may appear all positive, but below this is the opposite and the formulation: *I hate you as I hate myself.* When the hatred explodes, the author notes, it requires fortitude and a desire to cure the patient in order to tolerate the insults and threats. The discharge of this hatred enables him to accept his early love objects: teach him to feel like killing you, to tell you about it, and *not* to do it.

Theory & Therapy: Results & Issues

My own and others' analyses of schizophrenic patients open areas of theoretical consideration that become important issues, in terms not only of treatment strategy but of measurement of success and/or failure on the basis of the areas of personality difficulty that the patient has had opportunity to work out. Unfortunately, case studies present different emphases that preclude statistification. One report of analyses of schizophrenic patients[26] revealed that the paranoid ideas arise from aggressive impulses and form mirror images of the sadistic fantasies, adding dimension to the theory that paranoia results from the repression of homosexual wishes. The more severe phenomena of schizophrenia were found related to the greater intensity of paranoid anxiety,[26] the patient's omnipotent narcissism,[21] intolerable depressive anxieties[21, 31] warded off by narcissistic patterns of behavior, self-hatred,[25] infantile interdependency needs of symbiotic quality,[29] which tend to hypercathexis of perceptive truth often directly related to countertransference reactions. These latter enable the patient to distort the physician's predominating motives, such as an impatience, in order to emphasize his negative motives. This maneuver is part and parcel of the defensive organization. The emotional reality that the schizophrenic hates is the symbiotic reality that he can give up only when he no longer needs it. Attempts to remove it too soon too fast must be resisted by the therapist, who must focus primarily on the patient's anxiety and interpret the positive and negative transference.[22]

The therapeutic prospect seems to depend on the extent to which one can make the affects conscious and thus correct the falsification of reality. (In paranoia, the persecuting introject is displaced into the outer world, and transitions from paranoid mechanisms to those of melancholia and mania are observed.)

The omnipotent narcissism[21, 31] of the patient must be laid bare and integrated into the more normally concerned part of the patient. This is what is most difficult to bear. Facing it involves overcoming intolerable depressive anxieties whose source, in large part, is denial of envy of the analyst's capacity to give sustenance. This may, on the surface, present a very positive picture, because everything unpleasant may be discharged. These patients seem to feel that they contain all goodness, and have highly idealized self-images that they tenaciously hold. This position, of course, becomes a resistance of awareness to dependent feelings and anxiety.

The main goal of therapy[5, 6, 24] is not so much symptoms relief (that is, symptomatic relief or behavioral adjustment) as inducing the patient to form new structure. The ego defects are laid bare; artificial emotions are exposed. As the patient is able to tolerate and recognize them, he is encouraged to expose himself to those dreaded situations that provide the opportunity to check his fearful assumptions about the world. This process, with the help of analysis, will hopefully lead to the belated formation of a structure. The improvised falsified world affords a new identity to the patient: the point of recovery occurs when he realizes the falsity of the idea, has an opportunity for a major internal revision, and loses the feeling of being an automaton without a personality of his own.

Insight is very difficult to achieve, because the mutual acquiescence of the ego and superego in maintaining the reality of the psychotic ideas and experiences is a severe obstacle. Resolution of conflicts,[20] caused by unacceptable *id* impulses, adds strength to the elements in a patient's ego.

Summary

The clinical approach to long-term therapy of schizophrenia has a long heritage of experimental failures, which taught us to make claims cautiously, to continue to study and, most important of all, to realize that we are only helpers to the patient's continual efforts for optimum adaptations. Our skills and experiences in personal diagnostic processes, as well as our skills in helping a patient to maintain optimum ego functioning and remain in a compensated state, have grown greatly. The analysis of the psychosis-vulnerable ego, and the insurance of its maturation, are our greatest challenge still.

REFERENCES

1. Aichhorn, A.: An obituary, Int J Psychoanal *32*:51–56, by Anna Freud.

2. Bockoven, J. S.: Moral treatment in American psychiatry, J Nerv Ment Dis *124*:(#2) 167–194, 292–320 (Aug-Sep), 1956.

3. Bychowski, G.: On the handling of some schizophrenic defense mechanisms and reaction patterns, Int J Psychoanal *35*:147–153, 1954.

4. Cameron, M.: Introjection, retrojection, and hallucinations in the interaction between schizophrenic patient and therapist, Int J Psychoanal *42*:86–96 (Jan–Apr), 1961.

5. Eissler, K. R.: Remarks on the psychoanalysis of schizophrenia, Int J Psychoanal *32*:39, 1951.

6. ———: Notes upon defects of ego structure in schizophrenia, Int J Psychoanal *35*:(part 2) 141–146, 1954.

7. Freud, Anna: *The Ego and the Mechanisms of Defense*, New York, Internat Univ Press, 1948.

8. Freud, S.: *The Defense Neuropsychoses*, 1894. Translated in collected papers, vol. 1, London Institute of Psychoanalysis, Hogarth Press, p. 59.

9. ———: Further remarks on *The Defense Neuropsychoses*, 1896. Collected papers, vol. 1, p. 155.

10. ———: Psychoanalytic notes upon an autobiographical account of a case of paranoia. Translated in collected papers, vol. 3, London, Hogarth Press.

11. ———: *The Ego and the Id*, translated by Joan Riviere, London, Hogarth Press, 1927.

12. ———: *Introductory Lectures to Psychoanalysis*, translated by Joan Riviere, vol. 7, New York, 1914, p. 348.

13. Gitelson, M.: Psychoanalysis and dynamic psychiatry, Arch Neur Psychiat *66*: 280–288 (Sep) 1951.

14. Hendrick, I.: Ego development and certain character problems, Psychoanal Quart *5*:320 (Jul), 1936.

15. Hoedemaker, Edward: The therapeutic process in the treatment of schizophrenia, J Amer Psychoanal Ass *3*:89–109, 1955.

16. Katan, M.: The importance of the nonpsychiatric part of the personality in schizophrenia, Int J Psychoanal *35*:119–128, 1954.

17. Mann, J., and Semrad, E. V.: Conversion as process and conversion as symptom in psychosis, *in* Deutsch, Felix, ed.: *On the Mysterious Leap from the Mind to the Body*, New York, Internat Univ Press, 1959, pp. 11–26.

18. Meyer, Adolph: A Dynamic Interpretation of Dementia Praecox, Clark Univ Monographs, Twentieth Anniversary Series, 1910, pp. 1–9.

19. Pious, W. L.: The hypothesis about the nature of schizophrenic behavior, *in Psychotherapy of the Psychoses*, chap. 2, New York, Basic, 1961.

20. Rosen, J.: *Direct Analysis*, New York, Grune, 1953.

21. Rosenfeld, Herbert A.: On the psychopathology of narcissism—a clinical approach, Int J Psychoanal *45*:(parts 2, 3) 332–337 (Apr to Jul), 1964.

22. ———: Object relations of the acute schizophrenia patient in the therapeutic situation, *in* Solomon, Philip, MD, and Glueck, Bernard, Jr., MD, eds.: *Recent Research in Schizophrenia*, Psychiat Research Report #19, Amer Psychiat Ass.

23. Rycroft, Charles: The analysis of a paranoid personality, Int J Psychoanal *41*: (part 1) 59–69 (Jan-Feb), 1960.

24. ———: An observation on the defensive function of schizophrenic thinking and delusion formation, Int J Psychoanal *43*:(part 1) 32–39, 1962.

25. Sarvis, Mary A.: Paranoid reactions, perceptual distortion as an etiological agent, Arch Gen'l Psychiat *6*:157–162, 1962.

26. Schmiedelberg, M. A.: Contribution to the psychology of persecutory ideas and delusions, Int J Psychoanal *12*:331–367, 1931.

27. Schroeder, T.: Psychoanalytic method of observation, Int J Psychoanal *6*:155–170, 1925.

28. Searles, H. F.: Anxiety concerning change as seen in the psychotherapy of schizophrenia patients with particular reference to the sense of personal identity, Int J Psychoanal *2*:74–85, 1961.

29. ———: The place of neutral therapist—responses in psychotherapy with a schizophrenic patient, Int J Psychoanal *44*:(part 1) 42–55, 1963.

30. ———: Transference psychoses in the psychotherapy of chronic schizophrenia, Int J Psychoanal *44*:(part 3) 249–281, 1963.

31. Segal, Hannah: Depression in the schizophrenic, Int J Psychoanal *37*:339–343, (Jul–Oct), 1956.
32. Semrad, E. V.: Experiences in Treatment of Schizophrenic Patients, read before the Mass Mem'l Hosp, Boston Univ Group, Mar 7, 1962, in process of publication.
33. ———: Discussion of Dr. Herbert Rosenfeld's paper, (see ref. 22).
34. ———: The treatment process, Amer J Psychiat *3*:426–427, 1954.
35. Semrad, E. V., and Day, M.: Techniques and procedures used in the treatment and activity program for psychiatric patients, *in Changing Concepts and Procedures in Psychiatric Occupational Therapy*, Amer Occupational Ther Ass, Dubuque (Iowa), Brown, 1959.
36. Spotnitz, H.: The narcissistic defense in schizophrenia, Psychoanal Rev *48*: (#4) 24–43, 1961–62.
37. Sullivan, H. S.: Conceptions of modern psychiatry, the first William Allenson White Memorial Lecture, Psychiatry *3*:1–117, 1940.
38. Waelder, Robert: The principle of multiple function, Psychoanal Quart 5:45, 1936.
39. Whitehorn, J. C.: Guide to interviewing and clinical personality study, Arch Neur Psychiat *52*:197–216 (Sep), 1944.
40. Whitehorn, John: Mental disorders, the psychoses, *in Cecil's Textbook of Medicine*, ed. 6, Philadelphia, Saunders, 1943, pp. 1513–1527.
41. Winnicott, D. W.: Transitional objects and transitional phenomena, Int J Psychoanal *34*:89–97, 1953.

EDWARD H. KNIGHT, MD, MODERATOR
Touro, LSU

14

Panel: Schizophrenia

PANELISTS: DOCTORS BRUCH, DONNELLY, FINCH, GIBSON, SEMRAD, SHAGASS

DR. KNIGHT

TODAY WE HAVE HEARD A COMPREHENSIVE COVERAGE OF MOST OF THE MAJOR *views and attitudes regarding this condition we call schizophrenia. Everyone seems to agree to the value of a total organismic approach. [The schizophrenic illness is viewed as multidimensional with interlocking physiologic, psychological and sociological perspectives. It always seems to stay a few steps ahead of us, and we keep pursuing.] To get still another chance to catch up, we'll have the members of the panel speak briefly and, perhaps preferably, react and respond to one another. Dr. Gibson?*

DR. GIBSON: I was glad to have Dr. Donnelly speak of the importance of a therapist's belief that there is a psychogenic cause of schizophrenia and of his having some theoretical approach to it, because, in effect, I presented the conceptual model I use. This matter puts us in a strange position. As therapist, we must have a conviction about our ideas; yet as scientist, we must acknowledge the weaknesses in our system. I do not know how to avoid this.

The central point of my thoughts was a need-fear dilemma; Dr. Semrad spoke of something similar. My ideas come from my direct observation. The patient struggles to handle the dilemma by trying either to cling to an object when his need is dominant or to avoid an object when his fear is dominant. I feel fairly secure about this part of my conceptual model, because it is something that goes on between the patient and me. Of the origin of the dilemma, I feel less certain. I did suggest that it can come about through a disturbance in integration and differentiation, and that this disturbance leaves the schizophrenic with a defect that could be characterized as a vulnerability to disorganization, a relative lack of autonomy and poor reality testing. Before we can prove any concept of that sort, we would have to do a great deal of work with children. I would be interested in hearing Dr. Finch's reaction on that point—whether he feels that any of the work that he does, particularly with young children, seems to substantiate my concept of a dilemma. I would like, if there is an opportunity, for Dr. Donnelly to comment further on the desirability of dealing with hostility in the patient. We may be in disagreement. I suggested that I do not focus on hostility a great deal, the hostility that the patient may experience toward me. I do not confront the patient with his hostility very vigorously because I feel that this might break off a relationship that is crucial. I would be interested in knowing whether Dr. Donnelly would agree or disagree. Another question occurred to me:

Dr. Shagass spoke about drugs. I certainly feel that drugs have a place in helping establish a relationship, and I use them, even though I did not with the particular patient presented. My question is: Can the use of tranquilizing drugs sometimes interfere with ego growth? For example, if you resolve a conflict by lessening hostile feelings, does this take away the motive force, so to speak, for the ego structure to develop to handle such feelings?

DR. KNIGHT: *Thank you, Dr. Gibson. I think we ought to adhere to our order of presentation, so Dr. Finch?*

DR. FINCH: I would agree that of all the places in the human life span where one might find even more obvious proof of this need-fear situation, children are an excellent place. I won't elaborate on that at the moment. Two or three points I wanted to make.

The first is to stress that in our work, at least, the infantile autistic child, the symbiotic child and the borderline child are all parts of a continuum. One reason we've come to believe this is that they go up or down like musical scales and you can, with treatment, move one of them up the scale. If something goes wrong, one of them can go down the scale. I think, although some workers have felt early infantile autism is a totally different syndrome from all the rest, that we have come to look on it as part of a continuum.

Another point that I think worthy of mention concerns treatment. We often assume that if we can recognize and adequately diagnose the child very early, perhaps during the second year of life, we ought to have a much better chance with treatment. We have found that even when we do, we are faced with how to change the parents rapidly enough to reverse the child's illness. If one puts the mother into classical therapy and this is effective within the next two or three years, the child has meantime become worse. We have one child now that we have managed to take out of a home after watching her become increasingly autistic from 15 months to 30 months. We put her in a foster home. The parents (the natural parents) had so many children that they were overburdened, had little left for our patient, and agreed to placement.

This child is beginning to respond primarily because we got her early. Now the big problem isn't the child but the mother, who has begun to feel guilty about giving her up, and we can't keep her out of the picture in a way that will enable us to proceed effectively. So early recognition in and of itself, while good, doesn't necessarily solve the problem.

One thing about which I would have to disagree mildly with Dr. Leon Eisenberg, who has written, as you know, a great deal about this subject, is that speech in the early psychotic child is evidence of a better prognosis than lack of speech. Now, the sickest child that you saw in the film, Linda, when she was admitted wouldn't eat, was untrained, mute, about as lacking in ego as possible. Yet she has done the best job of all these children. Debbie, who came in as rather an appealing little television commercial repeater, looked as if she had all the qualities to move right up the ladder, but has remained much less improved than Linda.

One other point that I would mention. That is, when we first started to work on the residential side of these children, we'd been taught that you shouldn't expose them to students. This would ruin everything. We are a large teaching institution—student nurses and medical students, student OT's, student social workers and others. We soon had to give up, to go ahead and let the students see the patients and interact with them. It doesn't bother the children as long as there is one central therapeutic figure who will remain. If you change the primary therapist everytime students rotate, then you have trouble; but these children do remarkably well being exposed to a new group of students of various disciplines if they keep their therapist.

The final point that I would make has to do with countertransference of professional personnel. If you overload a ward with these children, you begin to have massive ward countertransference and loss of interest toward and irritation with the children. The ward personnel begin to beg to have some children with a little more ego so they can find some more rewards in their day to day work. Therefore, I think it is a mistake to have a whole ward of these youngsters. There is the added usefulness of mixing degrees of illness for benefit to the children themselves. One other useful activity is regular team meetings of the ward personnel every week wherein they can air their feelings and their ability to work with these children. The unfortunate countertransference problems are markedly improved when such meetings are held.

DR. KNIGHT: *Thank you, Dr. Finch. Dr. Bruch, I noticed that there was no particular decline in the business of the Rib Room or the Esplanade today in spite of your paper on obesity.*

DR. BRUCH: By and large, I have recognized several themes going through all of the papers. The one easiest to recognize is the concern with what is organic and what is psychological. We cannot deny one or the other. As Dr. Donnelly and Dr. Gibson have emphasized, if one wants to be therapeutically effective, one needs to have the conviction of a developmental concept of this disorder. I seem to be less troubled by the seeming contradiction between an organic and psychological approach.

I have spent a large part of my professional life dealing with patients who are obviously somatically disturbed, and I have become more and more convinced that there is an experiential background. I feel more secure in stating this since some work has been done that presents experimental evidence that something as grossly abnormal as a metabolic disturbance, which is a prerequisite for perpetuating obesity, can be created by exposing young animals to abnormal feeding experiences. This work was done by Parson and his co-workers in Charlottesville, Virginia. They took litters of rats. One group had the normal life of laboratory rats, namely, they were kept in cages with free access to food. The experimental littermates were put into cages with access to food restricted to two hours out of 24. What happened to these restricted rats is that they grew fat. They learned to grab food and to take it so fast that they ate more than the unrestricted rats. The organism learned to process this extra food through increased lipogenesis. Now all the old questions—what is heredity? what is metabolic? what is purely psychogenic?—are superseded by this type of experiment.

I feel that all this is applicable to human obesity, that all obese patients suffer from some kind of metabolic disorder. We can look on this now as the outcome of abnormal early experiences and the establishment of abnormal patterns. The cycle can be interrupted mechanically and metabolically. More important appear to be efforts to retrain the organism through more appropriate experiences.

The important question is whether this can be done. From animal observations, we have learned about critical periods of learning. Once a function has missed being learned, it is sometimes exceedingly difficult, or even impossible, to establish it at all. It seems that these critical periods in humans are not as limited, and that a certain capacity for development persists. If we have an active and optimistic outlook about the chance of being therapeutically helpful, of making people capable of learning later in life, after they have reached the status of being patients, then we must rely on a certain flexibility of the learning capacity. In areas in which this does not persist, or in which there is no rudiment of functioning, no change can be expected. It is a common experience, something to which many have referred, that even a well treated schizophrenic retains a certain liability, a schizophrenic core or something. This seems to refer to those areas in which no early experiences have been made, with severe failure or deficiency in learning appropriate responses, so that there is no awareness, even rudimentary, of some functioning capacity. . . . I think that what I just said was too complicated. I hope, however, that somebody will ask about this so that I may clarify it later.

DR. KNIGHT: *Thank you, Dr. Bruch. Dr. Shagass, would you continue?*

DR. SHAGASS: I think that we have a persistent confusion between etiological concepts and what happens when we intervene therapeutically. Now, there is no necessary paradox between a therapist's being confident that what he wants to do to help a patient is going to help that patient and, at the same time, his being able to admit that he doesn't know the cause of the condition that he is attempting to help. We do a lot of things in medicine to help people suffering from disorders whose cause we don't know. It is not necessary to believe that a particular experience that one is attempting to bring out in a psychotherapeutic exchange was the cause of later behavioral disturbance. It is part of the process, whatever it is.

The position of drugs is similar, and I have found myself in the position of presenting a paper showing how drugs have not made any specific difference with respect to the natural history of schizophrenia, except that they allow rapid, easy intervention and the effects are much more predictable. Dr. Donnelly talked about the varieties of therapists and how some do well and some don't do well; there is less variation with drugs. In fact, what Dr. Donnelly didn't mention was that in the studies of Whitehorn and Betz, the "bad" therapists did just as well as the "good" ones when insulin coma was added to the armamentarium. The point here is that there are many things going on that we can't specify but, if we avoid doing things that hurt the patient, the patient seems to have something within him to help him get better, a "normalizing" factor on which all therapy may depend, providing we learn how to use it properly.

Dr. Gibson asked about whether the drugs interfere with ego growth. I don't know that I can answer that specifically. We do know that, in the work of Dr. Else Kris, the patients on drug therapy who had been ill for some time in hospitals were able to go out in the community, to go back to school, to reenter their marriage relationships. A number of her patients have given birth to babies who are in good shape and growing normally. Behind Dr. Gibson's question I discern the basic idea, which comes mainly from study of the psychoneuroses, that you have to make a patient anxious in order to have him cooperate in psychotherapy, and I don't know whether this applies to schizophrenia. I wanted to ask Dr. Gibson whether, in describing the ego defect in schizophrenia, he is saying that this is the proper way to look at schizophrenia. I favor this view. It seems to me that, in schizophrenia, we are dealing with an ego defect state just as one may regard sociopathic antisocial reactions as superego defect states. And I wonder whether an entirely new way of formulating the situation isn't called for here.

DR. KNIGHT: *Thank you. Dr. Donnelly?*

DR. DONNELLY: Of the interesting points raised, let me comment first on the question of the conceptual model with which one operates. In many if not most situations in life, individuals operate with all sorts of models without being sure with absolute certainty that the theoretical model is correct. Most observations, and inferences from them, are based on the assumption, conscious or unconscious, of the structure of such models; equally accepted is the understanding that, given new, sound information, the structure of the model may be modified. The whole of our social structure is so formed historically.

As Dr. Shagass mentions, there is no antithesis in the therapist's belief that his plan of treatment will help the patient and his recognition that he does not know the exact etiology of the patient's disorder. In other areas of medicine, this situation has always been accepted: omniscience has never been prerequisite to therapy. A research attitude during therapy has played a significant role in most discoveries in the etiology of disease.

Therefore, I believe that a psychotherapist should possess two qualities or capacities. The first is the ability to develop a working conceptual model of normal personality structure with recognition of the dynamic interactions within the personality and, in addition, with the individuals with whom the patient interacts. The model must be capable of modification, as the forces, in quality and in degree, vary with a given individual or from person to person. It must account in broad outline for the origin of symptoms and their interrelationships, for the forces that deviate from the normal, and for the counterforces that may be mobilized to modify in the direction of normality those pathologic forces. Success in the latter operation is an important aim of therapy and, of course, reduces or resolves the symptoms. With such a theoretical model, the therapist enters the therapeutic relation and tries to build a picture of the dynamic structure of the patient. The better the conceptual model the easier it is to construct quickly the model for the particular patient. Inherent in this whole approach is confidence that he has the capacity to assist the patient. Moreover, the prototypic conceptual model will reflect the specific orientation of the therapist—and his degree of sophistication. Thus, the purely organically oriented therapist will utilize a largely organic framework, while the psychologically oriented therapist will use a dynamic model reflecting his particular training or the degree of divergence from it.

My personal opinion is that all therapists operate with their own conceptual model. Some, however, do not realize that they do so, while others are unchangeably committed to a model as though it were based on absolute truth.

The second quality of the therapist is the capacity to recognize that, no matter how explanatory his conceptual model may be, nevertheless the complexity of the human organism is such that the ultimate model must take into account normal and abnormal physiology as well as normal and abnormal psychology and that, with respect to each individual patient, the model must be capable of modifications logically consistent with the structure of the model. This, therefore, calls for a research attitude. Outside the therapeutic relationship he should also have an investigatory approach. In his thinking about the individual patient, he presumably would be capable of bringing into consideration many kinds of information, data, theories, which would be inappropriate in the context of the therapeutic hour. In other words, one should not bring into the therapeutic relationship all the doubts, questions, and agreements or disagreements with others who postulate their individual findings and theories regarding etiology and pathology of the condition.

This is particularly relevant in the treatment of the schizophrenic, whose ego-boundaries are ill-defined and who is searching for his own identity. Often the intellectual processes of the schizophrenic patient have developed in a particular direction as the result of pathologic relationships from early childhood onward. That the therapist has *his* ego-boundaries is important because, in the therapeutic contact, the ego-boundaries of the therapist become the corresponding limits of the patient. Treatment objectives include that of having the patient recognize these boundaries as a prologue to further maturation. This attitude enables one to accept the patient as an individual in his own right even if ego-boundaries do not exist for him.

But this lack of ego-boundaries is included in the conceptual model of the personality of the patient and, utilizing the model, the therapist hypothesizes that certain emotional experiences, present and past, are at the root of the illness. Of these, anger, rage, helplessness, and guilt are present to a pathologic degree. Few will question that anger is a major problem to the schizophrenic patient. It is perhaps the major factor leading to his characteristic withdrawal.

Dr. Gibson asks whether I would comment on the need to discuss the patient's hostility with him. First, I want to stress that I avoid the use of the word "hostility" not only in teaching residents and in case discussions with psychiatrists, but also especially with patients. I do not like psychiatric jargon. I believe its use frequently implies either lack of clear meaning or lack of precise thinking. Quite frankly, I get very confused when listening to some psychiatrists and psychologists because the same word has so many different meanings, each depending on the person using it. I do not use the word "hostility" just as Dr. Bruch doesn't use the word "oral." I know what anger is and I believe everyone else knows what anger is. If there is evidence of anger towards a person, then I have no hesitation to talk about it. If the person exhibits anger towards me, this necessitates at that moment a decision what to do. If the patient is beginning to get angry about something or someone (this happens at different stages of therapy), I endeavor to correlate the situation with the conceptual model. This frequently enables me to understand what is going on in the interview and to place it in the historical context of the patient. I then have no hesitation in gently pointing out to the patient his anger, the apparent, immediate cause, and the desirability that he examine the situation to discover if there is something he might learn about his pattern of so reacting. The arousal of anger has important connotations and, if important, why avoid them? To avoid the presence of anger or to avoid its recognition by the patient is not helpful because when one person gets angry with another, especially on an irrational basis, all sorts of feelings may arise, guilt, anxiety, and so on. To allow these delayed reactions to complicate the therapeutic relationship is not desirable.

Dr. Shagass mentioned that, in the series of studies by Betz and Whitehorn, patients did equally well on insulin therapy whether treated by D&O or by P&A therapists. This permits different kinds of interpretations, some biologic, some psychological. For example, all received the same biologic intervention. But in insulin treatment there are also concomitant psychological experiences, and some theorists hold that these are of primary significance. As far as a conceptual model of schizophrenia is concerned, psychiatrists who may deny the occurrence of biologic changes, either of a genetic, etiologic or symptomatic nature, simply are unsophisticated in their knowledge about the disorder. The principle of multideterminaton is well documented in psychopathology. The problem involves how much and at what stage.

DR. KNIGHT: *Thank you, Dr. Donnelly. Dr. Semrad?*

DR. SEMRAD: Apropos the question of etiology, the answer is very simple: we do not know. This presents areas of work in which different disciplines with different tools and skills can pursue clues developed through their own experiences and bring them to bear on the overall problem. At the Massachusetts Mental Health Center, our many laboratories devote themselves to pursuits in biochemistry, neurophysiology, pharmacology, psychopharmacology, electroencephalography, polygraph, tissue culture, sociophysiology, psychology, community psychiatry, as well as in the fundamental clinical areas.

My own studies have progressed from one of the more impersonal processes to others of psychotherapy and psychotherapeutic processes. A study done in the early forties, gross as it was, still leaves me puzzled as to its possible significance, especially in its therapy implications. Chronic schizophrenic patients who "did not get well enough" to return to a community adjustment were studied by pneumoencephalograms (PEG) and electroencephalograms (EEG): 42% had both abnormal PEG's and borderline or abnormal EEG's, and 20% showed normal PEG's and normal EEG's. There was no consistent relationship between the character of the EEG tracings and the findings from the PEG.

Since return from military service in World War II, as a teacher and clinician focused on dysfunction of integrated personal functioning and the resultant difficulties therefrom, I nevertheless aid and encourage those of my residents desirous of becoming skilled in other areas to help us with our continuing puzzlements.

Formulation of knowing and understanding the patient as a person in terms of the views of his experience, and helping residents do the same, can be an all-consuming assignment. My experience leads me to believe that psychodynamic psychiatry can be learned and taught effectively only in the ongoing clinical situation. The young psychiatrist needs the experience of individual validation as he faces the difficult task of trying to understand and utilize psychodynamic concepts in the realistic, commonsense context of his previous life and training. He needs a basic frame of reference, namely, the patient, in order that formulation and communication of psychodynamic concepts be possible for operational validation in this area of his professional work. Psychodynamic psychiatry, essentially an American development, is concerned with the whole man, the person as a person, in his genetic, somatic, behavioral, interpersonal and social aspects, as seen from the viewpoint of psychoanalysis. This brings into focus an overall area for residency teaching, broadly stated as the individual's total make-up and probable reactions at any given moment determined by all the forces, early and late, external and internal, past and present, that have played on him and are playing on him. Particular caution is necessary that extrapolations from the use of one tool to explain the data obtained by another tool be guarded against to avoid useless debate on issues that do not reflect the patient as the primary referent with full acknowledgment of the way, and the type, and the significance of the information obtained. The person as a psychodynamic biologic unit is an entity available for study without the necessity of postulating a leap from body to mind, or vice versa. For me, it is less a question of a leap than that of a gap, that is, in our knowledge of the conversion process, which has to be filled. It all depends on whether the right methods will be chosen for its investigation. Thus, as knowledge and understanding grow, therapeutic endeavor, as well as therapeutic processes may also change.

The patient as a person becomes the area of preoccupation—hence the subtitle of my chapter: *Formulation of the Clinical Approach.* What I try to say can really be more simply stated, that is, a patient comes to us with a life history. In his progressive development, he has achieved a certain competence, or perhaps better said, a limiting incompetence for successful adaptation to life's vicissitudes. These patients are highly skilled in getting along by avoiding contact with people, by avoiding responsibility in contact with people, and by viewing life as they would like it to be rather than as it actually is. This theme runs through the three chapters of Semrad, Gibson and Finch. Such a person gets along in life up to a point and then, instead of just being a limited person, or a special character in the community, or a denier, projector or distorter, he becomes a patient.

The first question that comes to my mind is: What happened that made the difference? Here this person was getting along such as he was, and then something happened that he could not get along any more. In essence, there are not many different things that happen to human beings. Either their somatic structure becomes impaired in functioning (I always remember the PEG and EEG studies and note with growing interest the more refined, better tooled studies like those of Sachar, Wolff and Menzer, *et al.*) or somebody dies who is very crucial in their life of ambivalent mutuality, or they succumb to the frustration of object need. The last is usually most difficult to diagnose. Often the patient is aware only of not feeling well and goes from doctor to doctor and may have a succession of diagnoses indicating lesser efficiency in functioning as a person. State hospital records attest the number of patients who have successive diagnoses of neurotic reaction, reactive depression, and finally schizophrenia. In the old days we used to ask: Did we miss the diagnosis the first time? Today we probably would say the diagnosis was correct in terms of the functioning level that the burdened patient was manifesting at the time he was seen by the physician.

Frustration of object need simply means that the person is no longer having need satisfaction that he had been used to and which was essential to his getting along. The first therapeutic task is to help the patient identify what is missing. Can he make up for it, or does he have to accept the inevitable that he is not going to get it back? In the setting of a need-satisfying relationship, the first item on the agenda of therapy is to help the person integrate this impasse in his life that necessitated his psychosis.

A therapeutic strategy must be based on a consummation of the clinical context of who is doing what to whom (person), when (time), where (place), how (style), why (purpose), and negotiate around the vital life issues. The fact that the patient regressed because he chose to or was forced to affected his relationships with the important people in his life. They feel assaulted by the patient who regresses whether they can acknowledge it or not. Relationships are disturbed and have to be mended before the patient can get back some security, regain his reputation, and again be held in a less ambivalent state of affection.

The "long haul period" is devoted to this purpose. During this period, therapists are apt to get very frustrated because the patient wants to talk about his object relationships and cannot comply with associations relevant to intrapsychic issues. It takes a long time for a patient to regain enough stability in his own milieu before the major task of helping him study himself as a psychosis-vulnerable person can be undertaken. The clinical material available is the patient's own experience that he brings to the treatment situation, as well as the experience he gains from his relationship with the therapist. It is most important not to underestimate the patient's strength and reliance on his defenses against object anxiety. He denies, projects and distorts and identifies initially on an aggressive basis. This is quite a different psychopathology from that observed in the defensive organization of the neurotic patient who presents, essentially, defenses against the instincts. Thus the patient's avoidance defenses have to be dealt with first. They not only determine the overt features of the clinical symptomatology but serve the purpose of keeping out of awareness painful impasse-creating issues, and thus preclude their solution.

May I highlight a most relevant observation stressed by Dr. Gibson and Dr. Finch of features common with those of my patients' overt behaviors and what they imply for therapeutic strategy. Dr. Finch showed us three types of patients. The first little girl showed mostly object fear. The second patient showed object clinging. The third patient showed object redefinition, thus demonstrating features of behavior that Gibson related in terms of severity of illness observed in the course of a patient's recovery. These allowed for planning and judgments of the patient's progress in therapy. The reactions I described viewed in a recovery profile are essentially the same, albeit I termed them patterns of response. I think that the deepest regression and the necessity for the patient's remaining stuck in it are essentially a clinical manifestation of object fear and necessitates denial patterns of behavior. As the ego becomes more integrated and bears the affect more successfully, the patient presents manifestations of object clinging, which I include under projection patterns. As ego integration progresses, object redefinition and distortion patterns in this service come into clinical view. As the patient's reliance on these narcissistic patterns of defense becomes less, great unhappiness in the patient, sadness, depression and/or psychotic depression present clinically. One is repeatedly impressed from the study of regression and recovery profiles how the narcissistic, namely, projection, distortion and denial patterns are in the service for avoidance of unbearable, intolerably painful depression in these patients. By helping the patient experience his depression and do the necessary work to achieve it, object redefinition ensues along with growing security in self as an entity. It is in the disorganization and reorganization of the ego that these clues to therapeutic strategy are to be sought and the many associations of them in somatic indices documented.

DR. KNIGHT: *Thank you. Are there comments from the panel?*

DR. BRUCH: Yes, I would like to ask what to me is an important question. I agree fully that in dealing with a schizophrenic, or any other patient, avoidance of psychiatric jargon is, of course, essential. Dr. Donnelly says that if a patient shows anger, he takes up the anger; I might be inclined to do the same. But what do you do when a patient does not feel anger and he is unable to identify it? This is the orientation under which I approach a schizophrenic patient. To me, the important aspect is his failure of having learned how to identify such sensations. As long as he does not recognize anger and I tell him that is what he feels, he is left with the old situation, that *somebody else* knows. I do not know whether you have observed it, but if you have, how do you feel about this gap in recognition, that he acts like angry but is unable to feel it.

DR. DONNELLY: In short-term psychotherapy, this lack of recognition by the patient of his anger is one of the more important aspects of treatment, and it is most important that the individual be helped to recognize it. But, of course, anger is only one emotion or response with which one has to deal with the schizophrenic patient. I have discussed anger mainly because Dr. Gibson asked how I deal with it. Sometimes the pathway to the recognition of anger is through the recognition of guilt feelings arising secondarily to angry feelings.

The conceptual model that I use for work with schizophrenic patients includes the hypothesis that the patient has never been able to have satisfactory communication with either parent, but especially with the mother, that the interaction of child and mother was such that the child's natural desires to do even things customary to his age were restricted, and that the patient was never able and never allowed, certainly never encouraged, to communicate his feelings, especially those of frustration and its derivatives. Even a tantrum was followed by more frustration. He gives up trying to communicate at any level because of the ensuing helplessness and hopelessness. The latter may develop at a very early age, because of this failure to communicate, and gain recognition of his natural desires to be allowed to decide some things for himself.

Some patients are apparently unmotivated, therefore, and, when admitted to hospital, are not good treatment subjects at least from a psychotherapeutic standpoint. To get the patient involved is an immediate objective. Here history taking is the key. Usually, the history initially is in terms of recent events and situations. By questions carefully directed, one can elicit information about occasions recalled by the patient in which frustration and anger would be the normal responses. By concentrating on his feelings on such occasions, one is able to judge how capable the patient is of recognizing anger in himself. By comparison with his recognition of angry feelings in others, one attempts to evaluate how he identifies anger. As history taking proceeds, one attempts to uncover his feelings on occasions when his recognized important desires were frustrated. With adolescent and adult patients who have been able to adjust sufficiently to be able to go to school and to make some, if marginal, adjustment in their environment, few if any cannot recall some experience of anger.

If one is still unable to elicit a history of recognized anger and if the patient does not exhibit such feelings, one must utilize the events within the hospital setting, sometimes manipulating the management of the patient's program, to discover his methods of coping with frustration. In my experience, patients who do not exhibit overt anger in even a mild degree tend to deal with difficulties by *marked* withdrawal, and they are not candidates for short-term psychotherapy. Interference with this pattern may be the approach, resulting in the expression of this emotion. In my opinion, some of the difficulty arises out of interpreting the presence of anger when the patient does not feel it. In these situations, it is my opinion that the recognition of the anger is repressed, not that the anger has never been experienced and cannot be identified by the patient. Sometimes, too, it is necessary to distinguish between righteous anger, not regarded by some schizophrenics as anger, and unjustified anger. This distinction, I believe, is related to the very strong and punitive superego of the schizophrenic.

Interpretations based on all sorts of theories are not at all helpful with such patients. Interpretations are most effective when made in the context of the present or recent past without emphasis on psychological development in infancy and childhood. Schizophrenics can think and reason on a step-by-step basis as long as the definitions are agreed on. The concreteness of thinking, supposedly typical of schizophrenia, is a peculiar phenomenon much more complicated than recognized. Many schizophrenics are able to discuss philosophy, that is, classical philosophy, say of Spinoza or Hegel, giving good theoretic and accurate accounts. It is not that they are incapable of abstract thought; they often are and can use it defensively. But for the schizophrenic, the particular abstraction is as specific and concrete a thought as the words *stone*, *moss*, or *gathering*. He then talks about the abstract concept as though it were a single precise entity. This is not unlike the way lawyers talk about legal concepts.

DR. BRUCH: If I understand you correctly, what you do with a schizophrenic patient is to help him first to identify the sensation in the experience of anger.

DR. DONNELLY: I regard each schizophrenic patient as having a problem that is a challenge to me. Can this patient be helped as a result of the relationship with me—the therapeutic relationship? I know that it is impossible to do anything for the patient if he is not really going to get involved, so the next important objective is to put the decision back on the patient. Does he or does he not want to get well? Does he want help or is he prepared, if he is a hospital patient, for perhaps permanent hospitalization? This I regard as a key to short-term psychotherapy. One must constantly get back to what the patient wants, and one has to make him face up to some of the emotions that, as Dr. Semrad and others have mentioned, he is trying to avoid. If the therapist cannot break through the barrier of denial and avoidance, it is difficult for the patient to confront what he is attempting to avoid. Anger is often a central problem, but the patient may also have experiences of fear, guilt, helplessness, and such, which are major difficulties and which may have to be dealt with before the problem of anger. If the patient does not exhibit angry feelings, dealing with his problem of underlying anger may have to be deferred until later. If he does show anger, I utilize the occasion immediately.

DR. BRUCH: That was the essence of my question. Is he avoiding it, or has he never learned how to identify it. I must admit that I was a coward this morning. I used Lidz's definition instead of giving my own. I feel, like him, that the schizophrenic suffers from a deficiency in not having had the necessary experiences. How much is it the essential aspect in the interaction between physician and patient that, in contrast to the past environment, we are a predictable agent, someone who can help him in identifying things about which he has remained confused in the past. That is why I entered into this discussion on hostility and anger. Even if we are simple and direct in grasping a situation, we first must help a patient with a new learning experience. The problem is not that he avoids admitting his anger, but that he has never been able to be discriminatingly aware of the fact that this unpleasant feeling *is* anger and not something else. Whatever the sensation may be, he seems to be covering it up. By our saying "avoiding," we express it as if he were doing something he should not be doing. Actually, we are dealing with a deficit in his development, of never having had the experience of how to identify feelings.

DR. DONNELLY: In short-term psychotherapy, I work on the hypothesis of the principle of homeostasis, that an individual in similar circumstances will react in a certain way, physiologically, psychologically, emotionally. I presume and believe that anger is one of the experiences common to all human beings. I presume that in the past the patient will have experienced what we, or should I say I, call anger or angry feelings. He may not recognize them as such at the moment they occur.

DR. BRUCH: There I disagree with you. My concept of the schizophrenic is that though he may have had all kind of experiences similar to those of other human beings, he has not had consistent help from the adult environment in organizing them, in symbolizing them as something reproducible, and thus becoming able to recognize anger, for example. This morning, I used the example that we all have nutritional needs, but to be able to identify them as hunger, and to differentiate them from fatigue or anger, appears to be something that these patients have not learned. I try to stay away from the secondary misinterpretations, and try to focus on this cognitive aspect in human experience and development. Thus, we come to a dynamic understanding of the thinking disorder in schizophrenia.

DR. GIBSON: I brought up the issue of hostility in the schizophrenic. I certainly would not suggest that a patient's anger be avoided or ignored. It never helps to avoid an area of the patient's feelings, no matter what they are. What I am suggesting is that we seldom need to confront the schizophrenic with his feelings of anger. I find that most schizophrenic patients are all too aware of these feelings, that what they need is some assistance in controlling them. I often find it helpful to go beyond the feelings of anger to the feelings of helplessness. It follows from what I said about the schizophrenic's need-fear dilemma in his object relations that he is almost always struggling with a sense of helplessness and futility about his relationships with people. I struggle to let the patient know somehow that I can withstand his anger, and have an awareness of the dilemma that confronts him as he and I try to achieve and maintain a therapeutic relationship.

DR. KNIGHT: *Perhaps we should comment on some of the other panelists' opinions about this topic. Dr. Gibson has referred to a basic ego defect. It seems to me that the fundamental issue is whether we are dealing with an innate or acquired ego defect or with a "conflict." Perhaps underlying some of our discussion is the idea that there is a psychological conflict that leads to pathologic reactions. With this concept, the traditional method of dealing with defenses, resolving conflict and opening the way to growth is employed. Whereas if one conceives of an innate ego defect, then things are completely different. There is a defect in basic learning experiences that precludes or distorts ego formation so that conflict in the traditional intrapsychic or interpersonal sense cannot occur.*

DR. BRUCH: That is the point which I have tried to make this morning. It seems to me that we all have been fascinated with pursuing these conflicts, defense mechanisms, and symbolic meanings. They all are on one level of functioning. In my efforts with a rather special group of patients, very sick patients, I have been sometimes successful by taking a step away from conflict and symbolic problems, and by focusing on the mental tools that they have for handling life situations. I avoid the word "defect," because it has too much the implication of something organic. I call it "deficit of experience." As Dr. Finch pointed out, we see it readily in children. But adult patients, too, amazingly often need help with identifying something they never have acquired. Only after they acquire these basic tools of orientation can we help them in recognizing the more sophisticated aspects of their problems. It so happens that many patients get well without our doing this consciously. I think that in long-term treatment, such as Dr. Gibson described, with his basic attitude, his being available in a predictable and very respectful way to his patient, such "tool formation" takes place without being consciously pursued. There is a difference in approach: Is it better to handle it on the level of conflict and symbolic and metaphoric interpretation, or on the level of helping the patient to develop the primary tools of orientation? I have developed the concept that it is the tools of orientation that are deficient in schizophrenics, not because of brain defect, but because they have been deprived of the organizing experiences.

DR. KNIGHT: *Dr. Semrad?*

DR. SEMRAD: Could one put it this way? Dr. Donnelly stresses that one has to set up a situation where the patient gets involved. The only way I know of involving another person is to "touch" him, not physically, but touch him "at heart," so to speak, by responding to what in word or concept he does not feel able to confide in me. By observing nonverbal cues that betray affect, I can observe that he's either mad, sad, or scared, and stress the theme of his feeling the same at me, as we are trying to negotiate our relationship. In persisting to help him acknowledge this in my presence, I can demonstrate to him that he matters enough to me that I care enough to enable him to speak what he feels; in this way, I "touch" him, and he will respond.

DR. BRUCH: That is an important step. In helping him by giving a recognizable word or concept to identify these things himself, one must remember that none of this learning can take place without rapport. By the way, a book came out a year or two ago, by DesLauries, about treatment of autistic children in a fairly late state. He feels that physical touch, literally, is essential. He goes to the point of demonstrating physically—this is my hand and this is your hand—and this was also implied in Dr. Finch's film.

DR. KNIGHT: *This discussion, by distinguished psychiatrists deeply absorbed in the complex treatment of schizophrenia, is remarkable in revealing unexpected conceptual and communicative agreement. It is a credit to the panelists, and bodes well for the future of psychiatry, that such depth could be achieved in unrehearsed discussion of an area that has so long vexed and frustrated workers in schizophrenia.*

Fundamental optimism regarding prognosis is implicit in all the statements. The total psychobiologic and social nature of the illness is accepted, without recourse to the old debates of "organic" versus "psychological." The crux of treatment is psychodynamic psychotherapy, with emphasis on the individual's unique life and situation rather than on the therapist's theoretical position. Differences in theory are important for research, but the vital "contact" and closeness of the patient-therapist relationship, experienced and understood, are the essential ingredients of improvement. The nature of the growth processes thereby ignited, once such rapport is established, was one of the points of disagreement—a matter of "learning to have feelings" versus "learning to deal with feelings," or perhaps both. . . . We are sorry to end the panel.

Index

Subjects

Index of Names